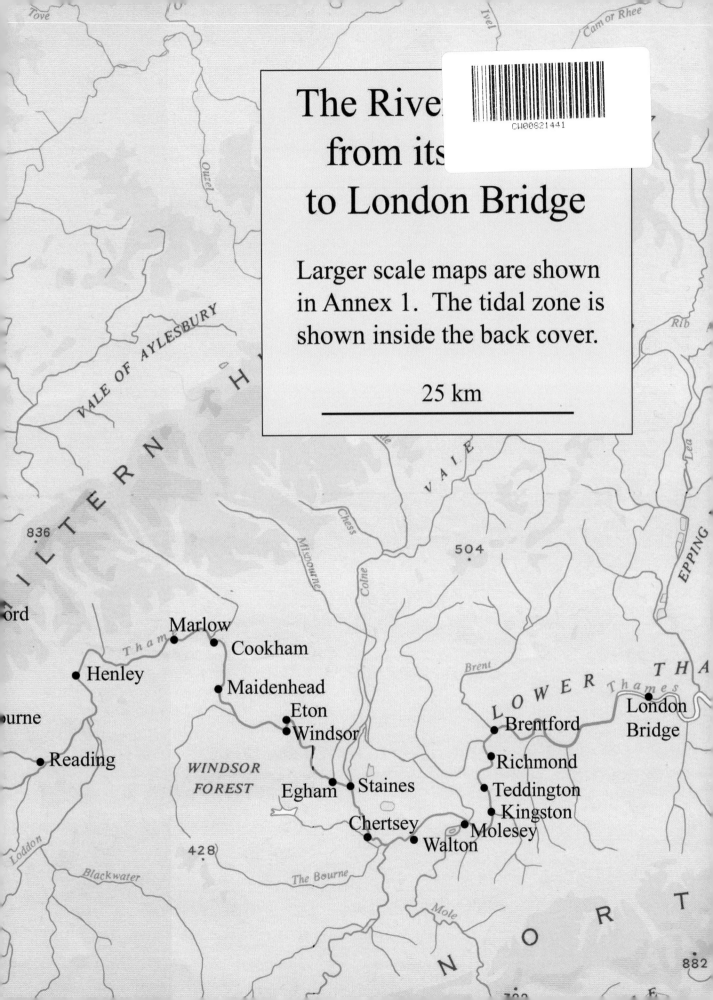

A History
of
Fish and Fisheries
of the
River Thames

David J Solomon

Fluvial Books

A History of Fish and Fisheries of the River Thames
© David Solomon 2021

Figures, photographic editing, design and production by David Solomon and Yvonne C Solomon

ISBN 978-0-9574276-1-7

Published and distributed by Fluvial Books, Quiet Waters, The Street, Ewelme, Wallingford, Oxfordshire, OX10 6HQ. Email djsolomon47@gmail.com

Front Cover picture:- Gudgeon fishing, from Robertson (1875)

Rear cover picture:- Fishing at London Bridge in about 1750. Stonegate, London Bridge © London Metropolitan Archives (City of London).

Map inside front cover:- The River Thames showing the main towns on the river. Based on OS 1:625,000 physical map, 1957.

Map inside back cover:- Tidal Thames and upper estuary, from Anon 1964.

Preface

There have been quite literally hundreds of books written about the Thames, including quite a few on fishing the river. So why another one?

Hopefully this one is a bit different. It is not a fishing book in the conventional sense and does not presume to instruct on how to fish the river; I am far from qualified to pen such a work. Rather it tells the story of the fish and how they have been fished-for and managed over the centuries, how the management of the river for other purposes has affected the stocks of fish and the fisheries dependent upon them, and how we have arrived at the situation that prevails now.

So how am I qualified to write such a book? First and foremost I have been a lifelong angler, I understand fishing and I care passionately about both fish stocks and our sport. Second, I was born within a mile or so of the river and have known it all my life, and once again live within a mile or so of it. The first fish I ever caught was a gudgeon from the river more than 65 years ago. Third, because of my deep fascination with fish and other aquatic wildlife, I studied zoology at university, and undertook a PhD on fish biology. I then worked for fifteen years at the fisheries laboratories of the Ministry of Agriculture, Fisheries and Food in London and Lowestoft, before leaving to become a freelance fisheries scientist. In that role I undertook several pieces of work on the Thames and its tributaries, mainly for the Environment Agency and its predecessors. As a result of working on many different rivers I developed a deep interest in fisheries history, and have amassed a considerable collection of reports, pictures and other documents from the past. Finally, despite all the attention that the river has received from historians and writers in the past, no-one has attempted a work covering this particular field.

I hope that anglers will enjoy this book, even if it does not tell them how to catch more fish. I am confident that anyone with an interest in the management of the fisheries and environment of the river will find something to stimulate. Further, anyone with an interest in the river in general will hopefully find cause for thought in these pages.

David Solomon
Ewelme, Oxfordshire.
July 2021.

Acknowledgements

I am extremely grateful to the many individuals who have provided information or advice to me in researching and writing this book. These include, in alphabetical order, Keith Arthur, John Berry, Daryl Clifton-Dey (Environment Agency), Keith Elliott, John Essex, John Lawson, Stuart Manwaring (EA), and Martin Salter. I am sure I have omitted some and I apologise in advance for any such oversight.

The following have given permission for the reproduction of illustrations in their collections; Abingdon Area Archaeological and Historical Collection; London Metropolitan Archive (City of London); and the River and Rowing Museum, Henley on Thames; this is gratefully acknowledged.

I am very grateful to the staff and custodians of many libraries and local history archives for their help in locating sources and information used in this work.

Finally I owe a debt of gratitude to my family and friends who encouraged and advised me along the way.

Contents

CHAPTER 1

Introduction

Preamble

Although the Thames is arguably the most famous river in the world, it is physically quite unremarkable. The catchment area to the gauging station at Kingston, just upstream of the tidal limit at Teddington, is just 9,948 km². The Amazon is the largest catchment in the world at more than 7 million km², more than 700 times that of the Thames. The average volume of flow of the Amazon is about 209,000 m³/sec, more than 2,500 times greater than that of the Thames. And when it comes to other statistics it is equally modest; the highest point in the catchment is only 330 m above sea level.

But what it lacks in physical dimension it makes up for in sheer history. The Thames has generated a huge volume of literature and artistic work. At its mouth lies one of the most famous and historic cities, London, and on its banks upstream lie such iconic locations as the University of Oxford, Hampton Court Palace, Windsor Castle and Runnymede, where Magna Carta was signed. Its catchment is home to more than 12 million people, who depend upon it for their water supply, for disposal of their waste, and for recreation. In the past the river was also important as a communication link, and as a source of food. The fish stocks have been utilised by the local human population for thousands of years, and there has been some form of management of fisheries for at least the last thousand.

There have been hundreds of books written about the Thames, and thousands more include description and analysis as part of a wider treatment. In addition there are thousands of reports, scientific papers and scholarly articles covering the river, written over hundreds of years. An annotated bibliography of Thames literature from 1580 to 1980, produced by Ben Cohen in 1985, runs to 335 pages, and much more has been produced since then. This present work draws heavily on many published and unpublished documents (the reference list includes more than 170 works) but no attempt is made to achieve an exhaustive review. In addition, information is drawn from hundreds of press reports and other ephemeral sources, identified in footnotes.

Given the number of published works on the river, there are surprisingly few dedicated to fish and fishing. There are of course some; Peter Stone's 1997 book *Old Father Thames* is a classic, as are A E Hobbs' 1947 *Trout of the Thames* and James Englefield's 1912 *The delightful life of pleasure on the Thames*, Patrick Chalmers' 1932 *At the tail of the weir*, and several others. There are a number of "how and where to fish" style books of variable authority and usefulness, which are discussed in later chapters. One of the most informative of these, in that individual "swims" are identified, is Frederick Amphlett's *The lower and middle Thames and how to fish it* published in 1894; much of this work is reproduced as Annex 2 of this book. There are almost no books covering the fish and fisheries (as opposed to the fishing) of the Thames; the closest is Alwyne Wheeler's "The tidal Thames" published in 1979, but as its title tells it is restricted to that part of the river seawards of the tidal limit. Having said that, it is an important book written by someone who was there, involved in overseeing the recovery of the polluted estuary.

More general books about the river are too numerous to list, but one of my favourites is *The Thames Highway* published in two parts in 1914 and 1920 by Fred Thacker. Although mainly about navigation, it contains much useful information on the history of fish traps on the river, and is a lovely general history. The river has also been the inspiration for many of our most illustrious yarn spinners such as Charles Dickens (*Great expectations, Our mutual friend*), Kenneth Graham (*Wind in the willows*), Jerome K Jerome (*Three men in a boat*) and Robert Gibbings (*Sweet Thames run softly*). And its waterscapes have attracted such artists as Canaletto, J M W Turner, Whistler and Monet.

So it is against this formidable backdrop of a multitude of works by the great and the good that I pitch my humble effort, in the hope that I have identified one of the few niches in the history of the river that has not hitherto been exhaustively explored.

Fish in the Thames

The scope of this book is limited to the freshwater and migratory fish stocks, and the fisheries dependent upon them, in the main stem of the Thames including the tidal reaches. The tributaries warrant at least one volume in their own right, and the story of the marine fish stocks of the estuary is a continuing and fascinating one that must be told by others.

From the viewpoint of present-day fisheries, the history of the Thames really starts about ten thousand years ago. It is likely that no freshwater fish survived the last Ice Age in Britain[1] though some migratory species such as salmon, trout and char made use of any suitable rivers between ice events. The Thames was at this time a tributary of the Rhine. The exact course of the combined river is uncertain, but is believed that about 7,500 years ago it flowed SW from the confluence along what is now the English Channel, though at other times in pre-history it probably drained to the North Sea. Eventually the British Isles became separated from mainland Europe, and the link with the Rhine was severed. This one-time direct freshwater connection to the continent, shared at various times with the other East Coast rivers up to about Yorkshire, means that the fish fauna of this region is the richest in the British Isles; the Thames contains all the fish native to the British Isles with the exception of the char, whitefish and spined loach. There are also populations of other species introduced from Europe and further afield. The species to be found in the Thames are listed in Table 1.1.

Table 1.1. List of fish species occurring in the River Thames.

Common and Latin name	Notes	Chapter
Freshwater species		
Barbel (*Barbus barbus*)	Native, abundant.	10
Bleak *Alburnus alburnus*	Native, abundant.	22
Bream(Common) *Abramis brama*	Native, abundant.	11
Bream (Silver) *Blicca bjoerkna*	Native, local.	22
Carp (Common) *Cyprinus carpio*	Introduced, frequent.	12
Carp (Crucian) *Carassius carassius*	Native, infrequent.	22
Chub *Leuciscus cephalus*	Native, abundant.	13
Dace *Leuciscus leuciscus*	Native, abundant.	14
Minnow *Phoxinus phoxinus*	Native, abundant.	22
Gudgeon *Gobio gobio*	Native, abundant	16
Roach *Rutilus rutilus*	Native, abundant.	19
Rudd *Scardinius erythrophthalmus*	Native, infrequent.	22
Tench *Tinca tinca*	Native, widespread.	22
Perch *Perca fluviatilis*	Native, abundant.	17
Ruffe *Gymnocephalus cernua*	Native, abundant.	22
Zander *Stozostedion lucioperca*	Introduced, local.	22
Pike *Esox lucius*	Native, abundant.	18
Brown trout *Salmo trutta*	Native, local.	21
Rainbow trout *Oncorhynchus mykiss*	Introduced, infrequent.	22
Loach (Stone) *Neomachilus barbatulus*	Native, local.	22
Lamprey (Brook) *Lampetra planeri*	Native, local.	22
Bullhead *Cottus gobio*	Native, abundant.	22
Stickleback(3 sp) *Gasterostues aculeatus*	Native, abundant.	22
Stickleback (10 sp) *Pungitius pungitius*	Native, abundant.	22
Wels catfish *Silurus glanis*	Introduced, infrequent.	22
Grayling *Thymallus thymallus*	Native, local	22
Migratory species		
Eel *Anguilla anguilla*	Native, abundant	15
Smelt *Osmerus eperlanus*	Native, local.	23
Lamprey (Sea) *Petromyzon marinus*	Native, infrequent.	23
Lamprey (River) *Lampetra fluviatilis*	Native, local.	23
Sturgeon Acipenser sturio	Vagrant, infrequent	23
Salmon *Salmo salar*	Native, now infrequent.	20
Sea trout *Salmo trutta*	Native, local.	23
Twaite shad *Alosa fallax*	Native, local.	23

Governance of Thames fisheries

The history of legislation covering, alluding to and affecting Thames fisheries is long and complex, and includes both national and local provisions. The following discussion is in no way intended to be exhaustive, but just covers some of the more interesting and important developments.

Until about a thousand years ago there was little management of activities in, on and around the river except perhaps by local chieftains and lords of the manor who controlled all that they could in their own interests. However, Domesday showed that local fisheries were recognised and taxed by the year 1086 (see Chapter 5). At some stage the Crown assumed the right to govern over the Thames and other "Royal" rivers such as the Trent, Yorkshire Ouse and Severn[2].

About the year 1197 responsibility for managing the lower Thames from Staines (Map 8) out into the estuary was devolved from the Crown to the City of London and its Lord Mayor. The exact date is unknown, but several pieces of legislation from that time onwards refer to the existence of this arrangement. The first charter of James 1 in 1605 stated that the City of London had since *"time out of mind had exercised...the office of bailiff and conservation of the water of the Thames....from the bridge of the town of Staines... to a certain place called Yantlett"*[3].

These upstream and seawards limits of the jurisdiction of the City were marked with stone structures, variously known as the London Stones, City Stones or Boundary Stones (Figure 1.1).

Figure 1.1. London Stone at Staines (From Hall and Hall, 1859).

Most early legislation covering the Thames was predominantly concerned with navigation and the passage of boats, though it had a major impact on fisheries as weirs and other structures used for fishing were causing an impediment to navigation. The earliest record of general regulation of Thames fisheries is in Magna Carta in 1224, which translates as *all kidells* (fish weirs) *from henceforth shall be utterly destroyed through Thames and Medway and through all England except by the sea coast.* The weirs at that time were mainly for fishing and milling. This regulation was expanded upon by an Act of 1351 (25 Edward III, stat 3, c4):-

Whereas the common passage of boats, and ships in the great rivers of England be oftentimes annoyed by the enhancing of gorces, mills, weirs, stanks, stakes and kiddels, which were levied and set up in the time of King Edward, the King's grandfather and after, whereby the said ships and boats be disturbed that they cannot pass (in such rivers) as there were wont, shall be out and utterly pulled down without being renewed; and therefore writs shall be sent to the sheriffs of the places where need shall be, to survey and enquire and do thereof execution…

An attempt to define ancient fishing gear mentioned in old regulations.

At various points in this chapter, and later in this book, lists are given of methods of fishing that were being regulated. Many of the terms are archaic and difficult to define; some may be minor variations, or be local names, for nets and traps. The definitions below, such as they are, were found in Lloyd's Encyclopaedic Dictionary dated 1895. Some are not vey illuminating!

Blee. (contracted from bleak). The fish called the bleak.
Dray. Draw net.
Garth. A dam or weir in a river for catching fish.
Garthman. The owner of a garth or weir for catching fish.
Gorce. A weir. A pool of water to keep fish in.
Kiddle. A weir or fish trap formed of wicker or basket work.
Peterman. A fisherman [*an allusion to St Peter*].
Stank. A pool or tank.
Stalker. A kind of fishing net.
Trynk. A kind of fishing net, an old apparatus for catching fish.

The first reference to damage of fish stocks caused by weirs and traps appears in an Act of 1402 covering the whole of England and Wales (4 Henry IV c12) which reported the fry of fish being destroyed and fed to swine, *contrary to the pleasure of God, and the great damage of the King and his people*.

The orders put in place by the Lord Mayor in September 1584[4] are interesting as they incorporate many of the present-day tools for fishery management including prohibited methods and baits, mesh size regulations, size limits and close seasons. Methods banned altogether included dray nets and kiddels. Regarding mesh sizes; *no fishermen, garthmen, petermen, draymen or trinkermen, shall avaunce or set up any wears, engines, rowte wears, pight wears, foot wears, nor make any stalker nets, trynk nets, purse nets, casting nets, berd nets, pot nets, barrock nets at crooks, heaving nets, except that they be 2 inches in the mesh.* Blee nets had to be two inches and a half mesh. Fishing was prohibited in mill dams and locks. Close seasons were between *the nativity of our Lord and St Martins* (November 11) for salmon; *between Michaelmass and Christmas* for trout; *between 15 days before St Martins and 15 days after* for roach; and *between April 15 and August 15* for lampreys. Size limits included 14 inches for pike, 12 inches for barbel, and 6 inches for roach and dace.

In 1710 Parliament passed *An Act for the better preservation and improvement of the Fishery within the River of Thames; and for the regulating and governing the Company of Fishermen of the said River.* This allowed the "company" to appoint *one fit person to be the Master of the Mystery*[5] *of fishermen* and to make bylaws for the conduct of the company and for regulating the fishery and *reforming Abuses committed in the said Fishery*, subject to the approval of the Mayor and Aldermen of the City of London. However, the preamble of a subsequent Act passed in 1757 noted that *the said Company having ceased to act from about the Year 1727, and most of the members thereof being dead*, there was no effective regulation of the fishery. The 1757 legislation was entitled *An Act for the more effectual Preservation and Improvement of the Spawn and fry of the Fish in the River Thames, and the Waters of Medway; and for the better regulation of the Fishery thereof.* It declared that *no Person shall .... wilfully take, destroy, spoil, kill, or expose for Sale, or exchange for any Goods, Matter, or Thing, whatsoever, any Spawn, Fry, or Brood of Fish, or Spatt of Oysters, or any unsizeable or unwholesome Fish, or Fish out of Season, or bring such Fish on Shore for Sale, or use or keep any Net, Engine or other Device whatsoever, which shall be prohibited or declared unlawful in and by such Rules, Orders and Ordinances of the said Court of Mayor and Aldermen...".* It also required that any boat used for fishing was labelled with the fisherman's name and parish of residence. While the Act contained detailed arrangements for the application of the legislation, set-up of courts and committees and so on, it was light on specific rules; presumably these were the subject of bylaws.

Jurisdiction of the river upstream of Staines remained with the Crown, and from 1605 the navigation there was managed by a series of Upper Navigation Commissions. In 1857 the Thames Conservancy was established to take over the role of the City of London (ie with jurisdiction from Staines to Yantlett); and in 1866 their role was expanded to take over that of the Upper Navigation Commissioners. Thus for the first time since about 1197 the whole of the Thames was under single management. However, this arrangement lasted only 43 years as responsibility for the tidal reaches (deemed to commence 265 yards seawards of Teddington Weir) including the environmental and fisheries functions, was vested in the Port of London Authority (PLA) when it was established in 1909. Thames Conservancy continued to be responsibility for the non-tidal river until its powers were transferred to the Thames Water Authority in 1974; at the same time the new Water Authority took over the environmental and fisheries functions for the tidal river from the PLA. Thames Water Authority ceased to exist in 1989 and its fisheries and environmental functions were transferred to the new National Rivers Authority. This organisation lasted only seven years, being subsumed into in the Environment Agency in 1996.

Figure 1.2. Part of a scene at Staines drawn by William Havell in 1818. This captures a number of aspects of the management of the Thames at that time. On the far bank is the London Stone, marking the upstream limit of the jurisdiction of the City of London. The men in the punt on the right are engaged in the laborious business of ballasting, removing gravel to aid the passage of boats (see Chapter 2). In the punt on the left there are several wicker fish traps, of a type in widespread use for hundreds of years (see Chapter 5).

Maps

Maps are essential to a work such as this. The freshwater catchment, from the source to the tidal limit, including the tributaries, is shown on the map inside the front cover. The tidal reach is shown inside the back cover. Annex 1 comprises a detailed map of the main stem from source to London, covering ten pages. These are identified as maps one to ten, and locations mentioned in the text are cross-referenced to the relevant map.

Chapter 1 footnotes

[1] Varley (1967).

[2] Wisdom (1957).

[3] Wisdom (1957). Yantlett Creek is on the Isle of Grain, a little landwards of the mouth of the Medway. The Yantlett London Stone lies close to the mouth of the creek, and is beyond the area covered by this book.

[4] Strype (1720) and Griffiths (1748).

[5] This is an archaic use of the word "mystery"; "*a trade, an occupation, an employment, a profession*" (Lloyds Encyclopaedic Dictionary, 1895).

CHAPTER 2

The Thames environment

The nature of the Thames catchment

The Thames (at its tidal limit) drains 9948 km^2 of lowland Britain. About 50% of the catchment lies below 100 m above sea level, and the highest point is 330.2 m; only just over 1,000 feet. The mean rainfall is about 715 mm per year, varying between years and with location within the basin. Of this, only about 250 mm contributes to the natural flow of the Thames; the remaining 65% is lost to evaporation and plant transpiration without ever reaching the river, mostly during the warmer months of the year. The climate is temperate with rainfall spread fairly evenly through the year. Monthly mean air temperatures for the period 1960 to 1990 at Oxford, not far from the centre of the catchment, were lowest for January (4.1°C) and highest for July (17.1°C)[1]. Much of the catchment lies on permeable rock (chalk and limestone), so much of the potential river flow is from groundwater sources (springs). This results in a relatively stable flow regime, which is discussed further below.

Table 2.1. Characteristics of the present-day catchment of the Thames to the gauging station at Kingston[2].

Land cover	%
Woodland	16.1
Arable/horticulture	35.6
Grassland	32.2
Mountain/heath/bog	0.5
Urban	14.0
Geology	**%**
High permeability bedrock	43.2
Moderate permeability bedrock	9.7
Low permeability bedrock	22.0
High permeability superficial deposits	14.2
Low permeability superficial deposits	7.4
Mixed permeability superficial deposits	7.2

The natural state of the Thames

An important baseline for the consideration of the history of fish and fisheries in the river is to establish what the river would have been like before humans activities started to have an effect. This is really quite difficult as many human influences have been at work for hundreds if not thousands of years, and there are limited records to help us. One thing is certain – the river in its pristine state looked rather different to how it does now.

We are very fortunate in that, because the river is so important, flows have been measured and recorded for almost 130 years on a continuous basis, close to the tidal limit at Teddington (until 1974) and subsequently Kingston (Map 9). Even this record does not of course tell us what the flows would have been in the absence of human influence; for this we need calculated naturalised flows. Again, fortuitously, daily naturalised flows have been calculated for the whole period of the gauged record and are freely available from the National River Flow Archive (NRFA)[3].

The naturalised mean flow for the river at Kingston, for the period 1883 to 2011, was 78.4 m^3/sec, and the lowest flow – in the absence of human influence – of 7.37 m^3/sec would have occurred on July 7 1934. A usual measure of dry-weather flow is that which is exceeded for 95% of the time; or to put it another way it is the flow below which the river falls on average for 18 days per year. This is termed the Q95 flow and the naturalised Q95 for the whole period was 19 m^3/sec. The calculated highest natural flow would have been 806 m^3/sec on November 18 1894. The ratio of Q95 to mean flow, at 24.2%, is relatively high indicating a fairly stable flow regime. For comparison, the ratio for a "spatey" river system, the Tamar, is 9.78%; and for the River Test, a river fed almost entirely from groundwater sources, it is 51.6%.

In contrast, the actual gauged mean flow of the Thames for the same period was 65.2 m^3/sec, the lowest flow zero (for several weeks in 1976), and the Q95, 7.52 m^3/sec. The main reason for the differences between naturalised and gauged flows is the abstraction of water for supply; while much of that used in towns upstream of Kingston is returned to the river and its tributaries as treated sewage effluent, water for London is taken upstream of Kingston and the effluent returns are all downstream of the tidal limit. Thus, on average throughout the period 1883-2011, the flow of the Thames at Kingston was reduced by 13.2 m^3/sec (16.8%); the dry-weather flow (Q95) was reduced by 11.6 m^3/sec (61.2%); and the lowest flows to zero. The highest flow of 806 m^3/sec was reduced to 800 m^3/sec, a reduction of less than 1%. It is thus at times of lower flows that the relative impact on the river has been greatest, exactly when the habitat is at its most sensitive and vulnerable. The issue of abstraction is discussed further below.

Weirs for milling, fishing and in particular navigation have had a dramatic effect upon the habitat of the river, in deepening the water column and reducing the velocity. An invaluable insight into the more natural state of the river comes from a report on a survey of the river from Reading to Isleworth undertaken by the famous engineer John Rennie in 1794, before there were any locks between Boulters (Map 7) and the estuary. Rennie was instructed to examine the obstacles to navigation in the river and to make suggestions for their remedy, including the possibility of one or more canals to bypass significant stretches.

Table 2.2. Results of Rennie's survey of 1794.

Reach	Length yards	Fall inches	Length m	Fall mm	Fall mm/km
u/s Boulters to Maidenhead Bridge			0	0	
Maidenhead Bridge to Monkey Island	3575	35	3268	889	271
Monkey Island to Boveney	4018	61	3674	1549	421
Boveney to Windsor Bridge	3858	54.5	3527	1384	392
Windsor Bridge to Datchet Bridge	3172	56.5	2900	1435	494
Datchet Bridge to the lower end of Old Windsor	6130	66	5605	1676	299
Lower end of Old Windsor to Staines Bridge	5716	72	5226	1828	349
Staines Bridge to Laleham Ferry	5444	61	4977	1549	311
Laleham Ferry to Chertsey Bridge	2354	38	2152	965	448
Chertsey Bridge to upper end of Stoners Gut	2904	45.5	2655	1155	435
Upper end of Stoners Gut to Opposite lower end	1042	6	952	152	159
Opposite lower end of Stoners Gut to Shepperton	1116	11.5	1020	292	286
Shepperton to Walton Bridge	2453	32	2243	812	362
Walton Bridge to Sunbury	2872	47	2626	1193	454
Sunbury to Hampton	3636	44.25	3324	1123	338
Hampton to Hampton Court Bridge	1898	26.5	1735	673	387.
Hampton Court Bridge to Ditton Wharf	1910	19.5	1746	495	283
Ditton Wharf to Kingston Bridge	3178	29	2905	736	253
Kingston Bridge to Teddington Ferry	2974	25.5	2719	647	238
Teddington Ferry to Twickenham Ferry	2515	22.75	2299	577	251
Twickenham Ferry to Richmond Ferry	2119	27.25	1937	692	357
Richmond Ferry to Rails Head at Isleworth	1364	4.25	1247	107	86
Rails Head to Kew Bridge	3892	31.25	3558	793	223
Kew Bridge to Mortlake	2867	18	2621	457	174
Totals (mean)	**71,007**	**834.25**	**64,928**	**21,189**	**(326)**

The main problem was the shallow nature of the river and the fast currents. Rennie described many "shoals" (banks of gravel) covered by fast-flowing shallow water. In many places the depth was maintained only by the barges scraping along the river bed, with extensive though somewhat laborious dredging or "ballasting" in places (Figure 2.1). Near Old Windsor there was a reach with only three or four inches depth across most of the channel. Between Windsor Bridge and the present location of Victoria Bridge, a reach now intersected by Romney Lock and Weir (Map 8) , there was *a continual shallow, and the river is very rapid, moving at a rate of 3 miles per hour* [about 1.3 m/sec]. Between "Laylam Gulls" and "Doomsday Bushes", a distance of 1.5 miles with a fall of 5.5 feet, the current was said to be *considerable above three miles per hour*; and between Kingston and

Teddington Ferry (about 1.5 miles) the velocity approached three miles per hour. Rennie rather obscurely described the Thames:-

If the country through which a river passes, was of a homogeneous quality, the river would have a gradual declivity; but when otherwise, shoals are formed, and the course of the river becomes irregular, the hard places resisting the effects of the stream, and forming so many dams over which the fall of the water is in many cases very considerable, whereas the water in the spaces in between runs deep and languid.

The river Thames partakes to a great degree of this last supposition.

The results of Rennie's survey show a fall in water surface level of 0.326 m/km (1.72 feet/mile) over the 64.93 km (40.34 miles) between Boulters and Mortlake (Map 10). Rennie also noted that the river channel was filled with abundant growth of aquatic plants. This abundance was not just due to the shallower, faster-flowing water – it was also the result of the water being much clearer than in later years. Before the advent of the power boat (first steam, later internal combustion engine driven) boat traffic caused little wake and wash, and at times of low flow at least the water was very clear. James Englefield described punting in the 1860s at Maidenhead; *the angler has the bed of the river constantly under his keen observation, with its luxuriant plant life, the bright shallows, deep holes and all the wonders of the watery realm of lavish Nature's providence.* He described how a lost diamond ring could be clearly seen on the "clean and sun-lighted gravel bottom" in three feet of water.

Figure 2.1. Dredging or "ballasting" by hand on the Thames. The man on the left is forcing the bucket into the gravel shoal while his colleague winches it along and then to the surface. The meagre results of their efforts so far can be seen scattered on the bottom of the punt. Note that the punt has to be firmly secured with four stakes (ryepecks) driven into the river bed. From Robertson (1875).

Figure 2.2. We have few meaningful images of how the Thames looked in its natural state. When this picture of Maidenhead Bridge (looking upstream) was composed in about 1790 there were no navigation weirs of locks between here and the sea, and the river was relatively shallow and fast flowing. However, significant dredging was taking place and clearly sizeable vessels were able to navigate. The emergent rushes (probably common club rush, *Schoenoplectus lacustris*) well out in the stream indicate shallow areas. From Dalton (1794).

We have no large free-flowing lowland rivers left in England to liken to the natural Thames; the nearest approximation is perhaps something like a larger version of the Dorset Stour, or maybe the lower River Wye.

Thames tides

The action of tides has a profound effect upon the Thames from Teddington Weir seawards, and at times both recent and past, somewhat upstream of Teddington too. However, the situation is complicated with a number of factors affecting the tide level at different times and different locations. Needless to say this has had a significant effect upon the distribution of freshwater, brackish and saltwater fish, and of the fisheries dependent upon them.

Over the period of recorded history there have been some major shifts in high and low tide levels, and thus the extent of penetration of tidal and salt-water influences, due to both natural fluctuations and man-made factors.

Since the last Ice Age the mean sea level in Northern Europe has risen by about 25 metres relative to the land surface, which has itself risen to a lesser extent due to the removal of the weight of ice bearing upon it. However, superimposed upon the resultant trend of rising tide levels have been a number of shorter-term reversals[4]. The best recorded of these took place in Roman times, evidenced by differences in the top height of quays constructed during successive phases of reclamation of tidal areas.

The overall trends in levels of high and low tides in the City of London over the past 2000 years are shown in Figure 2.3. A number of features are apparent. First, the decreases in both high and low tide levels during Roman times are clear. Since then there has been a continued increase in high tide level, accelerating somewhat in the last 500 years. In the past 1000 years the low tide level has been falling steadily, increasing the tidal range from less than two metres to more than five. Also shown is the mean high water (spring tides) level at Twickenham; this is of the order of 0.5 m higher than in the City due to the funnelling effect of the tidal reach between the two. This is the same effect that leads to the creation of the Severn Bore. High water at Teddington is about an hour after that at London Bridge.

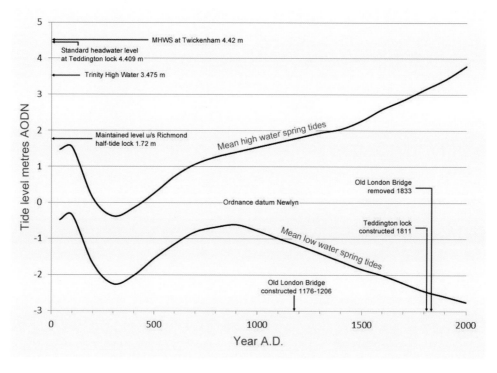

Figure 2.3. Tide levels at London Bridge over the past 2000 years, with some present-day levels indicated along with timing of some human influences. AODN = above Ordnance Datum at Newlyn.

Human activities that have modified the tidal regime include the reclamation of marshes and mudflats narrowing the channel, and the construction and eventual removal of the old London Bridge. There has been a crossing close to the present London Bridge for about 2000 years, but the first stone bridge was constructed between the years 1176 and about 1206. This gradually became the iconic image of so many paintings, with about twenty narrow arches, and many houses and even a church built on the bridge itself. The houses were in fact removed between 1758 and 1762 to increase the road traffic carrying capacity, and the bridge itself was finally replaced in 1833. In turn this bridge was replaced by the current modern bridge in 1973.

14

Figure 2.4. Old London Bridge at low tide from the seaward side in about 1600 . The starlings and the narrow channels between them are clearly illustrated. The water wheels for pumping the water supply occupy the three channels on the right.

The bridge that was replaced in 1833 represented a major obstruction to the free flow of water in the Thames, and had a significant effect upon water levels both upstream and downstream, and on the penetration of saline water landwards. Each of the 19 support piers was built upon what was effectively a small artificial island called a "starling". They were constructed of elm piling filled with rubble. The tops of the starlings were covered at high tide, but at half-tide and below the flow of water, on both the flood and ebb tides, was restricted to the twenty narrow channels between them. Until 1762 the total width of the 20 channels between the starlings was 249.25 feet, or about 76.0 m. The total width of the river at the bridge site was 900 feet or 274.4 m; the effective width of the river was therefore reduced by about 72%. The rapid flow between the starlings had eroded the river bed somewhat, but nonetheless the cross-section area of the channel was very much restricted. At the peak of the ebb tide flow there was a level difference of up to five feet (1.52 m) through the bridge, and up to 14 inches (0.36 m) on the flood tide. This head-drop was exploited by mill wheels situated in the four channels closest to the north shore, and in 1750 these were used to pump water for supply throughout much of London (Figure 2.5). However, the head-drop made navigating through the bridge very hazardous at times, and many accidents occurred. Near low tide the only passage through was in the narrow channels between the starlings; the widest of these was only 19 feet (5.8 m). Near high tide the water channels were wider, but the shallow water over the starlings was a great hazard for boats with a significant draft. In 1762, at the time of removal of the houses on the bridge, the opportunity was taken to remove one of the piers with its starling to create a larger bridge span known as the "Great Arch"; this gave a channel with a width of 58 feet 6 inches (17.8 m) between starlings. In an attempt to maintain the head drop for the water pumps the two channels closest to the south shore were blocked, but this was not enough to regain the head drop and great problems were experienced maintaining the supply. The well-known engineer John Smeaton was immediately summoned to come up with proposals to remedy the situation. In his report[5] he calculated that the output of the pumps had been reduced by about 35% by the changes in water level, and he proposed a series of measures, including blocking further channels and reducing the depth and width of others, to recover the old regime. However, by 1820 all the waterwheels had ceased operation due to water quality concerns and because consideration was being given to replacing the bridge with a new one that was more navigation-friendly.

Figure 2.5. Water-wheel installed in one of the channels between starlings at London Bridge, used for pumping water for supply. From Beighton (1731).

The next London Bridge was built between 1824 and 1831 and was designed by the eminent engineer John Rennie. He died before construction began, and overseeing the work was entrusted to his two sons, John Jr and George. The new design was a five-arch affair representing minimal obstruction to free flow of the river. It was built just upstream of the old bridge, and during construction the two bridges stood in parallel. Once the new bridge was completed demolition of the old one took place, taking about a year. Once removal was complete the tidal regime both below and above the bridge was greatly altered; a thorough assessment of the situation was made by the Rennie brothers[6].

At Richmond Bridge the tidal range was greatly increased by the removal of the old London Bridge. The high tide level was only increased by a matter of a few inches, but the low tide level fell by more than three feet at spring tides. The drainage of areas surrounding the tidal river was greatly improved, and barges, which had previously required towing by horses to work landwards from Putney to Richmond, could now use the flood tide to make the passage in a few hours. Not all the impacts were beneficial, however. Salinity landwards of London Bridge increased markedly with the new tidal regime, pushing the freshwater fish community landwards. Navigation between Richmond and Teddington Lock was complicated by the shallow water at low tide, and a drop in low tide level seawards of the new bridge caused some problems for shipping there. An article in "The Times" many years later[7] described conflicting views on how the issues between Richmond and Teddington might be addressed; exposure of unsightly and noisome mud at low tide had been added to the problems of navigation. Two engineers appointed by the Thames Conservancy (TC) recommended dredging a channel 100' (30 metres) wide to allow boats to pass at all states of tide. Another engineer, representing the town of Richmond claimed that this would not be effective at addressing the exposed mud problem and that a lock and weir at Richmond was the answer. The argument was still raging ten years later in 1884;

A memorial to the Home Office authorities has been drawn up by the Richmond Select Vestry with reference to the condition of the river within their district. It states that during the past dry season the state of the Thames between Teddington and Isleworth has been worse than has ever been known at any period in its history; that the greater part of the bed of the river has been without water, and where exposed, slime, forming huge mud banks, has taken the place of pure sand and shingle; and that such a state of things is destructive to all enjoyment of the beauty of the river, is dangerous to health, and ruinous to property in the valley of the Thames.[8]

Eventually a bill for construction of a structure to address the problem was placed before Parliament with the catchy title *The Richmond Footbridge (with Removable Sluices), Lock and Slipway Bill.* This was to be a weir to retain landwards water level at about mid-tide height, and a lock. Even at this stage TC were still opposing the scheme, though to be fair they acknowledged that it would achieve the desired effects landwards of the structure, but were concerned about the potential siltation effects seawards. The bill was enacted in May 1890, and TC took on responsibility for construction and operation. The scheme was completed in 1894; the structure is shown in Figure 2.6.

The retained level is 1.72 m AODN, about mid tide, allowing adequate depth for navigation upstream at low tide, and covering the mud banks. For about two hours either side of high water, the three 20-metre-wide sluice gates are lifted clear of the water, and boats may move freely (and free of charge) in both directions. When the sluices are closed, passage is made via the lock. Each year in November the sluices are raised throughout the tidal cycle for a few days, allowing the river to drop to the levels that prevailed before construction of the weir and lock. This is done to allow inspection and maintenance, and is an event eagerly exploited by archaeologists and mudlarks[9] alike.

In 1897 Amphlett examined the impact of the new half-tide lock on the angling between Richmond and Teddington Weir. He considered that the former favourite swims at Richmond were now not nearly so productive, and that at Twickenham it has become much more difficult to locate the fish. However, he considered conditions for spawning much improved, and he looked forward to better sport in future years. It seems that the fish and the anglers soon adapted to the changed conditions, and good fishing was restored.

There is some doubt about how far landwards the tide affected the river before the construction of the lower-river weirs between 1811 and 1815, and before construction of the old London Bridge. De Mare (1958) suggests that the effect of the tide was felt as far upstream as Staines (Map 8), and Herbert (1966) suggests that this was the reason for the setting of the upstream limit of the jurisdiction of the City of London established in about the year 1197 (See Chapter 1). This casual and unsubstantiated claim would appear to be unlikely to be even remotely true. First, at the time of the establishing of the limit of jurisdiction the tidal range was much less that at present, with high tide level about 2 m lower (Figure 2.3). Second the standard tailwater level at Penton Hook (the first lock downstream of Staines, Map 9) is at 12.6 m AOD; the bed is likely to be less than 3 m lower, say 9.5 m AOD. High tide level at London Bridge at the time was of the order of 2 m AOD. Even allowing for the funnelling effect of the narrowing channel, and the backing-up effect of freshwater flow, a tidal influence that far landwards is virtually inconceivable. A limit of tidal influence at Molesey or Sunbury is more realistic, even without the restricting effect of the old London Bridge. Pennant in 1790 stated that *just above Kingston it feels the last feeble efforts of a tide*, though that of course was still affected by the old bridge; Teddington Weir and Lock were constructed in 1811.

Figure 2.6. Richmond half-tide lock and weir, looking seawards, in about 1910[10]. The tide is low so the sluice gates are lowered; the grooves in which they fit can be seen above the gates in the centre three arches. The anglers are taking advantage of the retained level landwards of the structure.

As a result of a continuing trend towards higher tide levels, the spring high tide overtops Teddington Weir with increasing frequency. The water level recording at Kingston (about 2 km upstream of Teddington) between November 4 and 6 2013, shows small peaks of level of up to 0.5 m at high water (Figure 2.7) . At such times the crest of Teddington Weir is completely drowned-out.

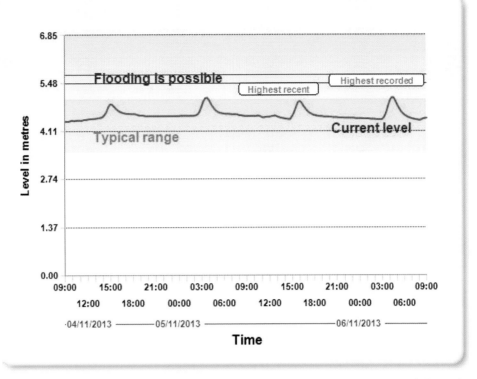

Figure 2.7. Water level at Kingston between November 4 and 6, 2013, showing the effect of high spring tides overtopping Teddington Weir. From Environment Agency website.

Salinity

Between the freshwater river and the open sea there is a gradient of salinity levels, the dynamics of which vary with freshwater flow and time within the spring/neap tidal cycle. This has fundamental significance for the distribution, wellbeing and movements of fish.

As fresh water enters the tidal zone its salinity level is virtually zero; the salinity of the North Sea is around 34 mg/litre (parts per thousand or ppt) of sodium chloride (salt). The salinity increases as one passes down through the tidal zone and estuary, the value at any point varying with freshwater flow to the estuary and state of tide. Typical values along the estuary at high water (HW) spring tide and LW neap tide are shown in Figure 2.8. As the salinity of the estuary is such a dynamic situation it can be difficult to identify the effect of individual variables such as freshwater flow. One approach is to consider the location of the point in the estuary where the salinity reached a certain level (say 12.5 ppt) at a particular state of tide (for example mid-tide, half way between LW and HW) during extended periods of settled flow conditions. During the third quarter of 1949 when freshwater flow to the estuary was very low and stable (averaging only 5m³/sec), this point was 11 km seawards of London Bridge. This contrasts with a period of high freshwater flow (first quarter of 1951, mean freshwater flow 229 m³/sec) when it was located 48 km below London Bridge[11].

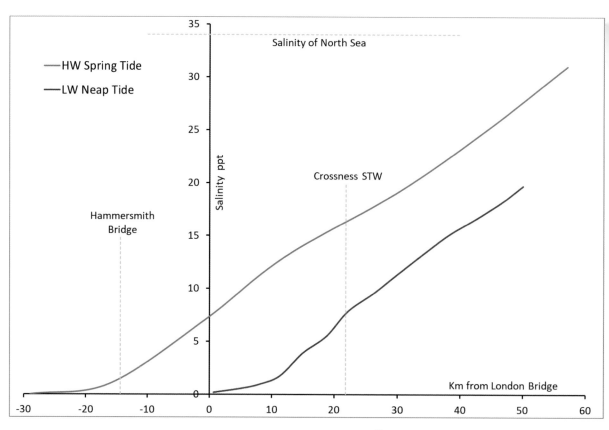

Figure 2.8. Level of salinity along the estuary at HW spring tide and LW neap tide[11].

Freshwater fish species differ with respect of their salinity tolerance range, and tolerance varies with temperature and other environmental factors. Generally speaking, most species are comfortable at a salinity level up to about 12 ppt, which approximates to the salt content of their body fluids. Taking perch as an example, in an experimental study survival was not affected by 13 ppt at 12 and 15°C, but at 25° half the fish died in 62 hours at 13 ppt. Growth may be affected at lower levels of salinity; in the perch study, body weight increase at 10 ppt was about half that observed at 4 ppt[12].

Given that most species are comfortable at 12 ppt it can be seen from Figure 2.8 that they are likely to find the environs of London Bridge acceptable in terms of salinity at all states of tide, at least at times of average flow. Suitable conditions also prevail for perhaps 10 km seawards at high tide, and 30 km at low tide. The extent to which fish move up and down river with the tide is uncertain; it is most unlikely that they will not do to some extent. It would be easy in terms of swimming effort to just "go with the flow"; typically the tidal excursion of the estuary (the distance up and down river that a typical molecule of water would travel up and down river on a typical tide) is of the order of 14 km[11]. A fish could use the current to carry it over the same path, while remaining throughout in similar conditions of salinity and other water quality parameters, whereas remaining in one location would require swimming effort and would subject the fish to a range of environmental conditions.

Chapter 2 footnotes

[1] Hulme and Barrow (1997).

[2] National River Flow Archive, Centre for Ecology and Hydrology.

[3] www.ceh.ac.uk/data/nrfa/

[4] Brigham (2001)

[5] Smeaton J (1763) The report of John Smeaton, upon the questions proposed to him by the committee for improving, widening and enlarging London Bridge.

[6] "On the course, dimensions, inclinations, and velocities of the River Thames, and the effects which have been occasioned by the removal and rebuilding of old and new London Bridges, according to the observations and experiments which have been made on the river during the years 1832, 1833 and 1834, by Messrs. George and John Rennie". Report of the Fourth meeting of the British Association for the Advancement of Science, held at Edinburgh 1834; published 1835.

[7] The Times, September 1 1873.

[8] Globe, December 27 1884.

[9] "Mudlarking" is the term given to the practice of searching the intertidal areas for items of value or interest. Originally it was a source of income, especially for youngsters, but nowadays it is mainly concerned with finding historical artefacts, and on the tidal Thames is allowed only under licence. Maiklem (2019) gives a fascinating account of modern-day mudlarking, including at Richmond when the level is lowered.

[10] Postcard published by "WHA", no 3975

[11] Data from Anon (1964). The HW readings were taken on April 27 1949 (mean freshwater flow to estuary 18.4 m^3/sec), and the LW readings on 6 April 1949 (mean freshwater flow 42.4 m^3/sec).

[12] Overton *et al* (2008).

22

CHAPTER 3

Man and the River Thames

Boats and navigation

There have been boats on the river for almost as long as man has lived alongside it, for several thousand years. Early boats would have been used for fishing, crossing the river, and for local transport of people, animals and produce between settlements and villages. The river would have been beset with shallows and rapids, and long distance navigation would have been fraught with problems, especially for upstream travel. The Romans had sea-going boats of course, but how far up the Thames they would have been able to bring them is uncertain.

One of the earliest known Thames boats is an oak dugout which was recovered from the river bed near Walton on Thames (Map 9) when the anchor of a dredger became fast in it. The boat, in an excellent state of preservation, is on display at the River and Rowing Museum in Henley (Figure 3.1). It is carved from a single oak tree trunk, and has been carbon-dated to between 405 and 530 AD. The capacity has been calculated as more than 1.4 tonnes so it was clearly capable of carrying a useful cargo. It would have been propelled by poling or paddling, as the banks were probably too overgrown to allow effective towing by animals or humans.

Figure 3.1. One of the earliest boats known on the Thames, dated at between 405 and 530 AD. See text for details. Photograph reproduced by kind permission of the River and Rowing Museum, Henley.

Early boats would also have been used for fishing activity, in setting traps and setting and hauling nets. In general, however, early boats and boating would have had only minor impact upon the fish and the fisheries exploiting them.

At some stage sails were adopted as a mode of propulsion; many old etchings show quite large boats and barges with sails. Using this method of transport must have been a very skilful business beset with problems; the narrow and often fast-flowing waterway, numerous shallows, variable winds, river meanders, tree-lined banks, and bridges that would require the sails and mast to be lowered. An additional complication arose when the construction and operation of mills started to impinge upon navigation. Efficient milling relied upon a head of water, and on lowland streams such as the Thames this generally involved some sort of head-retaining structure or weir. This had two immediate effects upon boat activity. First, by raising water level for some distance upstream it slowed the current and deepened the water, making many short-distance journeys on these reaches much easier. Second, however, the weirs themselves represented a severe impediment to passage upstream and downstream, and interfered seriously with longer-distance trade. Smaller boats could be dragged or "portaged" overland to bypass the weirs, but for larger boats the technique of "flashing" evolved. This involved an openable or removable section of the weir, through which downstream-moving craft were flushed, and upstream-moving craft could be winched (Figure 3.2).

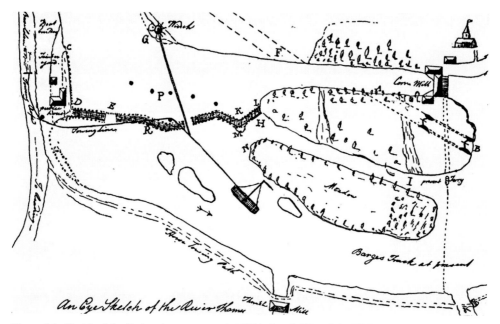

Figure 3.2. Sketch of the flash weir arrangement at Whitchurch (Map 6) in 1786, showing the location of a proposed pound lock[1]. The pound lock was built the following year but was placed in the channel between the two large islands, and the weir was reconstructed to run from the tip of the southernmost island.

As navigation became more organised two major developments aided navigation. The first was the pound lock – basically the same as those on the river today. These started to appear in about 1630, and are discussed further below. The second was the development of the tow (or towing) path alongside the river, with the space between it and the river cleared of

Figure 3.3. A barge being towed by a horse on the towpath at Hurley (Map 7) in about 1830. The direction of travel is downstream, hence only a single horse is required. Note the short mast used for fixing the tow rope. From Fearnside (1850).

trees. This allowed craft to be hauled by teams of men or horses. To haul a 200 ton barge upstream apparently required a team of about 50-80 men, or 12-14 horses[2].

Until the 19th century, the boat traffic on the river, being propelled by oar, pole, wind or towing, involving minimal underwater disturbance, had only a minor direct effect upon fish and fisheries – though of course the development and operation of navigation locks and weirs, and the towpath, had significant impact. However, the introduction of powered boats had a much greater effect.

The first powered craft on the Thames were steam driven, and they started to appear in about 1813. Steam launches soon became the favourite playthings of the rich, whose behaviour left much to be desired. Wheeldon (1878) wrote:-

Everywhere I go I hear like complaints made both by residents and visitors…. against the abominable thoughtlessness and selfishness displayed by those who…. possessing a specimen of these nasty toy steamers, go shrieking with their whistles up and down the river reaches, destroying that very quiet which induces wealthy men either to build for themselves, or rent at an enormous figure, the splendid mansions that adorn the banks of the stream, washing away the banks by the high rate of speed at which the craft are driven,

The Thames Bore

Figure 3.4. Sketch showing the havoc caused by a speeding steam launch in 1882[3]

and doing all that in them lies to make both themselves and their snorting, wheezing little tugs thoroughly objectionable.

In 1874, increasing boat traffic at Maidenhead caused James Englefield to give up his *delightful life of pleasure* there and move to Marlow, then a much quieter place. He wrote:-

The locality was fast becoming a very fashionable resort in summer time, and then the trout fishers quiet pastime began to be interfered with by a good deal of commotion occasioned by the increase in river traffic of pleasure boats etc, and even a few steam launches invaded the peaceful scene.

Figure 3.5. A "Punch" cartoon[4] from 1869 entitled *Captain Jinks (of the Selfish) and his friends enjoying themselves on the river.* This was drawn by Frederick Walker. The artist whose punt is being thrown about on the left is George Leslie, author of "Our River".

26

Figure 3.6. This picture, taken a year or two before the First World War, captures the atmosphere of the Edwardian era Thames boating holiday, with the house boat, gramophone, punt, bare feet and fishing rod. From a glass plate negative in the author's collection

Jerome K Jerome disliked steam launches; in *Three men in a boat* he wrote:-

We had a good deal of trouble with steam launches that morning. It was just before the Henley week, and they were going up in large numbers; some by themselves, some towing houseboats. I do hate steam launches: I suppose every rowing man does. I never see a steam launch but I feel I should like to lure it to a lonely part of the river, and there, in the silence and the solitude, strangle it.

The Field even went as far as publishing[5] the name of one particularly recalcitrant craft, presumably in an attempt to "name and shame":-

Anglers and others are much troubled in these waters (Streatley) by two nuisances. First, we have the steam launch, Undine, whose owner drives her up and down the river at full speed, and never vouchsafes the grace of an "easy" to punt or pleasure boat. He has his pleasure, and others may look out for theirs.

The second nuisance referred-to was shooting moorhens:-

One sportsman of this class so amusing himself the other day nearly made a heavy bag, for in the open river, and knowing that the boat was there, he fired and wounded a young gentleman, who was in it with his sister enjoying the river, and not expecting to be shot. He might just as easily have been killed as wounded.

And some people think that oafish behaviour is a recent phenomenon!

Table 3.1. Details of navigation locks on the Thames. See text for explanation of the statistics.

Lock	Date first construct	km to next lock d/s	Head loss mm 1860	Head loss mm 2013	SHWL M AOD
St John's	1790	1.85		850	71.139
Buscot		5.37		1690	70.286
Grafton	1892	2.98		1110	68.604
Radcot		4.23		1480	67.497
Rushey	1790	6.92		1820	65.987
Shifford	1896	7.63		2230	64.179
Northmoor	1896	6.21		1240	61.958
Pinkhill	1791	2.38		1050	60.705
Eynsham	1928	4.37		840	59.648
Kings	1928	1.81		770	58.809
Godstow	1790	3.87		1570	58.049
Osney	1789	3.73		1890	56.459
Iffley	c1632	2.70	1016	810	54.568
Sandford	1632	7.38	1829	2690	53.763
Abingdon	1790	4.15	1829	1890	51.049
Culham	1809	4.52	2134	2410	49.171
Clifton	1822	4.80	914	1030	46.756
Days	1788	6.37	1524	1580	45.739
Benson	1788	10.46	1372	1870	44.138
Cleeve	1787	1.00	1016	890	42.277
Goring	1787	6.55	1524	1770	41.387
Whitchurch	1787	3.67	914	1010	39.631
Mapledurham	1777	7.08	1524	2050	38.616
Caversham	1778	4.23	1372	1440	36.559
Sonning	1773	4.68	1219	1630	35.119
Shiplake		4.80	1016	1550	33.466
Marsh	1773	4.59	1372	1330	31.93
Hambledon	1773	5.89	1422	1440	30.165
Hurley	1773	1.03	1016	1050	29.145
Temple	1773	2.70	1219	1230	28.096
Marlow		6.44	1676	2160	26.852
Cookham	1830	3.35	1219	1300	24.722
Boulters	1772	3.43	1829	2390	23.404
Bray	1845	5.10	533	1460	21.046
Boveney	1838	3.75	1067	1470	19.585
Romney	1797	4.83	1626	2010	18.085
Old Windsor	1822	4.94	1219	1740	16.12
Bell	1817	4.33	1448	1820	14.411
Penton Hook	1815	3.13	762	1220	12.578
Chertsey	1813	3.32	914	1220	11.346
Shepperton	1813	4.75	1600	2030	10.14
Sunbury	1812	4.79	1219	1870	8.122
Molesey	1815	7.74	1524	1850	6.257
Teddington	1811		762	2680	4.409
Richmond	1890				

Not only did these powered craft disturb the peace and quiet of the river and often spoil fishing, they also had an impact upon the riverine environment to the detriment of fish. The wash eroded banks, uprooted aquatic plants and muddied the water, interfering further with plant growth and the fishy habitat.

Internal combustion engines only served to increase motorised boat traffic and disturbance on the river. At first these would have been inboard mounted units, often based on car and truck engines, but through the 20th century outboards grew rapidly in popularity. By 1973 there were more than 25,000 pleasure boats registered on the river, twice as many as in 1889; but in the later year the great majority would have been outboard powered, whereas in the earlier year the great majority would have been manually propelled. With outboard engines discharging their exhaust under water, and until recently being two-strokes, they would also have been discharging significant levels of oil, the greatly increased impact of boating on the water environment is obvious. However, boat usage peaked in the period 1973-1981 with over a million lock passages made each year; by 2004, lock passages were down by 40% on the peak, and boat registrations down by 25%[6]. There has been an increasing trend towards cleaner four-stroke technology for outboards, and electric boats are once again increasing in popularity, so hopefully pollution from internal combustion engines will become a thing of the past.

Navigation weirs and locks

The construction and operation of the weirs and locks for navigation purposes had a fundamental and effectively permanent impact on the habitat of the river. Some on the upper river have been in place for hundreds of years, but the lower river was finally tamed in the early 19th century. Details of the locks are shown in Table 3.1.

The first column gives the lock name, and the second the date of original construction. All have been reconstructed a number of times over the years. The third column gives the length of the reach downstream to the next lock. The fourth column gives the head loss at each lock in the year 1860; the total head loss of structures between upstream of Iffley Lock (Map 4) and downstream of Teddington Lock (at low tide) was 41.63 m. The next column shows the head drop in 2013; the total head loss at structures over the same reach (upstream of Iffley to downstream of Teddington) was 52.89 m. The last column gives the Standard Headwater Level (SHWL) for each lock above Ordnance Datum. This is the level of the crest of the weir, and is the level that would occur if there were no nett seawards flow. It is the target condition for operating and typically the levels are just a little above the standards – see Figures 3.7 and 3.8. The tailwater level is managed through control of the next weir downstream; the Standard Tailwater Level (STWL) at each weir is the same as the SHWL of the next weir. Thus almost the whole of the head loss of the navigable length of non-tidal river occurs at the weirs and locks, at least at times of low to medium flows.

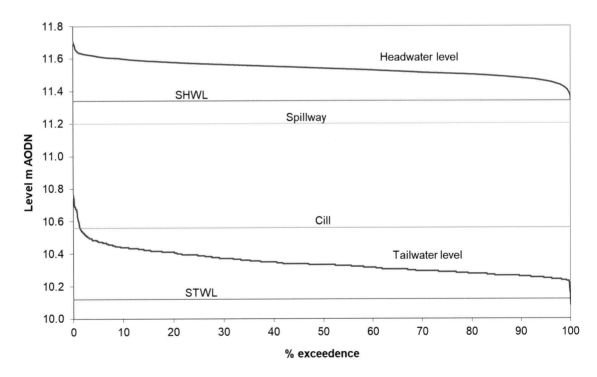

Figure 3.7. Headwater and tailwater levels at Chertsey Lock and Weir (Map 9) during 2005. It can be seen that typically both levels are 0.2 to 0.3 m above the standards (SHWL and STWL).

29

Figure 3.8. Chertsey Weir in about 1910, and in August 2009. In both cases upstream level is just above SHWL, and the weir sill in the foreground is just spilling. In 1910 control was effected through the deployment of rhymers and paddles (centre of picture), whereas nowadays automated sluices are used (far side of weir).

Water supply

The main supplier of water for domestic and industrial purposes throughout Greater London is Thames Water Utilities Ltd, generally known as Thames Water. They take most of their supply from the river between Datchet (Map 8) and Surbiton (Map 9), both for direct supply and to replenish their storage reservoirs. The rules under which water may be abstracted from the river are set by the Lower Thames Operating Agreement, between

30

Thames Water and the Environment Agency. The maximum abstractions allowed at each abstraction point are shown in Table 3.2.

Table 3.2. Maximum Thames Water takes permitted under the LTOA.

Source	Daily maximum take	Equivalent to
Datchet	2273 Ml/day	26.3 m³/sec
Staines	682 Ml/day	7.9 m³/sec
Laleham	1364 Ml/day	15.8 m³/sec
Walton	1264 Ml/day	14.6 m³/sec
Hampton	109 Ml/day	1.3 m³/sec
Thames-Lee Tunnel	682 Ml/day	7.9 m³/sec
Surbiton	109 Ml/day	1.3 m³/sec
All sources, daily max.	5455 Ml/day	63.1 m³/sec
Annual average, all sources	1818 Ml/day	21.0 m³/sec

When reservoir storage is satisfactory, there is a requirement to leave a flow over Teddington Weir of at least 800 Ml/day (9.5 m³/sec); this is downstream of all the abstraction points. However, if reservoir storage is depleted, reduction in the residual flow is permitted, in 100 Ml/day steps, down to 300 Ml/day. There are a series of control curves for this reduction based upon current total reservoir storage; all the reservoirs are part of a conjunctive use scheme. The control curves vary with the time of year; for example, at the start of the "dry season", in April, a reduction in residual flow from 800 Ml/day is permitted when the reservoir storage is at 95% capacity, whereas in December reservoir storage must be at 75% or below to trigger such a move. Any step below a residual flow of 600 Ml/day requires demand control measures, such as a hosepipe ban, to be in place.

As discussed in Chapter 2, the average reduction in flow due to abstraction between 1883 and 2011 was 13.2 m³/sec. In the early years of this period the take was much less than this figure; and between 2008 and 2017 the average reduction[7] was 22.5 m³/sec.

Chapter 3 footnotes

[1] From Thacker (1914), who obtained the image from the Thames Conservancy.
[2] Chaplin 1982
[3] The Graphic, Summer Number, 1882.
[4] "Punch" magazine, August 21 1869.
[5] Field, September 20 1873.
[6] The history of boating on the Thames; www.simonwenham.com
[7] Data from National River Flow Archive, www.ceh.ac.uk/data/nrfa

HENLEY-ON-THAMES.

From Leslie (1888).

32

CHAPTER 4

Water quality

"Dirty old river" are the opening words of "Waterloo sunset" by the Kinks, words by Ray Davies 1963. While probably justified at the time the lyrics were written, the water quality of the tidal river has improved considerably since then; and the fish have responded.

The history of Thames water quality is long and well-recorded; the tidal river and estuary is perhaps the most researched waterway in the world.

The non-tidal river, and most of the tributaries feeding the non-tidal river, have never suffered overwhelming water quality problems. Running waters of high quality have a remarkable capacity to deal with limited inputs of potentially polluting discharges, especially those that take effect through depletion of oxygen, without great impact upon their biota. However, once this capacity is exceeded, damage can be immediate and considerable. The lack of heavy industry within most of the catchment has meant low levels of contaminants have entered the river above Teddington. This is not to say that there have not been threats to the river, or that this happy state of affairs occurred without vigilance on the part of the appropriate authorities. In the year 1886 the owners of 77 gas works and chemical factories were prosecuted by the Thames Conservancy for polluting the non-tidal reaches of the river, and statutory notices were issued to the local authorities of Oxford, Abingdon, Wallingford, Reading, Henley, Marlow, Cookham, Windsor and Eton requiring them to discontinue discharging sewage into the river[1]. The smaller towns were able to comply readily with the conservators' notices, but for Oxford, Abingdon, Reading and Windsor more radical action was required. Each of these towns developed extensive sewage farms covering many acres which continued in use for much of the ensuing century. Windsor, for example, constructed a three mile long, 54 inch diameter, brick tunnel to carry raw sewage to Ham Island at Old Windsor; I recall vising the Ham Fields Sewage Treatment Works (STW) on a school trip in about 1960.

There were apparently a number of fish mortalities around 1909 due to tar-spraying of roads, but adoption of less toxic bituminous material solved this problem. For the mostpart, the water quality of the non-tidal river has remained good enough to support most species of freshwater fish, including salmonids, throughout recent history.

In contrast, the tidal river and estuary, and many of the tributaries flowing into them, have in the past been very heavily polluted, to the extent that long reaches have for considerable periods of time, been entirely fishless. From the time of earliest settlement of the London area its inhabitants have used the river and its tributaries for waste disposal. As with the non-tidal river, the natural resilience and inherent ability to absorb and process a fair level of abuse meant that water quality was not an overwhelming problem – at first. In 1828, a third of the water supply of London was still being supplied from the tidal Thames, and a further fifth from the tidal Lee at Old Ford. However, soon after this the growth of London and the increased loading of sewers meant that the natural capacity of the waterway was exceeded, and water quality deteriorated rapidly.

The water quality of the tidal Thames has been much studied, and only a summary is appropriate here. There is a good assessment in the Government report "Pollution in the tidal Thames" (Anon 1961); most of the following description up to that time is derived from there. The work of the committee making that report was in turn based upon a vast and scholarly scientific investigation commenced in 1948 (later published as Anon 1964).

In 1827 a petition to Parliament stated that:-

The water taken up from the river Thames at Chelsea for the use of inhabitants of the western portion of the Metropolis being charged with the contents of the great common sewers, the drainings of dunghills and laystalls, the refuse of hospitals, slaughterhouses, colour, lead and soap-works, drug-mills, and manufactories, and with all sorts of animal and vegetable substances, rendering the said water offensive and destructive to health, ought no longer to be taken up, by any of the water companies, from so foul a source.

A Royal Commission on Metropolitan Water Supply reported in 1828 on the state of the tidal Thames. They noted that, over the previous decade:-

..the well-ascertained fact of the disappearance of fish from those parts of the river, to such an extent as to have led to the almost entire destruction of the fisherman's trade between Putney Bridge and Greenwich; and upon the circumstance that the eels imported from Holland can now with great difficulty be kept alive in those parts of the Thames where they were formerly preserved in perfect health.

The Commission attributed the deterioration in water quality to the waste products of industry, including the manufacture of coal gas; to the disturbance of sediment by steam boats, and to the result of increased availability of water supply to houses and the adoption of the flushing toilet; *for where refuse animal and vegetable material used to be collected, and from time to time removed for the purposes of manure, it is now indiscriminately washed into the sewers, and conveyed into the Thames...*

However, it was more than twenty years later that the Metropolis Water Act of 1852 required all intakes from the tidal Thames to cease by 1856. With the pressure from water consumers removed, more and more sewage found its way into the river, and in 1860 Joseph Bazalgette and others recommended a scheme to intercept the majority of the sewage above the existing outfalls to the river, and discharge it instead seawards of the Metropolis on the ebb tide. The scheme was adopted. The Northern (Beckton) and Southern (Crossness) outfalls, located about 18 and 21 km seawards of London Bridge respectively[2] (map inside rear cover), were completed in 1864, and the remainder of the works, including the Thames Embankment by 1875. The history of the issues and the steps taken to deal with them is well told and beautifully illustrated by Stephen Halliday in 1999. It appears that there was an improvement in the situation in the immediate metropolitan area, but the scheme just exacerbated problems in the immediate vicinity of the new outfalls. This was partially solved by precipitation of the solid matter from the effluent, and carrying the resultant sludge to sea in ships to be dumped many miles seawards.

The improvement in the metropolitan area was described by Brougham in 1873[3], when he made an inspection on the river from Wandsworth upstream:-

The first person I came in contact with was John Peters, whose honest though quaint vernacular convinced me that he was one of the best type of his class. He gave me some interesting accounts of how his father some fifty years ago used to take the salmon, and also what he had done in his day; but to come to a more recent date, how he considered the water in the river was getting more pure, banks only a few years back covered with mud to the depth of two or three feet being now a comparatively clean bed of stones, the result being a larger body of fish this year than he has known for years; he added that the water was so clear he would willingly drink it. I found the boats were principally working between Wandsworth and Kew Bridge, and were mostly among the flounders, which we found of a fair average size.

The steady increase in the population of London and the associated volume of sewage put increasing stress upon the river, but superimposed on this were the various improvements in sewage treatment; there was thus distinct fluctuations in water quality through the latter part of the Victorian era.. Following the improvement associated with Bazalgette's scheme in the early 1870s deterioration once more set in and the distribution of fish in the tidal river more declined for ten or more years.

Domestic sewage was not the only unsavoury problem in Victorian times; there was also the "dead dog nuisance"![4]

The Thames Conservators have taken steps to mitigate the dead dog nuisance by the offer or twopence per body for every one put under ground at Teddington. Doust, the lockkeeper, is authorised to witness the funeral obsequies and pay the fees. The great aversion and prejudices, not to say superstition, upon the part of those most likely to avail themselves of this seasonable offering, may possibly militate against so desirable a measure. Would it not be better to employ a few men for a week or two, whose duty should be to perform this sanitary duty than leave it to the chance offices of the necessitous? And here a caution is necessary to all who would approach so repulsive an object not to let the putrescent body touch the hand, for if there is the slightest wound or scratch most serious results may follow the contact. The son of a friend of mine, in the enthusiasm of angling, searched a "Thames pet" for gentles[5], and the poor lad has not yet recovered the use of his right hand.

FARADAY GIVING HIS CARD TO FATHER THAMES;
And we hope the Dirty Fellow will consult the learned Professor.

Figure 4.1. Cartoon from Punch, July 21 1855; evidence of "the dead dog nuisance" (see text).

From about 1890, for a period of about 15 years, there was once again a distinct improvement in the water quality of the estuary, and consequent return of many species of fish that had vacated the area[6]. In 1893 whitebait and shrimp fishing boats were operating ten miles upstream of their recent former limits. In 1895 there was a sudden improvement in the distribution of fish throughout the area, with marine and brackish species moving landwards and freshwater species moving seawards to meet in London. Whitebait abounded at Greenwich and flounders returned to the upper estuary at Chiswick, for the first time in twelve years. Smelt were caught at Kew and Isleworth, and good catches were made at Teddington Lock. Lamperns (river lampreys) appeared in good numbers at Hammersmith. Shoals of dace, roach and bleak appeared at Putney, and some roach and dace were seen and a few caught at Westminster and London Bridge.

Sadly, with increasing discharges a renewed water quality decline set in around 1910; this shows clearly in Figure 4.2 in the difference between the oxygen concentration for the period from 1900 to 1905, and that for 1920. The situation remained very poor for the next forty years, as the population of and thus effluent from London increased, and two world wars diverted attention and resources from schemes that might have improved the situation.

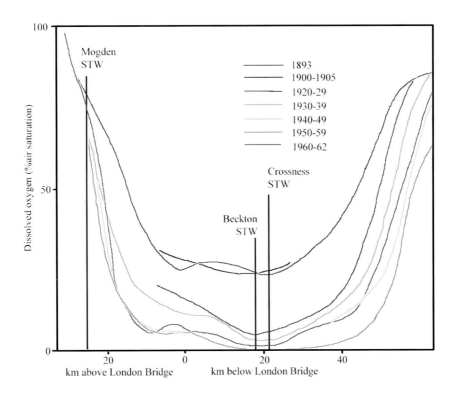

Figure 4.2. Dissolved oxygen sag curves for the period 1893 to 1962. The concentration shown is that occurring during the third quarter of the year, when freshwater flow to the estuary was around 13 m³/sec. Redrawn from Anon (1964).

37

However, infrastructure developments in the years following WWII gradually led to an improvement in the situation. In 1955 new sedimentation works were commissioned at Beckton, and in 1959 a diffused air activated sludge plant started treating about half the volume of sewage there; completion of the process occurred between 1972 and 1975. Full activated sludge treatment was commissioned at Crossness in 1963. Overall, commissioning of these works resulted in a reduction of about 80% in the polluting load discharged from the Northern and Southern Outfalls. This, coupled with improvements in the effluent from Mogden (see map inside rear cover) and other STW upstream, allowed a recovery of the dissolved oxygen throughout the tidal zone (Figure 4.3). This was accompanied by a great repopulation of the "oxygen sag" zone by fish; freshwater, estuarine and marine. Almost as soon as fish reappeared, a programme of sampling based upon fish recovered from the water intake screens of Thameside power stations developed[7].

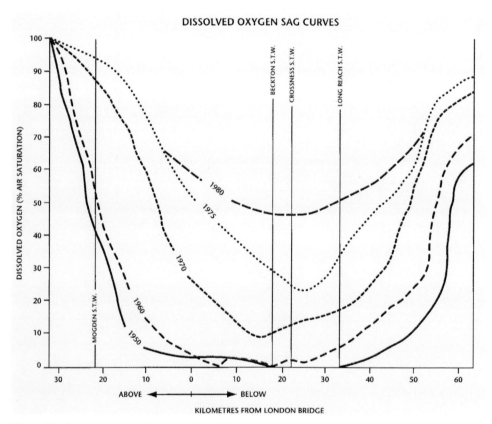

Figure 4.3. Oxygen sag curves for the period 1950 to 1980. The length of estuary represented is the same as in Figure 4.2., but the data are a little different, being the mean oxygen concentration for the period April to September. The outfall from Mogden STW is at Isleworth. From Environment Agency (1997).

The chief problem that remains with regard to water quality in the tidal Thames is that of combined sewage overflows, or CSOs. Domestic and industrial sewage is conveyed in the same sewers as surface drainage from streets, roofs and so on. After anything greater than light rain the capacity of the system to carry and process the increased volumes involved is exceeded, and a significant part of the effluent is discharged untreated directly to the Thames. In a typical year something of the order of 39 million cubic metres of combined untreated sewage is released into the tidal river in about 50 separate events. These cause a significant deterioration in water quality, and in the worst cases major fish kills can occur.

To a significant extent, the worst effects of CSOs are mitigated by deployment of the Thames Bubbler, a 600 tonne vessel operated by Thames Water Utilities which can inject up to 30 tonnes of oxygen directly into the river. It is deployed when the oxygen level falls below, or falls rapidly towards, 30% of the air saturation level (about 3 mg/litre depending on temperature).

About ten years ago an ambitious scheme was devised to deal with the CSO problem, and is currently under construction. The Thames Tideway Tunnel is a 7.2 m diameter sewer more than 30 km in length, much of it running beneath the bed of the tidal river. The first stage, completed in 2016, runs from Abbey Mills on the River Lea (one of the worst offending CSO sites) for 6.5 km to Beckton STW. The second stage, a 25 km tunnel from the outfall of Mogden STW to Abbey Mills, is currently under construction and is due for completion in 2025. When complete the tunnel will intercept 21 of the 71 CSOs directly, and a further 12 indirectly; the remainder, mainly limited volume outfalls, are being addressed through upgrades of the STWs at Mogden, Crossness, Beckton, Riverside and Long Reach. The tunnel will represent a major storage volume in its own right, with additional storage capacity at Beckton. The sewage thus retained will then be treated and discharged to the estuary. The benefits to the environment and to fish stocks between Isleworth and Beckton are likely to be tremendous.

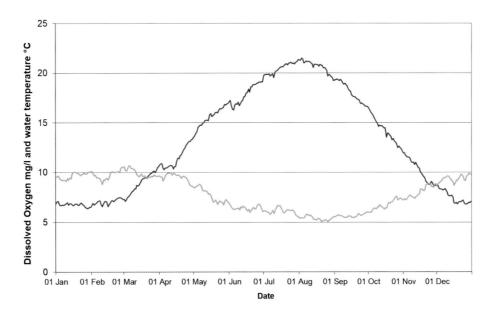

Figure 4.4. Average water temperature (red line) and dissolved oxygen level (green line) at Cadogan Pier, by calendar date, 1986-2008. Data from Environment Agency.

In Figure 4.4 the mean levels of temperature and dissolved oxygen at Cadogan Pier (23 km seawards of Teddington Weir, map 10) over a 23-year period are shown. It is not unexpected that temperature is highest and dissolved oxygen lowest (the worst combination for fish) in the late summer. While the new Thames tunnel will do little to change the water temperature, it will certainly help the dissolved oxygen situation by minimising the impact of CSO's which undoubtedly contribute significantly to the present reduced levels.

Chapter 4 footnotes

[1] Barclay 1963.
[2] See map inside back cover.
[3] The Field, September 20 1873.
[4] Field, May 18 1867.
[5] Maggots or larvae of bluebottles and other flies used as bait by anglers. The term "gentles" is still used by some.
[6] Cornish 1902
[7] Wheeler 1979

CITY NAVIGATION COMMITTEE INSPECTING THE NUISANCES ON THE RIVER.

From Punch, 1844

40

CHAPTER 5

History and development of food fisheries

Methods of capture

The fish of the Thames would have been exploited for food from the moment that our ancestors arrived on the banks of this productive river many thousands of years ago. Fish such as pike, perch, chub, roach and dace, as well as a number of smaller species, would have been readily visible in the clear water, and presented an immediate challenge to our hunter-gatherer forebears. Attempts to catch them by hand are likely to have been ineffective and tools to aid capture would quickly have been developed. Indeed, intelligence on such critical life skills is likely to have spread quickly and the earliest colonisers of the South of England would almost certainly have brought some folk experience with them. Spears and other projectiles are likely to have been the earliest technology deployed, followed by trapping, netting and hook and line fishing – there is prehistoric evidence of all these methods.

Spears were in use in Europe at least 400,000 years ago, and their use in fishing persists to this day in many parts of the world. National legislation made spearing illegal in England and Wales for taking salmon in 1861, trout in 1878, and freshwater fish in 1923. Use of eel spears continued to be legal, though the fish are not actually impaled by these instruments but are caught between tapered tines and are undamaged. However, the use of a spear upstream of London Bridge for any species, including eels, was prohibited by the Thames Conservancy Byelaws of August 1893.

Figure 5.1. Stakes that formed part of a Saxon fish trap in the tidal Thames at Chelsea in 2019. Carbon dating puts construction between AD 660 and 890[1].

Figure 5.2. Seine netting between Twickenham and Isleworth (Maps 9-10), about 1750. The anglers on the right are likely to have been unimpressed! From Phillips (1951).

There is evidence of fixed fish traps being used in tidal waters from ancient times; these were generally constructed to capture fish on the ebb tide so that the catch could be collected at low tide. Remains of several such traps are still to be seen at several points on the tidal river, for example at Isleworth and Chelsea (Figure 5.1; Map 10).

Seine nets, that is a wall of netting that is used to surround the fish and haul them to the bank, have been in use for thousands of years; an ancient Egyptian drawing shows a seine net being used[2] . Thames regulations from the 16th century refer to stalker nets, trynk nets, purse nets and berd nets, most of which are believed to have been forms of seine. Casting nets, weighted sheets of netting that were thrown over shoals of fish, were also used from early times; the same 16th century regulations refer to casting nets and heaving nets.

Seine nets in use on the Thames are shown in Figures 5.2, 5.3 and 5.4. In early days the lower edge of the net was held down by stone weights, with either a hole or a groove around them to aid securing with rope or twine. Some were of natural limestone almost "as found", some were worked to improve their form, while others were made from fired brick clay. These weights often became detached and lost, and examples are still occasionally to be found among the gravel in shallow water. Drawings of a few recovered from the Thames are shown in Figure 5.5; the ones shown are believed to date from between the 13th and 14th centuries.

Figure 5.3. Seine netting in the upper reaches at Radcot Bridge (Map 2) in about 1790[3].

Figure 5.4. Seine netting and dip netting at Westminster (Map 10), 1756[4].

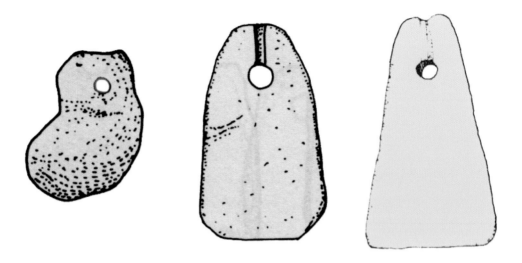

Figure 5.5. Seine net weights (stone) found in the Thames[5]. Left; probably "as found", but with drilled perforation; centre; worked limestone; right; fired brick clay. Redrawn from Steane and Foreman (1988).

Figure 5.6. Wicker fish trap from the 15th or 16th century, recovered from the moat at the Tower of London, somewhat squashed. Stone weights are still attached. The Petri dishes contain fish bones recovered from the trap. Also shown is an eel spear. Museum of London.

44

Perhaps the most widespread fishing technique involved the use of mesh traps of some form, some of which were very local in design and specific to the Thames. Hoop nets (Figure 5.7) were set overnight with their open end downstream, to intercept any fish moving upstream. A wide range of species was exploited by these nets; Robertson listed perch, pike, chub, roach, dace and even moorhens and otters as being "fair game" for the method.

Figure 5.7. Hoop net hanging up to dry. From Robertson (1875).

Eels were trapped with three different specialised sets of gear, all in use over several hundred years. The first two intercepted adult eels on their downstream migration to the sea. First, many mills incorporated eel traps based upon near-horizontal iron bars which allowed the water to drain through but not the eels (or indeed any other fish or waterborne debris). The bars were inclined so that the wriggling of the stranded eels caused them to fall into a collecting trough at the downstream edge. This led to a catch box where the eels would stay alive almost indefinitely; eels were generally distributed and sold live.

Figure 5.8. Lowering eel bucks. The side-arm allows removal of the captured fish. From Robertson (1875).

Second, eel bucks were large basket traps set into weirs or causeways with a head drop.

They could be raised for emptying and for protection when not in use (see figure 5.8). Details of many installations on the Thames are given in Annex 3. Bucks would also trap other species of fish moving downstream, or even salmon migrating upstream when they rested and dropped back a little immediately upstream of a weir (see Chapter 20).

The third widespread eel capture method was the grig, or "weel" (Figure 5.9). These are smaller baskets, which are laid on the river bed overnight to catch exploring and feeding eels. Although eels were usually the target catch for these traps, on occasions a wide range of species were caught. Englefield recorded one basket set during coloured water conditions yielding five eels, three crayfish, a coot, many minnows, a bullhead, four small pike and a drowned water-vole. Grigs could be purchased around the year 1900 from a Mr Bambridge of Eton; these cost 5 shillings (25p) unweighted, or seven shillings and six pence (37.5p) weighted[6]. Eels were of course also captured by other more general fishing methods such as hoop and seine nets, and night lines.

Figure 5.9. A Thames eel grig. Note the weight tied to the basket to hold it to the river bed. Lantern slide, origin, exact location and date unknown.

Figure 5.10. This picture of Marlow Weir, engraved in 1818[7], shows gear for several Thames fishing methods of the time. To the left a raised eel buck is visible. In the punts are a seine net, two eel grigs, and a rake for gudgeon fishing (see chapter 16). Beneath the grigs can be seen bundles of cut willow osiers, used for making grigs and bucks.

The use of willow twigs for making fish traps and baskets for produce gave rise to a significant local industry, osier production. This was suitable use for low-lying islands (eyots or aits) and riverside areas as frequent flooding made them unsuitable for most other forms of agriculture. Osier growing and processing is described in detail by Robertson and Cornish.

Young willow plants were reared for a year in nurseries, and planted out in specially-prepared ground in late winter, a one foot gap between each, in rows two feet apart. Weeding was essential at least twice a year for two years, though once the osiers became established their own growth shaded out further weeds. The harvested rods were single year growth and up to nine feet in length. The rods were cut close to the ground, leaving only the bases of each osier (Figure 5.12). Cutting, using a reaping hook, was done in early spring, and the

Figure 5.11. A modern copy of an eel buck, showing details of the design and construction. The inlet funnel tapered to a small diameter which made it difficult for the eels to escape once they had passed this point. Photograph reproduced by kind permission of the River and Rowing Museum, Henley.

rods sorted into four size categories called, from thinnest to thickest, Luke, Threepenny, Middleborough and Great. They were then bundled into "bolts" of 40 inches circumference for processing or sale.

Before processing, the bolts were stood in water for a month, until the rods started sprouting. The sap thus raised aided the stripping of the bark. They were then peeled of their bark using special tools called "breaks" (Figure 5.13). The stripped rods were then ready for making baskets, fish traps etc. In Figure 5.14, a series of eel grigs are displayed in front of a dozen or so workers engaged in osier peeling. The peeled bark was used as fertiliser for potato crops, or as a form of thatch for cow sheds and stables.

Figure 5.12. Osier harvesting. From Robertson (1875).

Figure 5.13. Osier peeling. From Robertson (1875)

48

Figure 5.14. Osier processing and the manufacture of eel grigs at Beesley's Rush Works, Fisher Row, Oxford, in 1901. From Cornish (1902).

A Public right to fish?

For many years there was a considerable debate regarding whether or not there was a public right of fishing in the Thames. As described in Chapter 1, downstream of the City Stone at Staines the rights were vested in the public and were managed by the City of London. But upstream of here, argument raged. Things seem to have come to a bit of a head about the year 1787, but it was over a hundred years later before it was finally resolved beyond all doubt.

The opening shot in the 1787 spat appeared to have been the establishment of an "*Association for the Public Right of Fishing in the Thames and for preventing the unlawful Destruction of fish*"[8]. The inaugural meeting was held at the Royal Oak in Reading on June 11, and subscription books were set up at several tackle shops in Reading, Henley, Marlow, Maidenhead and London. The second meeting was scheduled for July 24 in Marlow.

Apparently in response to this initiative, an advertisement appeared in the local press[9] threatening legal action against anyone fishing without permission on stretches of the river. It was placed by a group of owners of 31 fisheries and stated:-

The several Persons whose Names are hereunder written, Proprietors or Occupiers of the Fisheries in the different Parts of the Rivers Thames and Isis, observing that an Association is formed against their several properties, do hereby individually, and each for himself, give notice to all Persons, not renting any of their respective Fisheries, or having

Permission from the Owner or Occupier thereof, that they will be prosecuted by each and every of the undersigned Proprietors and Occupiers, upon whom trespass shall be made.

The following year, one of the above owners placed another notice; it stated that;

Whereas the Water belonging to John Phillips Esq: in the Parishes of Abingdon and Radley, hath lately been very much fished, This is to give Notice That if any one will give Information of any Person or Persons fishing the same with Nets, so that he or they may be brought to Justice, shall, on Conviction of the Offender or Offenders, receive FIVE GUINEAS Reward. All Persons are hereby cautioned not to angle or otherwise fish the said Waters, without actual Leave to be granted, as they will be prosecuted according to the Law[10]

Around this period a number of pamphlets were produced each purporting to prove that there was a public right of fishing within the river; three examples are Hodgson (1787), Allnut (1810) and Nash (1826). But they appear to have made little impression on the *status quo*, and little more then appears to have happened upon this issue until late in the 19th century. By then, the arguments over a public right of fishing centred almost entirely on recreational rather than commercial fishing, so further consideration of this issue is dealt-with in the next chapter, covering angling.

Some records of fisheries on the Thames

The earliest records of Thames fisheries come from the Domesday survey of 1086. In the seven counties comprising the catchment upstream of London Bridge there were at least 163 "fisheries" listed. Darby suggests that most references to fisheries implied some kind of fixed installation such as a weir or fish trap. This suggestion is supported by the occasional references to fishermen (as opposed to fisheries) paying renders, and to a single reference to a seine fishery in Surrey. Most of the fisheries were on the main river, but a significant minority were on tributaries such as the Wey, Colne, Wick (Wye), Loddon, Kennet and Thame. Most paid a rent as money, but 43 paid all or part as eel renders, totalling more than 19,000 eels per annum. Details are provided in Chapter 15. Further, most manors had one or more watermills, most of which would operate fish traps as a secondary source of income. Seventeen mills in the catchment paid all or some of their rent as eels, totalling more than 3,600 eels per annum. Thus in total, more than 22,600 eels were paid as rent per year in the catchment; the total catch would have been significantly more than this, though it is possible that the eel rent on mills represented most of their catch as fishing was not their main interest or income. All these numbers are minimum estimates as the Domesday recording is regarded as highly incomplete; for example, no fisheries are recorded anywhere in Wiltshire.

In addition to eel rent, a fishery at Petersham paid a rent of 1000 lampreys per annum.

Given the difficulty with distribution of food over large distances and the perishability of fish, it is entirely to be expected that freshwater fish were heavily exploited away from the coast, and that most of the catch was sold and consumed locally.

The history of fisheries around Oxford in the 15th to 18th centuries is described by Prior. There was an extensive "free" fishery in the Thames and its associated waterways, between Magdalen Bridge and Godstow, a total of about seven miles of waterway. Reference to this fishery as "free" indicates that it was separate (or free from) the ownership of the adjacent land, rather than meaning it was literally free for all. Having said that, control was vested in the City and fishing was allowed for all freemen of the city (a freeman was anyone who was not a slave, servant or employee). Management of the fishery was undertaken by water bailiffs, who, rather than receiving payment direct, paid the City for the privilege and made their income from perquisites and fines imposed on offenders. This arrangement ensured that the regulations, such as close times, gear restrictions and who could fish, were rigorously applied. For example, a notice in 1620 required all participating fishermen to bring their "tramills, castingnets, flagnetts, shownetts and all other nets and gynes" to be checked against the standard, presumably a check on dimensions and mesh sizes. In 1556 the City decided to lease out the fishing rights to a number of fishermen, thus denying other freemen of their right of fishing. Complaints from the disenfranchised appear to have been heard, and although the leases had been granted for 21 years, they were rescinded after only two years.

Pike were very highly esteemed as food in mediaeval times. In the latter part of the 13th century the price of fish was regulated by statute to prevent market exploitation, and the price of pike was fixed higher than that of salmon, and several times that of cod and turbot[11]. Calculation of the price per pound of various species sold in South Staffordshire in 1461, which depended upon assumptions regarding average weights, put pike at about 2½ d per pound compared to cod at around ½ d [12]. At these price levels pike are likely to have been sold to the rich rather than being consumed by the poor; John Gere was described as a "pikemonger" in 1452, and supplied fish to the Duke of Buckingham. Similarly, William Walis of London supplied large quantities of pike to Ann, Duchess of Buckingham in 1455-6[13].

A document from 1556 gives important information on what species were marketed in the Oxford area and the relative values of each. This is a list of the fish purchased and supplied during Lent 1555/6 to Thomas Cranmer, the former Archbishop of Canterbury who was sentenced to death by Queen Mary I, during his imprisonment in Oxford before his execution[14]. This is summarised in Table 5.1. The price shown is apparently the total for the fish to make a single meal for four people, so presumably the weight involved is broadly similar for each species. The period covered is February 19 to March 20; Cranmer was executed on March 21.

It is likely that the freshwater fish, with the exception of the salmon, were locally caught. The salmon may have come from the Lower Thames (see Chapter 20), and the sea fish probably came from London; they may have been salted or dried. "Stock fish" were sea fish that had been split open and died in the sun, without being salted. The predominance of "ling" is interesting. The ling is a deepwater species of the cod family occurring off Western Britain, but it is unlikely to have been a major commercial species at that time. It is suggested that the reference includes cod itself, which was otherwise a surprising omission from a list of commonly-marketed sea fish.

The high value of pike is again clear; 50% more than spring salmon. One surprising absentee from the list is gudgeon, one of the tastiest of the local freshwater fish.

Table 5.1. List of fish purchased during Lent 1555/6[15] to feed four people.

Species	Approx price pence (d)	Number of times served
Herring	3	49
"Ling"	7	46
Roach	6	19
Perch	6	16
Pike	12	14
Salt salmon	9	14
"Stockfish"	5	7
Eels	6	6
Fresh salmon	8	6
Thornback	8	5
Dace	6	2
Gurnard	9	1

Astonishingly, one still hears the tale of apprentices and salmon, about the Thames and many other rivers. As long ago as 1829 a correspondent in the Gentleman's Magazine wrote:-

It is rather a pleasant task than otherwise, to dispel illusions long current. An idea is prevalent that salmon was once so common in our great rivers that clauses were inserted in the indentures of apprentices to the effect that it should not be served as food more than twice, or thrice, a week. The most curious thing concerning the whole matter is that no proof of the existence of such an indenture can be found. Scores of people assert that they have seen it, and many have been sanguine as to their ability to lay their hands upon it. In no case whatever has it been forthcoming.

And in 1883, Fisheries Inspector Frank Buckland wrote *I am quite tired of hearing this story, and almost weary from hunting for an actual copy of an apprentice's indenture containing the clause.*

Despite more than 130 elapsed years since Buckland, still no-one has produced documentary evidence to support this old chestnut. The nearest I can come is to say that at one stage in my career I considered putting into any contract involving research on fishery history that I wouldn't have to hear the apprentice story more than three times a week.

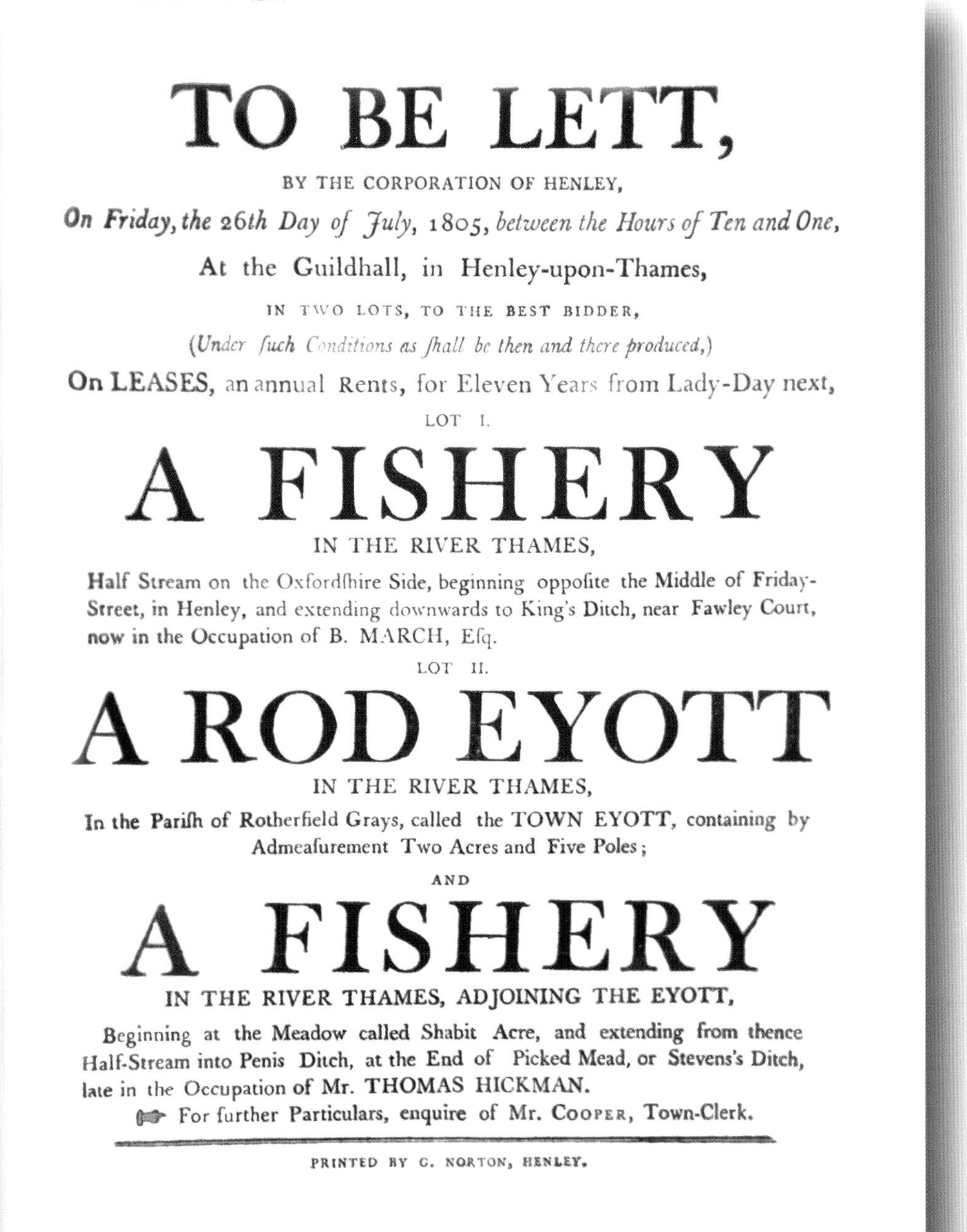

TO BE LETT,

BY THE CORPORATION OF HENLEY,

On Friday, the 26th Day of July, 1805, between the Hours of Ten and One,

At the Guildhall, in Henley-upon-Thames,

IN TWO LOTS, TO THE BEST BIDDER,

(Under such Conditions as shall be then and there produced,)

On **LEASES**, an annual Rents, for Eleven Years from Lady-Day next,

LOT I.

A FISHERY

IN THE RIVER THAMES,

Half Stream on the Oxfordshire Side, beginning opposite the Middle of Friday-Street, in Henley, and extending downwards to King's Ditch, near Fawley Court, now in the Occupation of B. MARCH, Esq.

LOT II.

A ROD EYOTT

IN THE RIVER THAMES,

In the Parish of Rotherfield Grays, called the TOWN EYOTT, containing by Admeasurement Two Acres and Five Poles;

AND

A FISHERY

IN THE RIVER THAMES, ADJOINING THE EYOTT,

Beginning at the Meadow called Shabit Acre, and extending from thence Half-Stream into Penis Ditch, at the End of Picked Mead, or Stevens's Ditch, late in the Occupation of Mr. THOMAS HICKMAN.

☛ For further Particulars, enquire of Mr. COOPER, Town-Clerk.

PRINTED BY G. NORTON, HENLEY.

Figure 5.15. A handbill advertising the sale of fisheries and osier beds at Henley in 1805. One cannot help wondering how Penis Ditch got its name! Another copy of this notice, held by the River and Rowing Museum, bears handwritten notes recording that Lot 1 went to John Fisher for £7 per annum, and lot 2 to Thomas Honey for £16 per annum.

Given the poor transport links and the lack of ability to keep dead fish "fresh" during distribution, many captured fish were kept alive in ponds until they were sold. In the years 1813 and 1815 my great, great, great grandfather, living in Benson, Oxfordshire, gave his occupation as fishmonger[16]. His house backed onto a pool formed off the Ewelme Brook which was called a "fish pond" in the Tithe survey of 1840. It is likely that he used this pond to store live fish captured in the River Thames a few hundred metres away.

Commercial exploitation of freshwater fish continued well into the 19th century. Alfred Church, writing in 1892 of his student days around 1850, described how fishing for gudgeon (a small species, see Chapter 16) around Mapledurham was excellent because of the eradication of their predators and larger competitors through netting:-

The keeper of the lock at Mapledurham, Shepherd by name, was the most inveterate destroyer of fish that the Thames has ever known. He rented the right of netting from the neighbouring proprietors, and "skinned" the river, to use the expressive term which is applied in such cases, relentlessly. There was no-one in those days to inquire into the size of the mesh, and with his bag nets and his flue nets, and other diabolical contrivances of misplaced ingenuity, he cleared the river of everything that was much above the size of a sprat.

Church added that the lock keeper sometimes would send as much as half a ton of fish at one time to Leadenhall Market in London; by this time the arrival of railways made distribution of fish much more efficient. But it was this very improvement in the logistics of distributing fish that probably in turn caused the demise of commercial fishing for coarse fish. As an alternative, sea fish were plentiful, readily available, inexpensive and generally preferable to eat.

Chapter 5 footnotes

[1] Cowie and Blackmore (2008).
[2] Whymper (1883)
[3] Ireland (1792)
[4] Thomas Sandby, 1756.
[5] Redrawn from Steane and Foreman (1988).
[6] Cornish (1902).
[7] "The weir from Marloe bridge", by William Havell. Published in 1818.
[8] Reading Mercury, July 2 1787.
[9] Oxford Journal, September 15 1787.
[10] Oxford Journal, August 2 1788.
[11] Yarrell (1859).
[12] Dyer (1988).
[13] Dyer (1988).
[14] Prior (1982).
[15] At this time New Year was still in March.
[16] Source; christening records for Cook's two sons.

CHAPTER 6

History and development of angling

The history of angling on the Thames is basically the history of angling itself. It is likely that fishing as a sport gradually evolved from fishing for food and profit. Rod and line was in use as a fish catching method in Roman times, and most early anglers would have kept the fish they caught, and eaten any that were palatable (and probably some that were not!). We know that angling as a sport existed by the time that the *Treatyse of fishing with an angle* (attributed to Dame Juliana Berners) was published in 1653, and the Thames was likely to have been at the forefront of the gradual evolution from fishing for food to fishing for pleasure. Dedicated fishing tackle shops are recorded in London as early as the mid 17th century (see chapter 9).

Figure 6.1 Fishing at Appleford (Map 4) in 1938. Angling was a very popular holiday pastime by then.

Figure 6.2.   Fishing at Teddington Lock in 1892[1]. On the bank there are eleven anglers in a few yards of river, with another sitting smoking and perhaps wondering where he can fit in between them. In contrast, on the extreme right of the picture there are two anglers fishing from a punt moored across the stream, with nearly the whole river their exclusive reserve.

By the 18th century a real class distinction had appeared among the ranks of Thames fishers. Requiring no licence and a minimal financial outlay in terms of tackle and bait, angling was a popular pastime among poorer folk who doubtless saw it as both recreation and a source of food. The result is that waters accessible to a large working population, such as the lower Thames, were often crowded with enthusiastic anglers. Those with rather more disposable income could travel further afield, and afford the services of a professional fisherman equipped with a punt (see Chapter 9). This allowed access to fishing locations that bank anglers could not reach, greatly increasing the scope of fishing and virtually guaranteeing exclusive enjoyment of the chosen swim. This in turn made pre-baiting the swim a viable option, with improved catches the result. This practice was particularly valuable in the pursuit of barbel, as described in Chapter 10. This distinction is well illustrated in Figure 6.2.

From the birth of angling, there was free fishing in the Thames downstream of the London Stone at Staines (Map 8), a charter granted to the City of London by King Richard I. Upstream of there the rights were the property of the riparian owner, but for the mostpart owners were very relaxed about defending their fishing rights, at least from the towpath. Indeed most anglers considered that there was a public right of fishing from the towpath and from boats, which led to a number of disputes. Something of the history of this saga with regard to netting has already been described in Chapter 5. But things came to a head regarding rights of angling in the last twenty years of the 19th Century, when several developments occurred. In November 1880 a public meeting in London established the Thames Defence Rights Association[2], with the aim of resisting encroachment on the rights of the public in the River Thames by riparian owners. The Committee included many of the great and the good in fisheries management of the period. The chairman was Francis Francis, and the committee included Bonvoisin, Geen and Ghurney from the (London) Anglers Association, R B Marston of the Fishing Gazette, and angling authors Greville Fennel and J P Wheeldon. In 1881 and 1882 the Association supported the defence of two fishermen in the Maidenhead area who were prosecuted by riparian owners for fishing on what they considered their property. Both prosecutions failed on the grounds that the plaintiffs had failed to demonstrate that they had an exclusive right of fishing at the locations concerned. The committee suggested that these results *dealt a heavy blow and great discouragement to persons who were, before the establishment of the Association, fabricating claims to exclusive rights from one end of the river to the other.*

An important document in terms of Thames fishery history is the 1884 report of the Select Committee appointed by Parliament *to inquire into the operation of the Acts for the Preservation of the Thames, and the steps which are necessary to secure the enjoyment of the River, as a place of recreation…* Scope was limited to the non-tidal river from Teddington upstream. Although the report itself was short, only ten pages, it was thorough and authoritative, and had appended nearly 500 pages of minutes of evidence, including long and detailed legal opinion on the issue of whether or not there was a public right to fishing.

The argument that there was no public right of fishing was presented by Stuart Archibald Moore, a barrister specialising in riparian and fisheries rights; he was later joint author of an authoritative book on the history of fisheries law (Moore and Moore, 1903). He argued that the fishing rights went with the ownership of the river bed, and that the fact that the river was navigable did not mean that the riparian owners did not own the river bed. This argument was countered by Percival Birkett, a solicitor representing the Commons Preservation Society. He argued that ownership of the river bed did not reside with the riparian owners as far as fisheries were concerned. The Select Committee supported Stuart Moore's view that no general public right of fishing existed on the Thames. While recognising the unique and complex nature of Thames fishing rights, they concluded:-

That the fisheries are or have been (the property of the Lords of the respective manors) and are now apportioned out among various owners, to whom the franchises have been granted in past times, seems indisputable, and it is therefore impossible to recognise anything like a general public right to take fish as now existing; and

Your Committee believe that the present relations between the owners of fisheries and the fishing public, especially so far as the latter are represented by numerous angling clubs, are generally satisfactory, and that the general public have only to know that their rights are imaginary to induce them also to be content with the extant system, under which permission is very freely granted by the owners of fisheries to the public for angling on the more frequented areas of the Thames.

Figure 6.3. Fishing downstream of Hurley Weir (Map 7) in 1876[3]. Soon after this it was finally established that riparian owners upstream of Staines had the right to control both bank and boat fishing, though this right was not usually exercised. Note eel bucks in background.

The conclusion of the Select Committee was challenged in a high-profile court case a few years later in 1891, in the case of Smith v Andrews. The plaintiff was a riparian owner, Mrs Annie Smith, who laid claim to a private right of fishing from near Maidenhead Bridge down to Bray. The defendant was a professional fisherman (ie an angling guide as all commercial netting had ceased by this time) who took clients fishing in the disputed water, despite several warnings. The judge found for the plaintiff, effectively ending any hopes of demonstrating a public right to fish in the river. One of the defendant's arguments was that the plaintiff and her predecessors had allowed fishing in the area for many years without challenge or complaint, but the judge felt that this had no bearing on the case. A full report of the judgement, which makes interesting reading, was printed in the Fishing Gazette dated May 23 1891.

After this, the situation apparently reverted to that described by the Select Committee, with riparian owners having a generous and laid-back attitude to their exclusive rights, with little challenge to *bona fide* anglers. In the 1960s I fished the Thames extensively, including the reach figuring in the Smith v Andrews case, without let or hindrance; indeed, I and I suspect most Thames anglers at that time still believed that there was indeed a public right of fishing from the towpath bank. Since then, much more of the riverbank has been held by local and regional angling organisations either for the exclusive enjoyment of their members, or in addition available to visitors on payment for a day ticket. The fishing from Staines downstream remains free, and it is usually possible to find free fishing elsewhere on public land and where the owner has not rented out, or does not defend, the rights.

Size limits

Rules regarding size limits have been in force for hundreds of years, though before the mid 1800s they were really aimed at commercial fishermen rather than anglers. One very early regulation was contained in an Act of Elizabeth I passed in 1558 (*A general provision for preserving the spawn, brood and fry of fish*). In this size limits were set for pike at 10 inches, salmon 16, trout 8 and barbel 16. Rules specific to the Thames were introduced in 1584 by Sir Thomas Pullington, Lord Mayor of London, who had jurisdiction over the river. The limits set were pike 14 inches, barbel 12, salmon 16, trout 8, tench 8, roach 6, dace 6, and flounders 6. Other species *are not yet assized*. In 1757 the Lord Mayor, Marshe Dickinson, issued a detailed set of rules, orders and ordinances governing Thames fisheries. Size limits set were 6 lb for salmon and 1 lb for trout; for other species a length limit was applied, but oddly the measurement was taken from the eye to end of the tail; pike 12 inches, perch 6, flounders 6, roach 6, dace 6, barbel 12 and chub, 9. The penalty for transgression was a fine of forty shilling (two pounds).

Jurisdiction of the Thames fishery passed to the Thames Conservancy in 1857 (lower river downstream of Staines) and in 1866 (upper river), by which time angling dominated Thames fisheries. Size limit byelaws from then on were clearly aimed at anglers, but with the same overall aim as before, preventing the killing of small fish. The 1883 Byelaws of the Thames Conservancy contained the following:-

No fish of the species hereinafter mentioned shall be taken in or out of the River Thames, or having been taken, shall be had in possession, or be exposed to sale on the River Thames, or on the shore thereof, or on any lands adjoining or near the river, of less than the respective sizes and dimensions following:- (this section is not intended to apply to any person who takes such fish accidentally, and forthwith returns the fish the same to the water with the least possible injury). (Sizes shown in Table 6.1)

Table 6.1. Thames size limits (extreme length), inches.

Species	1883	1914	1976
Barbel	13	16	15.7 (40 cm)
Bleak		4	3.9 (10 cm)
Bream	10	12	11.8 (30 cm)
Carp	10	12	11.8 (30 cm)
Chub	10	12	11.8 (30 cm)
Dace	6	7	5.9 (15 cm)
Flounder	7	7	
Gudgeon	4	5	5.1 (13 cm)
Perch	8	9	8.7 (22 cm)
Pike	18	18	23.6 (60 cm)
Roach	7	8	7.1 (18 cm)
Tench	8	10	9.8 (25 cm)
Trout	16	16	9.8 (25 cm)

New byelaws were enacted in 1914, in which the wording was revised along with many of the species size limits. The new wording read:-

No person shall take in or out of the Thames, or have in his possession, or expose for sale on the river, or on the shores or banks thereof, or within 100 yards either side of the Thames, any fish of the species hereinafter mentioned of less than the sizes and dimensions hereinafter mentioned (extreme measurements): (Sizes shown in Table 6.1.)

Provided that this byelaw shall not apply:-

To any person who takes any undersized fish unintentionally and at once returns such fish alive to the Thames, with as little injury as possible.

To any roach, dace gudgeon, bleak, or minnows taken from the Thames for use as bait, to be used by persons angling in the Thames. Provided that no person on the Thames, or on the banks or shores thereof, or within 100 yards on either side of the Thames, shall be entitled to have in his possession, or under his control, at any one time more than fifty such fish for use as bait, or take from the Thames by himself, his servants or agents, more than fifty of such fish on any one day.

Until WWII most anglers still killed most of the fish that they caught which were above the size limit. Keep nets had been developed by the early 20th century but were not in widespread use, and participating in fishing matches made killing the catch inevitable. However, even when not fishing in a match killing and keeping the catch was the general rule, even if most of the fish were not to be consumed or put to any other useful end. But after the war this changed rapidly, such that by the late 1950s few coarse fish were being killed (with the exception of pike), and the size limit regulations served little purpose in fisheries management terms. These size limits applied until the demise of Thames Conservancy in 1974. The new Thames Water Authority changed the size limits a little, taking the opportunity to "go metric". The 1976 byelaw size limits are shown in Table 6.1. This byelaw specifically stated that fish below the size limit could be retained in a keepnet for the duration of the fishing session, opening the possibility for "all-in" matches to be fished on the river (see Chapter 8).

Figure 6.4. A catch of seventy roach averaging more than 8 oz each, taken just over a hundred years ago. At that time it was usual to kill all the fish caught over the size limit (then 8 inches for roach, about 4 oz), even if there was little prospect of them being eaten or used in any way.

In 1961, Fishing Gazette printed an interesting exchange of correspondence on the matter of Thames size limits between two of the great anglers of the day, Fred J Taylor and Peter Stone. Taylor[4] argued that the rules were anachronistic, as few anglers retained fish by then; also that they precluded 'all-in' matches. He also argued that a reverse size limit would make more sense, allowing anglers to remove little fish (of which he argued that there were too many in the Thames) but not larger specimens. Stone[5] responded by agreeing with Taylor regarding the 'reverse size limit' idea, but arguing that holding 'all-in' matches would be a retrograde step in fisheries management terms. Support for the idea that there were too many small fish and that their growth was stunted came from a study of the fish populations in the reach of river between Caversham and Sonning weirs. This was funded by the London Anglers Association, and was conducted by Reading University. A preliminary report on the investigation[6] concluded that the roach were overcrowded and stunted, and recommended a reduction in numbers by encouraging anglers to retain small fish (though this was not legal at that time) and by encouraging populations of predators such as perch and pike. In the event nothing was changed and the rule forbidding retention of undersized fish remained in place until 1974.

The current byelaws are very different. National byelaws apply to the Thames, and these allow retention each day of one pike of less than 65 cm, two grayling between 30 and 38 cm, and up to 15 barbel, chub, common bream, carp, crucian carp, dace, perch, roach, rudd, silver bream, smelt or tench of less than 20 cm. Shad and eels must be returned to the water alive, but other species (effectively in the case of the Thames, gudgeon, bleak and pope) may be retained in unlimited numbers and of any size. Incidentally, the length to be taken was from the tip of the snout to the fork of the tail, in contrast to earlier bye-laws which measured to the tip of the tail. The logic behind these rules is baffling; why would the taking of up to 15 barbel of less than 20 cm be condoned?

Night fishing

Under Thames Conservancy rules, night fishing (angling) from the bank was permitted throughout the river until 1894, though night fishing from a boat was forbidden. The relevant 1883[7] bye-law read:-

No person shall do, aid or assist in doing the following things, or any of them, that is to say:-

Fish from any vessel, boat or punt, for or take, attempt to take, above Richmond Bridge, any fish except in the day time, that is to say between the beginning of the last hour before sunrise and the end of the last hour after sunset.

However, a blanket ban on night fishing upstream of Staines was introduced in 1894. The wording of the bye-law dated 1894 was:-

Bye-law 25. No person shall fish for, take or attempt to take, by any means whatsoever, in that part of the Thames as lies above the City Stone at Staines, nor from any vessel in that part of the Thames that lies between the City Stone and London Bridge, any fish, between the expiration of the first hour after sunset, and the last hour before sunrise.

The reason for this ban was made clear in a letter from the great A E Hobbs in the Fishing Gazette[8] in 1960:-

Dear Sir, Sixty seven years ago I as Hon Sec to the then Henley Fisheries Preservation Association, was invited by the Conservators of the Thames to assist them in their deliberations in regard to revising the Rules and regulations of their Fishery By-laws. In those days there was a considerable amount of night poaching with large casting nets and small flue nets; the By-laws were revised to check this offence and are in force today.

In the intervening years great changes have occurred and a large proportion of the private fishing above Staines in now rented by clubs and associations, therefore it is the main responsibility of such clubs to do their own keepering. Believing that the majority of anglers are good sportsmen I would not now oppose night fishing, and feel that they would do their best to prevent breaches of the By-laws by uninformed and junior anglers.

Yours faithfully, A E Hobbs.

There was a considerable correspondence on this issue, including a letter from Richard Walker[9] (who also favoured permitting night fishing).

Thames Conservancy were not moved by these arguments, but one of the first actions taken by the new Thames Water Authority in 1974 was to drop the night fishing ban.

The etiquette of pre-baiting swims

Mention has already been made of the practice of pre-baiting swims during the day or days before fishing. There was a definite etiquette involved in respecting others' efforts in pre-baiting swims, and there was a convention of marking such spots by leaving a ryepeck (see Chapter 9) jammed into the river bed. Wheeley describes it thus:-

Should one man bait a swim, it is arrant poaching on the part of another to take advantage of that baiting for his own sport. The professional who deliberately allows, or takes a customer to fish a swim baited by some one else would never, after such a flagrant breach of etiquette, be employed by me. There are two sides to this question, however, as I cannot see that any one has a right to bait a swim and say that he only shall fish that swim for perhaps a week straight off; this may mean the monopoly of the best barbel-swim in a mile or more of water. Again, ryepecks are left to mark some of the baited swims (or those supposed to be baited) for days and days together; meanwhile the angler who is a sportsman leaves that particular spot alone, perhaps being debarred from trying a really good pitch.

A disagreement between two well-known anglers regarding a baited swim resulted in protracted correspondence in the press, and legal proceedings. John Jones and J W Gant were staying at the French Horn at Sonning in September 1876, and in conversation Gant let slip that he had been groundbaiting a swim for barbel fishing for a few days. Jones arose early the next morning and fished the swim before Gant arrived. Gant accused Jones of unsportsmanlike behaviour, writing in a note to The Field[10] "*there is no way I could write sufficiently expressive to convey my contempt*", and giving Jones' full name and address. A lively correspondence ensued over the following months, culminating in a court case for libel being brought by Jones, contending that he was entitled to an apology or damages for having been maliciously charged by the defendant with unsportsmanlike behaviour. The jury found for Jones, and the judge granted damages of one pound, plus costs[11]. The costs far exceeded the value of the damages granted. This was not the end of the matter, for at the next meeting of the Piscatorial Society, of which Gant was Treasurer, a collection was proposed by fellow member Mr Jardine to contribute to the court costs, and an astonishing sum of £52 10 s was raised in a few minutes. Members further demonstrated their support of Mr Gant by voting him as chairman for the occasion of their annual dinner[12].

Thames angling records

Although there is no official repository for listing record fish and catches from the Thames, various lists have been prepared in the past. The ones described here were made in 1955, 1973 and 2018.

The 1955 list was published in the Fishing Gazette on May 7, 1955, and was updated by correspondence over the following weeks. No details of captor, location and date were given. The 1973 list is from the Woodbine Angling Yearbook 1973 Edited by Colin Graham. This gave more information on location, captor and date but these details are not reproduced here. The 2018 list is taken from the Thames Anglers Conservancy website, where they maintained a rolling list of records. Details of captor and date are provided. However, at the time of writing (March 2021) the list has not been updated since 2018. Where larger fish are known to have been caught recently they are described in the individual species chapters. The somewhat surprising situation of some of the fish in the later lists being smaller than those listed in the earlier ones arises where the compiler has felt for some reason that the earlier record was unreliable.

Table 6.2. Thames angling record fish in 1955, 1973 and 2018.

	1955	1973	2018		
Species	**lb-oz-dr**	**lb-oz-dr**	**lb-oz-dr**	**Captor**	**Date**
Barbel	14-6-0	13-8-0	19-8-0	Dave Broady	Jan 2018
Bleak	0-5-8		0-3-8	N D Sizmur	1963
Bream	10-14-0	11-4-0	10-13-0	Rob Inns	Nov 2015
Bream (Silver)	4-0-0		1-14-0	Stuart Manwaring	Jan 2015
Carp (Common)	16-15-0	30-8-0	40-5-0	Duncan Green	Sep 2011
Carp (mirror)			48-7-0	Steve Shenfield	2017
Catfish			64-0-0	Jamie Drylie	Aug 2010
Crucian carp	1-8-0		4-2-0	Justin Gray	Sep 2014
Chub	7-1-0	7-1-0	9-4-0	Dylan Docherty	2007
Dace	1-3-8	1-0-0	1-3-0	R Page	Jan 1964
Eel	2-8-0		8-5-0	Matthew Kendall	Aug 2016
Grass carp			30-1-0	Tim Hughes	Aug 2009
Grayling	1-12-0				
Gudgeon	0-4-4		0-4-8	G Cedrick	1933
Perch	4-0-0	4-5-4	6-4-0	"Bill"	Mar 2014
Pike	29-8-0	30-0-0	34-2-0	Colin House	Dec 2011
Roach	3-9-12	3-9-12	3-5-0	David Booth	1927
Rudd	2-0-0	3-13-0			
Ruffe			0-6-0	Paul Sullivan	Aug 2011
Tench	5-4-0		8-11-0	Duncan Green	Jun 2013
Brown trout	15-0-0	16-15-0			
Salmon			14-5-0	Michael Hargrave	Aug 1993
Zander			13-12-0	Ashley Stockbridge	Nov 2009

Numbers of anglers fishing the Thames

It is very difficult to estimate how many anglers there were enjoying their sport on the Thames at any time in most of the last few hundred years. It was clearly a very popular pastime judging from the extensive literature on the subject, the number of angling societies and the large number of tackle shops and manufactories from 1700 onwards. The Freshwater Fisheries Act of 1878 authorised fishery boards to issue licences for catching trout and coarse fish. Most boards promptly did so, and the number of licences sold gives a good indication of the number of anglers fishing in each river or area. However, the Thames Conservancy and the Lea Conservancy chose not to do so; no licence was required to fish for freshwater fish in the Thames until after the formation of the Thames Water Authority in 1974. Estimates of potential licence sales for the combined Thames and Lea catchments conducted between 1970 and 1977 ranged from 255,000 to 400,000[13]; however, these were suspected of being too high as Thames Region licence sales in 1977/8 totalled only 147,000. Regional licences were replaced with a single national licence with the formation of the National Rivers Authority in 1989. However, there has been a marked decline in sales of trout/coarse fish licences sales nationally over the years; reportedly 39.4% between 2011 and 2018[14]. This is discussed further in Chapter 24.

The roach pole

No history of Thames fishing would be complete without mention of the London roach pole. The history of the development and history of poles is told in Michael Nadell's exquisite book "Poles apart", published in 2013. The roach pole is descended from crude early fishing rods that used a fixed length of line attached to the tip of the rod, but it evolved into a thing or great beauty and grace. The advantage over a standard rod lay mainly in its length (up to 24 feet = 7.3 m) which allowed great control of trotted float tackle. Perhaps more intimately bound-up with the angling history of the River Lea than that of the Thames, it nevertheless played an important part in the latter. Lea poles tended to be shorter than Thames poles, reflecting the more limited dimensions of that river.

Although a pole could be fished with a length of line up to the length of the pole itself, it was at its best when fished with a short line, with just a couple of feet between the rod tip and the float. This allowed the swim of the float to be controlled exactly, holding back a little at times to allow the bait to rise in the current. This also made the strike very direct, allowing the angler to "hit" the slightest dip or waver of the float. In order to land the fish the angler would remove the lower sections of the rod one by one, until the remaining sections were about the same length as the line between the tip and the hook. The fish could then be swung to hand, or netted if its size warranted.

As its name implies, the roach pole evolved as a tool to catch smaller fish that could be played on a tight line. Occasionally, however, a larger fish would be hooked inadvertently. While this often resulted in a smash, sometimes surprisingly large fish could be defeated by exerting careful control. In Chapter 10 there is a graphic description of a successful fight with a large barbel hooked on a pole, and I used to catch many stillwater tench using this technique.

As mentioned, the best roach poles were creations of great beauty and are very collectable. Michael Nadell has a collection of more than 60 London cane poles representing "*150 years of London's fishing history*"; many of these are pictured in his beautiful book.

Other angling matters

During the 19th Century anglers started to get organised into local clubs and regional organisations, to protect and develop their interests. This important development is described in Chapter 7. Match fishing is discussed in Chapter 8, and Chapter 9 covers a range of services associated with angling.

Chapter 6 footnotes

[1] The Graphic, September 3 1892. Artist A W Cooper.
[2] Report of the Committee of the Thames Rights Defence Association (About 1883) 8 pp. Copy in Reading Central Library.
[3] The Pictorial World, October 14 1876. The artist was J Temple.
[4] Fishing Gazette November 4 1961.
[5] Fishing Gazette December 9 1961.
[6] London Anglers Association, Members Handbook 1962.
[7] Bye-laws for the Protection, Preservation and Regulation of the Fisheries in the River Thames, from Cricklade in the County of Wilts, to Yantlet, in the County of Kent. July 19 1883.
[8] Fishing Gazette November 26 1960.
[9] Fishing Gazette November 12 1960.
[10] The Field, September 16 1876.
[11] The Field, July 29 1877.
[12] Fishing Gazette July 20 1877.
[13] Spillett (1979).
[14] Anglers Mail November 5 2018.

CHAPTER 7

Organisations and Societies

Angling is often a solitary pastime, and many fishermen feel no need to belong to any society or organisation; to this day many prefer to be independent, viewing their hobby as a method of escape from the rigours and constraints of organisation. However, during the 19th century it became clear that a number of developments on the Thames, including water quality deterioration, poaching and breaches of the fishing regulations, and navigation, were having a serious negative impact upon stocks of fish. In many cases the rules for proper protection were already in place, but were being flouted in the absence of effective enforcement. This stimulated the setting-up of a number of organisations specifically to further the aims of good fisheries management and the interests of anglers.

The first, and probably the most effective and long-lasting of these societies, was the Thames Angling Preservation Society, TAPS for short. The inaugural meeting took place on March 17, 1838, at the Bell Inn, Hampton. The founder members were Mr Henry Perkins of Hanworth Park, C C Clarke of Twickenham, Edward Jesse of Hampton, Dr Henry Jepson of Hampton, Richard Kerry of the Bell Inn, Hampton, W Whitbread of Eaton Square and David Crole of Strawberry Hill. These were all gentlemen anglers in the practice of hiring professional fishermen to provide punts, bait swims and to generally attend to their needs. The Society's "area" was very specific; the River Thames within the jurisdiction of the City of London, from the City Stone at Staines to Richmond. One of their first actions was to approach the Lord Mayor of London, Sir John Cowan, with whom the responsibility of conservation of this part of the Thames lay, to negotiate powers for assistant bailiffs appointed by, and financed by, TAPS. These provisions were agreed and the society "set out its stall" with a notice in the "Morning News" on January 1 1839:-

Thames Angling Preservation Society.

To Anglers. It is admitted by anglers that the River Thames is, perhaps, the finest river in the kingdom for the amusement of angling, but that, owing to the destruction of the fish by persons using unlawful means, inconceivable injury is continually being done to the sport, and consequently to such of the fishermen whose bread in many instances is chiefly derived from their attendance on anglers. These considerations have induced some gentlemen in the fishing villages on the banks of the Thames, between Staines and Kew Bridge, and their neighbourhood, to form themselves into a society, bearing the above name, for the general preservation of the fish, but particularly in the fence (close) *season, when depredations are more easily and more destructively commuted. The society (at present consisting of 110 subscribers) besides contributors, is directed by a committee of gentlemen residing in or near the fishing villages, which has been occupied for a considerable time in making the necessary arrangements for carrying into effect the objects contemplated, and in overcoming some obstacles which presented themselves; and having succeeded as fully as they could reasonably expect, has now the pleasure to inform Thames anglers that the preserves in the river between Staines and Richmond Bridge are staked or otherwise secured against unlawful netting; that posts are placed at the preserves describing their situation and extent, in which no fishing is permitted except by angling, and that assistant water bailiffs are appointed to various districts along the river, whose duty is to detect illegal fishing by whomsoever committed, and to lay informations against all persons found offending against any of the " rules orders, and ordinances" made, framed, and set down in writing by the Court of the Mayor and Alderman of the City of London.*

The committee is sanguine as to the beneficial results which will arise from the rigid enforcing of those "rules, orders, and ordinances". Much good, indeed, has already been effected, owing, as the committee believes, to the rewards offered by the society on the conviction of offenders to their own personal efforts, and to the influence of their admonition. In order, however, to bring into full and effective operation the objects of the society, it is obvious that a considerable charge will necessarily be incurred in staking the preserves, and on other indispensable precautions, besides an annual expense for assistant water-bailiffs' wages, towards which no assistance can be procured but from subscribers and others who may be desirous by their donations of furthering the objects of the society.

The committee, therefore, most anxious that no persons shall be excluded from the society on the score of expense, has determined that the annual subscription be one guinea only, to commence on the 1st day of March in each year, about which time it is intended to convene a meeting of anglers in London, when a statement of the finances of the society, and how appropriated, will be submitted, and every useful suggestion receive its due attention. In the meantime books are left with Mr Barth, Cockspur Street; Mr Bowness, Bellyard, Temple Bar; Mr Eaton, Crooked Lane; Messrs. Bond and Sons, Cannon Street; at the Bell Inn, Hampton; and Mr Leece, the collector, Strand-on-the-Green, for the insertion of the names of persons disposed to afford their pecuniary aid, to any of whom as may be most convenient.

The committee cannot help expressing its hope, and belief, that many true lovers of angling will on this occasion gladly come forward with their support, that an amusement so inoffensive and interesting to themselves may be by their joint and strenuous endeavours restored to its former state, and that the fishermen to whose experience and knowledge of the river, anglers are frequently indebted, and who have for so many years subsisted on their patronage, may not be now deserted, and ultimately ruined through the want of timely exertion.

By order of the committee, DAVID CROLE, Hon. Sec. Hampton, January 1, 1839.

Figure 7.1. TAPS bailiffs intercepting poachers[1].

The Society made a prompt start with its campaign to control illegal fishing; in April 1839 they brought a prosecution against a Brentford fisherman for catching dace and gudgeon out of season. He was found guilty and fined £5[2].

On May 22, a meeting of the society was held, chaired by Henry Perkins. It was resolved that five part-time bailiffs were to be appointed, to *prevent the fishermen from using improper nets and from taking fry*. A *liberal subscription was entered into to carry the objects of the society into execution*[3]. The society's bailiffs were, through the agreement of the Lord Mayor, empowered:-

to enter any boat, vessel or craft of any fisherman or dredgerman, or other person or persons fishing or taking fish or endeavouring to take fish, and there to search for, take and seize all spawn, fish, brood of fish, and unsizeable, unwholesome, or unseasonable fish, and also all unlawful nets, engines or instruments for taking or destroying fish as shall then be in any such boat, vessel or craft in and upon the river, and to take and seize on shore or shores adjoining to the said river, all such spawn, fish, and also all unlawful nets, engines, and instruments for taking and destroying fish as shall be found.[4]

The new team of bailiffs were soon in action, and the importance of their endorsement by the Lord Mayor demonstrated. On August 24 1839 several fishermen appeared at a special court at the Mansion House, presided over by the Lord Mayor himself. They were charged with illegally fishing at night, with nets of smaller mesh than the law allowed. Apparently the men put up quite a fight with the bailiffs; they explained that they thought that they were *just men employed by the Thames Angling Preservation Society*! The Lord Mayor said that he intended to stamp-out illegal night fishing, and proposed to appoint extra officers. The miscreants were fined fifty shillings (£2.50) each, with a warning that future fines would be doubled.[5] In the first six years or so of operations, TAPS brought 84 successful prosecutions, resulting in fines of £138 18s, and 29 nets were ordered to be burnt[6]. No doubt the deterrent effect of these actions was very much greater in terms of discouraging illegal fishing.

GROUP OF SOME OF THE MEMBERS OF THE THAMES ANGLING SOCIETY,
PHOTOGRAPHED BY MESSRS ROLFE, OF 4, HAYMARKET, PREVIOUS TO THE ANNUAL DINNER OF THE SOCIETY AT THE STAR AND GARTER, RICHMOND, ON THE EIGHTH OF JUNE.

Figure 7.2. A group of TAPS members gathering for the annual dinner at the Star and Garter, Richmond, on June 8 1858[7]. Well-known characters include W H Brougham (fourth from left, back row), H L Rolfe (extreme right; artist) and H Farnell (second from left, front row; author of several fishing guides referred-to elsewhere).

The notice issued on January 1, reproduced above, made reference to fishing preserves. These were areas, generally known as deeps, where no net fishing was allowed. TAPS patrolled all of these to discourage illegal fishing, and arranged for staking and addition of obstructions to thwart netting activity. The last to be established was at Kingston in 1857, and was protected by the sinking of the following obstructions[4]:-

Five old punts; two iron waggons; six two-horseloads of large brick burrs; twenty egg chests with tenter hooks; fifty large flint stones; ten tar-barrels, tenterhooked; two large sugar casks, tenterhooked; two punts loads of old iron gas lamps and other useful things; and three sacks of tin cuttings for the landing places along the shore. In addition, 450 stakes were driven into the river bed.

What the fish thought of all this junk being thrown into their habitat is uncertain, but they probably enjoyed the cover it provided.

The society continued to be largely comprised of gentlemen, as indicated by a drawing of members dressed for the annual dinner in 1858; bow ties, frock coats and top hats seemed to be the order of the day (Figure 7.2).

When the Thames Conservancy was established in 1857 they took on the responsibility for the river that had been held by the Lord Mayor. An application to continue the powers vested in the TAPS bailiffs was granted by the new body. Two year later the society pressed for a total abolition of netting between the City Stone at Staines and Richmond Bridge, a proposal supported by all the professional fishermen; they recognised that there was a much better living to be had from taking anglers out rather than by netting. The necessary byelaw was passed on January 23 1860, and henceforth the only legal nets used upstream of Richmond were a small cast net, not to exceed 13 feet in circumference, for catching baitfish, and an angler's landing net. In 1886, TAPS successfully pressed for the ban on netting to be extended downstream as far as the Chain Ferry at Isleworth[6].

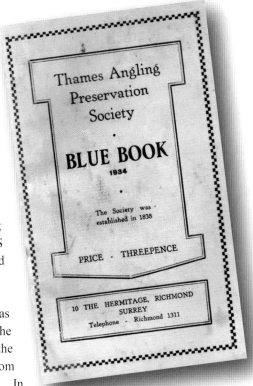

Regular prosecutions were brought for such offences as netting, setting night lines, and keeping fish below the legal size limits. In addition, from about 1860 onwards the river keepers became involved with transferring fish from various still waters to the river to supplement stocks. In 1864, 5,000 flounders were netted in the estuary and transferred to the river between Sunbury and Molesey, the species having disappeared from the area some years previously[8]. By 1866 the duties of the part-time keepers had become so expanded that the society had to appoint four full-time men[9]. The activities of the Society were not without controversy, however. In 1884 TAPS approached the Lord Chamberlain to do something regarding the depredations of the burgeoning swan population on the spawn of fish, especially perch which lay their eggs in clearly-visible ribbons in shallow water. They obtained permission for their keepers to *watch that portion of the river for the purpose keeping the birds away from those places where the spawn is deposited.*[10] This led to an acrimonious correspondence in the press with accusations of a *crusade against the swans*[11]. And in the same year, one of the part-time bailiffs, the Mayor of Kingston Alfred Nuttal, overstepped his authority and ended up in court. On seeing a fishing net hung up to dry on a steam launch owned by the solicitor employed by The Field, he boarded the boat and seized the net. The owner, Mr Powell, claimed that the net had not been used locally, but had been used quite legally some time earlier off Ramsgate. Nuttal retained the net and was sued by Powell with the result that the former had to pay the latter 20 shillings damages[12].

Although there had been various attempts at restocking by TAPS over the years, transferring unwanted coarse fish from other waters really took off as an activity in the 1880s. Examples over the ensuing years include "a ton" of fish from the large lake at Kew Gardens in 1881[13]; 10,000 roach, bream, carp, perch and chub stocked at Chertsey from a private lake in 1891[14]; two tons of fish from the reservoirs at East Molesey in 1901[15]; *"many thousands of bream, roach etc"* from Barnes Reservoirs into the Thames between Richmond and Twickenham in 1902[16]; and half a ton of fish from Worplesdon Mill Pond into the river at Chertsey and Weybridge in 1907[17]. And between 1919 and 1963, the society transferred nearly three million fish to the Thames. However, by the end of that period fish were becoming much more difficult to obtain as many of the potential "donor" waters had developed angling interest of their own[6].

Figure 7.3. TAPS netting a still water for fish for restocking into the Thames[18].

Figure 7.4. TAPS stocking the Thames with carp and tench netted from a still water[19].

Figure 7.5. TAPS netting at gravel pits at Old Ham, near Teddington, December 1925. Over two days more than 45,000 fish were netted and transferred to the Thames at Teddington and Twickenham[20].

The Society also attempted to rear young fish for release, using a side stream running from the Christian Spring at Hampton to the Thames. Production of juvenile salmon and trout was achieved but was deemed too expensive to be justified as a Society activity. In 1891 it was reported that Thames perch had been virtually wiped-out by a mystery disease[21]. The Society purchased a batch of 20,000 perch eggs from a fish farm (Solway Fisheries) to be hatched and raised at the rearing facilities[22], but this proved unsuccessful.

By the end of the 1960s the society seems to have lost its way somewhat, with the restocking programme being harder to maintain. It did not fold, however, and held healthy cash reserves in 1969 largely due to reduced outgoings. There was a restructuring in 1969, with a shift away from the "benign oligarchy" model that had served the organisation so well for well over 100 years to a more democratic model. A number of new posts were established including a Field Officer, an Assistant Secretary, and Equipment Officer and a Research Officer; this last post was filled by C Cargill, who in 1972 wrote a valuable history of TAPS on which this assessment of the later years is based. The society became very involved with the programme of experimental fishing matches in the tidal reaches, and spread its area of interest to cover the whole of the Thames.

As often happens with long-running organisations, their functioning can come to depend upon a few or even a single dedicated volunteer. In the case of TAPS this was the incomparable Dick Hodges, who was also involved in numerous other national and regional fisheries organisations. When Dick died in 2013, at the age of 91, it robbed far more than TAPS of his incredible energies. Basically TAPS passed away with Dick Hodges, 175 years after its inception.

Through the latter part of the 19th century, preservation societies based upon the TAPS concept started to spring-up further up the Thames. The first was the Great Marlow Thames Angling Association, founded in 1850. One of their main activities was stocking trout, and to support this they had developed their own rearing facilities. Up to 1880 they had released 4,723 trout into the river[23].

The Maidenhead, Cookham and Bray Thames Angling Association was next to be formed in 1874, and it ran from the downstream limit of activity of the Marlow Association down to Monkey Island. The inaugural meeting was held on March 30 at Lewis's Hotel (formerly and subsequently Skindles Hotel)[24]. Like TAPS more than thirty years earlier, it wasted no time in chasing up illegal fishing. An advertisement was placed in the Reading Mercury on April 25 for a Head Bailiff at a salary of £40 per year[25]. In July a prosecution was brought against one Henry Meads for laying a night line. He was found guilty and fined 2s 6d plus 11s 6d costs, and the line was destroyed. He was warned that any subsequent offences would be dealt with much more severely[26]. The following year the Association organised a conference on Thames fisheries management at Lewis's Hotel[27]. This attracted many well-known participants including Frank Buckland (HM Inspector of Salmon Fisheries), W H Brougham (Secretary of TAPS), Greville Fennell and James Englefield (well-known angling authors), and representatives from TAPS and the associations at Marlow, Abingdon and Oxford.

At about the same time the Thames Angling Association in Abingdon was established, followed four years later by the Reading and District Angling Association and the Windsor and Eton Thames Angling and Preservation Society.

The London Anglers Association (LAA) was founded in 1884 and has been a major player in Thames fisheries ever since. Its original aim was to negotiate discounted rail fares for members to travel to their fishing, but its role quickly widened as its membership increased. Membership was via affiliated clubs rather than as individuals. The early history of the LAA (up to 1924) and its relationships and rivalries with other organisations has been told in detail by W G Callcutt,

AVAILABLE FROM APRIL 1st, 1964, to MARCH 31st, 1965
PLEASE REFER TO NOTICE AT BACK OF THIS CARD

The London Anglers' Association
Memorial Hall, Farringdon Street, E.C.4

NOT TRANSFERABLE

This is to Certify that the Bearer Mr _____ is a Member of the above Association so long as he retains membership with the Duke of Wellington Angling Society,

NOT TRANSFERABLE

1964-65   Harold Morris.
                              President.
S.M.
5097
        Secretary, R.S.Davison.

This ticket must be produced, when demanded, on all Association Fisheries

N.B. ALL ENQUIRIES MUST BE MADE THROUGH THE ABOVE MENTIONED SOCIETY in a privately-published and much sought-after work that is strongly recommended to all with an interest in the politics of angling organisations.

The LAA had some fishing on the Thames, all upstream of Windsor, but were at the forefront of a long campaign to keep the fishing on the river free for all to enjoy. In 1949 they were founder members of the Federation of Thames Angling Associations, formed with the express aim of preventing any further loss of the free and open fishing on the river to individual clubs. The constitution of the FTAA included the aim that, as and when any fishing rights became available, they would be acquired by, or handed over to, the FTAA to manage for the benefit of all. Finance was provided by running the annual Thames Championship match. Unfortunately, after some years member clubs started to acquire Thames fishing which they did not make over to the FTAA, and in 1959 the LAA felt bound to withdraw from the Association. The LAA even went as far as to ban both its individual and affiliated members from fishing in the FTAA Thames Championship match, and from fishing the stretches of the river controlled by one of the "offending" individual clubs[28]. The impact upon entries for the Thames Championship was significant; only 927 in 1959, down from 1600 the year before[29].

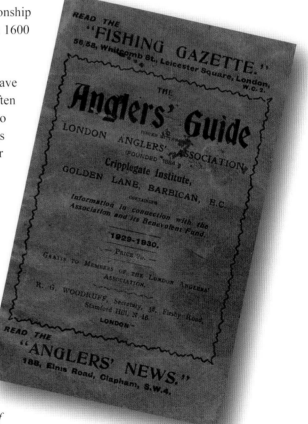

In addition to these large associations there have existed hundreds of smaller local clubs, often based at a popular pub. These existed to negotiate access to fishing, organise outings and matches, and to provide a social focus for anglers. In the close season and at colder times of year when outings were perhaps less frequent they often organised evenings of entertainment. Such a gathering of members of the City of London Piscatorial Society in 1907 was described thus:-

Surrounded by numerous friends and ladies, Mr G H Howard ("Dragnet") presided over the exceedingly successful social supper and musical evening, which took place on Tuesday evening, November 19, at Mason's Hall. After a repast, abundant and well-served, worthy of the high reputation of this historic establishment, the rest of the evening was devoted to music, under the very efficient direction of Mr David Isaacs. The programme was a long one, "but time was made for slaves," and listeners to the fine performances of the "Ariel Vocal Quartette" and other delightful items by various artistes, paid no attention to watches and clocks; the beautiful grace, "For these and all thy mercies", was finely given by the Quartette Party, as well as many charming glees and part songs, to the great enjoyment of the large party assembled, while many beautiful songs were well rendered by Miss Brooks, Miss Newman, and Daisy Howard, Messrs Davison, Wilmott, Goodier, and Allan Rayne also giving splendidly some capital songs, etc; some very good humorous musical sketches by Mr Archie Nash were also received with great applause. To conclude, Mrs Arthur Davison at the piano was a very efficient accompaniment throughout. The customary toasts, "The King", "CLPS", Visitors and Ladies", "The Press", etc, the last mentioned well-proposed by Mr Bridge Collins, and able responded-to by Mr Crumplen ("Old Izaak" of the People), were fully honoured, and votes of thanks to all that had so ably conduced to the success of the evening, not forgetting the very popular chairman, closed a delightful entertainment. Previous to the supper, there was an ordinary meeting, at which a new member was nominated, and fishing reports received. There will be a microscopical and scientific evening on Tuesday November 26.[30]

Two majors areas where clubs and organisations have contributed over the years are organising fishing matches, and arranging transport for their members to reach fishing venues. These are discussed in the following chapters.

Chapter 7 footnotes

[1] Illustrated Sporting and Dramatic News, April 2, 1881.
[2] Morning Post, April 10 1839.
[3] Morning Post, May 23 1839.
[4] Wheeldon (1883)
[5] London Standard, August 26 1839.
[6] Marston (1963).
[7] The Field, July 17 1858.
[8] London Standard, June 6 1864.
[9] London Standard, May 26 1866.
[10] London Standard, March 18 1884.
[11] London Standard, March 14 1884.
[12] Bury and Norwich Post, October 21 1884.
[13] Morning Post , March 28 1881
[14] Nottingham Evening Post, October 17 1891.
[15] Hull Daily Mail, September 9 1901.
[16] Evening Telegraph, July 24 1902.
[17] Manchester Courier and Lancashire General Advertiser, May 2 1907.
[18] Illustrated Sporting and Dramatic News, May 5 1877.
[19] Illustrated Sporting and Dramatic News, April 28 1877
[20] Fishing Gazette, January 23 1926
[21] Portsmouth Evening Echo, April 23 1891.
[22] Western Daily Press, May 25 1891.
[23] Reading Mercury, October 23 1880.
[24] Reading Mercury, March 28 1874.
[25] Reading Mercury, April 25 1874.
[26] Reading Mercury, July 25 1874.
[27] Reading Mercury, April 17 1875.
[28] London Anglers Association, Member's Handbook, 1962.
[29] The Field, December 10 1959.
[30] Fishing Gazette, November 23 1907.

CHAPTER 8

Match fishing

The latter part of the 19th century saw the development of organised fishing matches - as opposed to the companionable rivalry between friends sharing a fishing trip which has doubtless occurred for almost as long as the sport itself. Matches were organised by local angling societies and generally offered modest prizes for the largest catch by weight and/or number, and for largest fish. In early days the fish to be weighed-in were killed, and the weighing and prize-giving ceremonies were as much a part of the event as the fishing itself.

Figure 8.1. The weighing ceremony at the end of a fishing match of an unidentified London angling club in 1873.[1] This would appear to be a gentleman's event, with ties or bow ties the norm, and no less than ten top hats visible.

*The (*Anglers Association Shield Final*) was fished at Wargrave on Sunday last, Nov.17, between the Cobden AS and the Rainbow Trout AS. The match was well contested and led to a close finish, the Cobden winning by 9 oz – 3 lb 13¼ oz against 3 lb 4¼ oz, twelve fish to nine. Until late in the afternoon both clubs had four fish each, but the Cobden won in the last half hour. On the same day the Good Intent and the Brompton fished for six silver medals, given by Mr Stirling of Leyton Waltonians for the two semi-finalists, who were beaten by the finalists. This was also a very close match, the Good Intent leading all day until the last half hour, when Mr Locke caught eight roach, which won the match for Brompton AS by 8 oz. The weights were Brompton 5 lb 5 oz; Good Intent, 4 lb 13 oz. It was a most enjoyable outing. A saloon carriage had been chartered on the Great Western and the four teams and friends mustered about thirty-eight for the party. The utmost good feeling and fellowship existed between the teams and they parted at Paddington all satisfied that they had won and got beaten fairly, and content that they had had a good outing.*[2]

The above description is of the 1907 final of one of the longest-running and most prestigious matches generally fished on the Thames, the LAA Challenge Shield. It was a knockout competition fished by teams of six from LAA member clubs, and the venues for the semis and finals were kept secret until the day of the match. In all, 38 venues were available, of which 27 were on the Thames[3]. Thames venues therefore predominated; for example, in the 1971-72 competition all eight rounds were fished on the Thames, with the semis at Appleford and the final at Hurley. The photograph in Figure 8.2 shows what appears to be the victorious team probably some time around the 1930s[4].

Figure 8.2. The winning finalists with the LAA Challenge Shield ; no further details known.

Some of these matches involved many competitors and a considerable task of organisation. About 500 anglers from 27 clubs took part in a match at Bourne End on Sunday, November 23 1902, organised by the Central Association for the benefit of their Thames Restocking Fund[5]. The winner was C Watling with a weight of 5lb 2½ oz[6]. A total of 1,648 anglers in 85 teams took part in the Thames Championships in 1955; the top weights were 7 lb 1 oz for an individual, and 9 lb 8 oz for a team of eight[7].

An international match at Henley in 1905 was also a triumph of organisation by the Silver Trout Angling Society of London[8]. Competitors from France, Belgium and Germany took part as well as many from English clubs. Pegging-out the 500 swims started at 4 a.m., and covered a three-mile length of river between Henley and Hambleden. The competitors' trains were welcomed by a brass band playing the national anthem of the nationalities involved, and the day concluded with a dinner at Henley Town Hall. The match lasted five hours and was won by W Davis with an eight-fish catch weighing 2¾ lb.

Fig 8.3. The international match fished on the Thames between Henley and Hambleden in September 1905[9].

Year	Winner	Weight
1950	W Williamson	5-5-12
1951	A Bexley	31-5-6
1952	A A Jones	53-0-4
1953	E Beard	23-12-0
1954	D Blow	25-11-9
1955	W Nicholls	7-1-0
1956	Mrs W Messner	9-14-0
1957	G Powderham	16-3-8
1958	A Wrangles	18-12-12
1959	K Millad	62-10-2
1960	E Hayes	7-2-8
1961	R Vetterlein	23-11-4
1962	P Abbott	9-8-0
1963	C Willis	56-14-12
1964	G Redwood	20-10-0
1965	No match	
1966	T Bailey	8-4-8
1967	A Mitchell	10-4-0
1968	K Myers	9-5-4
1969	G Ormiston	13-12-0
1970	E Bowden	16-8-0
1971	R Mumford	20-4-0
1972	D Roberts	20-13-8
1976	L Price	72-4-0

Table 8.1. Winners and winning weights in the Thames Federation Championship (weight in pounds-ounces-drams).

Another long-running event is the Federation of Thames Angling Association Thames Championship. This was first fished in 1950, and at first attracted a large entry from throughout the region. However, following the split between the Federation and the LAA described in Chapter 7, the latter organised their own Thames Championship and member clubs did not fish in the Federation match. From this time on the LAA match was generally fished on the Lower Thames, and the Federation match on the Upper Thames from Radcot (Map 2) upstream. Incomplete lists of the individual winners of these competitions are given in Tables 8.1 and 8.2. The LAA match developed a large following, with more than 1400 contestants in 1969[10].

In recent decades there has been a general reduction of interest in and support of match fishing, not limited to the Thames. The National Championships expanded to six divisions of 80 teams each by 1992, but has since shrunk to two divisions. The LAA challenge Shield competition attracted 140 teams of six in 1971 (Graham 1972), but had dwindled to 18 teams of three by about 2016[11].

Year	Winner	Weight
1960	H E Mead	14-11-8
1961	D W King	11-14-0
1962	F Witcomb	5-13-0
1963	D Sleath	8-13-0
1964	D Howell	11-13-8
1965	J Hancock	6-11-0
1966	T Rose	6-0-4
1967	F Phillips	4-13-0
1968	K Kempsell	22-8-12
1969	K Kempsell	13-5-0
1970	B Gent	11-1-8
1971	J Rumball	13-1-0
1972	Barry Sawyer	6-11-8
1976	G Young	8-9-8
2008	Mick Hanks	170-11-0
2009	Ian Young	67-0-0
2010	Robert Wright	26-3-0

Table 8.2. Winners and winning weights in the LAA Thames Championships (Weights as Table 8.1.)

A factor that affected the popularity of match fishing in the Thames in earlier times was undoubtedly the size limit rules imposed by the Thames Conservancy. As described in Chapter 6, the size-limit regulations were introduced to prevent the killing of small fish at the time when most fish caught were killed. The rules required that any fish below the size limit were at once returned to the water, without injury. Thus in the early days when fish to be weighed-in were killed, matches were fished to the size limits . When keep-nets became the norm, with the catch being returned to the river after weighing at the end of the match, this rule was still respected; though it is uncertain if anyone tested whether retaining undersized fish in a keep net actually infringed the size limit rule. In his 1960 book on fishing the Upper Thames, Bill Taylor discussed the impact of the size limits on Thames match fishing. He suggested that they discouraged the *majority of roach match teams who will*

Figure 8.4. Many Thames matches were not pegged but were "rovers"; this sometimes resulted in a somewhat undignified race for favoured swims. But few matches could have exhibited such enthusiasm as the start of this under-14 junior match organised by North Oxford Angling Society in 1926![12]

only fish all-in and encouraged the belief, prevalent among Thames anglers, that match tactics do not pay off on the Thames. The result was that most Thames matches were local affairs that did not carry large prizes or significant sweeps (a system of allowing anglers to back themselves to win or be placed), and this situation did not attract the dedicated matchmen from the Midlands and North. Peter Stone recalled that retaining an undersized fish in a keep-net would lead to disqualification from many matches, so that he was always unsure about weighing in any fish on or only just above the limit.

Largely because of the size limit regulations and the unpopularity of the Thames among Midland and Northern anglers, only two National Championships took place on the Thames in the days before it was fished in more than one division, both in the early days of the competition. The first ever National was held at Pangbourne on October 15 1906, and involved only seven teams of 12 anglers. A total of 48 lb 4½ oz of fish was weighed-in, comprising 197 fish; 179 roach, 9 perch, 8 dace and a single chub. Northern teams took the top three places (Boston, Sheffield and Leeds) with the LAA team coming fourth. Boston anglers took the first three individual places, topped by F Beales with 19 fish for 4 lb 11 oz. The Fishing Gazette was rather critical of the performance of the local teams:-

There was no question of the river being entirely out of condition for the London style of angling, but the midlanders have demonstrated to the bigoted adherent of the roach pole

and tight lines how to catch roach when the conditions of the water render prospects of poor sport. London anglers must no doubt feel very depressed, especially when they take into consideration that the majority of the teams had never seen the river until the competition morning. The only thing for them to do is to practice the midlanders' style, and when they go to the Midlands next year they will be prepared to adopt either style of fishing. It may be that conditions then will favour the roach pole; but on Monday's form I have my doubts as to whether the cup will come back to London.13

The debate regarding whether the National should be fished to size limits raged on. The rules in most fishery districts, unlike the Thames, allowed "undersized" fish to be retained in keep-nets, and weighed-in at matches, as long as they were released after weighing. In 1926 the York Anglers Association waived their size limit rule in favour of fishing "all in". But the LAA continued their fight to have the National revert to size limit fishing[14].

In 1928, Reading and District Angling Association invited the National Conference of Anglers to fish the National Championship at Pangbourne, the venue for the 1906 match.[15] This was opposed by the Sheffield delegation, led by W Fox, because the match would have to be fished to Thames Conservancy size limits. Their resolution was carried, so that it was not possible to accept the RDAA invitation.

The national organisation apparently overcame its aversion to fishing matches to size limits, at least temporarily, as a second National was fished on the Thames in 1934. This was fished by 54 teams and was again won by a northern club, Sheffield Amalgamated. Again the top team included the individual winner, H Smith with 4 lb 3¼ oz. But no more National matches were fished on the river until after the size-limit rules had changed to allow all-in matches in 1973; the first for almost 50 years was a fourth-division match in 1981.

Many match fishers are very enthusiastic followers of this branch of the sport, only really fishing on their own to practice for matches. But the prize for sheer dedication should perhaps go to the late Ian Fisher, a tackle dealer from Wallingford. In 1993 he struggled for five hours to win a Jolly Anglers Club match on the Thames near his home town despite severe chest pains. The following day it was discovered that he had suffered two heart attacks during the match[16]. Twenty four years later Ian collapsed and died of another heart attack at the age of 68 after winning a Marston AC match on the Thames at Oxford with a catch of more than 52 lb[17]. His daughter nailed his fishing hat to a post near the spot where he collapsed with a note saying simply "Gone fishing".

In the "good old days" when kids still went fishing, junior matches were popular thanks to the dedication of local clubs and individuals. One long-running series was organised by the Jolly Anglers Club in Wallingford. The first took place in 1925[18] and was attended by the mayor and the headmaster of the local boys school at which many of the competitors were pupils. More than 40 youngsters participated in 1931[19], and the annual match continued until the war.

Matches are still held on the Thames, albeit fewer and smaller events than at the peak in the 1950's and 60's; the present-day situation is discussed in Chapter 24.

Chapter 8 footnotes

[1] Illustrated London News, October 18 1873.

[2] Fishing Gazette November 23 1907

[3] London Anglers Association Members Handbook 1962

[4] This is something of a mystery photograph. I found it tucked inside a copy of Calcutt (1924) when I purchased it a few years ago. My guess at the approximate date stems from the fact that there are 20 studs on the shield, suggesting that it was being contested for the 21st time. As the competition started in 1903, and was not fished in 1916-19, this suggests about 1927. However, this is pure guesswork; the shield appears to have started life in 1903 with a dozen studs, and the history of the growth in number is far from clear. Further, the style of dress suggests a somewhat later date, perhaps around WWII.

[5] Tatler, December 3 1902.

[6] South London Chronicle, November 29 1902.

[7] Fishing Gazette October 29 1955.

[8] Fishing Gazette, September 9 1905.

[9] Illustrated Sporting and Dramatic News, July 31 1915.

[10] London Anglers Association Members' Handbook 1970.

[11] Warwick Angling Society Website.

[12] Fishing Gazette, October 16 1926.

[13] Fishing Gazette October, 20 1906.

[14] Sheffield Independent, November 4 1926.

[15] South Yorkshire Times, May 25 1928.

[16] Aberdeen Press and Journal, February 11 1993.

[17] Oxford Mail, March 3 2017.

[18] Berkshire and Oxfordshire Advertiser, October 9 1925.

[19] Berkshire and Oxfordshire advertiser, September 18 1931.

T. COLLINS,

At his TRAVELLING TRUNK, FISHING ROD
and TACKLE MANUFACTORY,

MINSTER-STREET, READING, (from London)

MAKES and Sells all sorts of Travelling Trunks
and others of every description; Bonnet, Hat, Braide
and other Pasteboard Boxes, &c.; Ladies Red Trunks and
Caravans. Likewise all sorts of Fishing Rods and Tackle
in the greatest variety; the very best Kirby bent Hooks, sold
by no other person in Reading; silkworm Gut and Artificial
Flies, a curious sort of spun Fly Lines, and others. All the
above are actually sold as cheap as at any shop in London,
and every article neatly repaired.

Most money given for green Horse Hides.

N. B. Wanted an Apprentice of reputable parents: a
premium is required, and his friends to find him in cloaths;
he will be entitled to the freedom of the City of London.

Reading Mercury, April 6 1789.

CHAPTER 9

Angling; associated services

Professional boatmen

From the earliest days of sport fishing on the Thames, many anglers especially perhaps the wealthier ones, turned to a professional fisherman to guide them in their fishing. Many of these guides started life commercially fishing for food and other saleable products; and indeed, in Victorian times, many combined the two ways of life. However, as rules were gradually introduced to restrict commercial fishing more and more, and angling became a more popular pastime, many of these boatmen became full-time angling guides.

Figure 9.1. The boatman views the catch. The benefits of hiring a professional were usually greater than this![1]

The boats used for angling were almost universally Thames punts, long flat-bottomed craft with low gunwhales and plenty of room for the boatman and two or three clients. The craft was propelled using a single long pole. To fix the punt for fishing it would be either tied to mooring posts, anchored at each end using mudweights, or most often by using two long poles called ryepecks. These had a metal-clad pointed end which was pushed into the mud or gravel of the river bed. The flat bottom of the vessel allowed the use of kitchen chairs for the anglers comfort, though the boatman usually used one of the thwarts for sitting. The centre of the boat often housed a live-well for keeping live bait alive and the catch fresh.

Details of these arrangements are clearly apparent in many of the pictures throughout this book.

The duties of the boatman were to transport the anglers to a productive spot for whatever species was being sought, provide the bait, bait up the anglers hooks and help with other aspects of tackle tinkering, and to groundbait the chosen swim. This often involved baiting up the chosen swim for several days before the client wanted to fish, especially when bream or barbel were the quarry. In some locations it was a convention that the angler provided a picnic lunch and liquid refreshment for both himself and the boatman.

Another task for the boatman was raking the river bed to attract fish, especially when gudgeon fishing (see Chapter 16). However, it was also employed when seeking other species. Fennell (1867b) wrote:-

The rake has come again into fashion for roach, dace and chub fishing, and it has very considerably contributed to the success of the punt fisher. The method of using the rake upon these occasions differs from that pursued for gudgeons, which, for the latter, is made to pass over the gravel before the punt, and to disturb the exact spot fished. Not so in the present case. Here the puntsman takes his stand on the up side of the punt, and agitating the bottom above, sends down and under the punt the deposit, which allures the fish within reach of the boat.

Many angling gentlemen had favourite and regular professional boatmen, and doubtless treated them well in terms of gratuities; this would ensure good service in the future. The angling journalist John Englefield ("Red Quill" of The Field) recorded how in 1864 he engaged a Maidenhead professional, Andrews, for a day's pike fishing for a fee of 5 shillings for the day. He also promised to give the man a shilling for every pike caught in excess of five fish. In the event 18 fish were caught, and the boatman was handed a sovereign (one pound, or twenty shillings) for his day's work; *much to his satisfaction and to mine.* But Englefield added:-

but it taught me a lesson..... for when fishing by myself it was no uncommon thing to kill from five to eight jack per diem, without incurring unnecessary expense, and avoiding the endless and unedifying fish gossip of a professional, always at ones elbow, and too often without his temperance badge.

Reservations about using a professional fisherman were also expressed by Alfred Church writing in 1890. While accepting that handling a punt was a definite skill especially under difficult conditions he wrote:-

But it was a great thing to be able to do this without this same professional. He was expensive, not to say that his seven or eight shillings a day were not well earned; and he was apt to be something of a bore. I have kindly recollections of many of them – of the Cresswells of Marlow, of Rush of Streatley; of Stone of Henley too much given, I am afraid, to beer, ...

One advantage in nurturing a good relationship with a regular boatman was he could provide useful intelligence on current fishy activity. They would often spot trout feeding and mark them down for attention by a favoured gentleman (see Chapter 21), or make other useful observations:-

...ancient historians tell us of "shoals of roach" that used to "come down from the country", as low as the Temple and London Bridge; and of one John Reeves, a waterman from Essex Stairs, who used to watch daily for their arrival, and then go around and appraise his customers, aldermen or barristers learned in the law, as the case may be, who forthwith, to the prejudice of books and book debts, came out to catch them[2].

It is difficult to calculate the numbers of professional fishermen tending to the needs of Thames anglers at any specified date. Charles Dickens (son of the novelist), in his "Dictionary of the Thames" published in 1887, listed 185 "trustworthy" professionals available for hire. There were 37 listed for Teddington and the upper tidal reaches, 74 between Chertsey and Kingston, 30 between Maidenhead and Laleham, 27 between Reading and Marlow, and 17 upstream of Reading. How many "untrustworthy" individuals there were in addition is not recorded! Numbers dwindled during the 20th century; only 13 advertised in the Anglers News dated January 21 1939. I suspect virtually none existed after WW2. Friends and I occasionally hired punts in the early 1960s (without a professional) but they were all becoming dilapidated by then. I recall Tom Jones, who ran a boatyard near Romney Lock at Windsor, making a huge bonfire of old punts in about 1962. I did not appreciate at the time that I was witness to the end of an era.

Travel

Before the railways arrived around 1830 the only way for anglers to travel to their fishing, other than on foot, was by horse-drawn transport. Jesse (1836) describes some of the fisherfolk who used this means to reach Shepperton and Chertsey:-

It is somewhat amusing to notice the different characters and description of persons who visit some of the villages in the vicinity of the metropolis by which the Thames flows, for the purposes of fishing. I frequently have them as companions on the outside of our stage coach, and I must in justice to them say, that I invariably find them pleasant and good-humoured, generally full of sanguine and eager anticipation of excellent sport, though now and then casting a look at the sky, and asking the opinion of the coachman as to the probable state of the weather on the morrow. I observe that our coachman always treats these worthy disciples of Izaac Walton with great respect and civility, which I presume these open-hearted lovers of angling return by a small addition to the usual fee. I always think it a bit of good fortune whenever I find myself placed on the roof of the coach near these light-hearted fishermen, with their rods between their knees, and their fishing baskets properly secured. There is a sort of freemasonry amongst the anglers which speedily makes then become acquainted with each other, and then commences an agreeable relation of their exploits in the piscatory art.

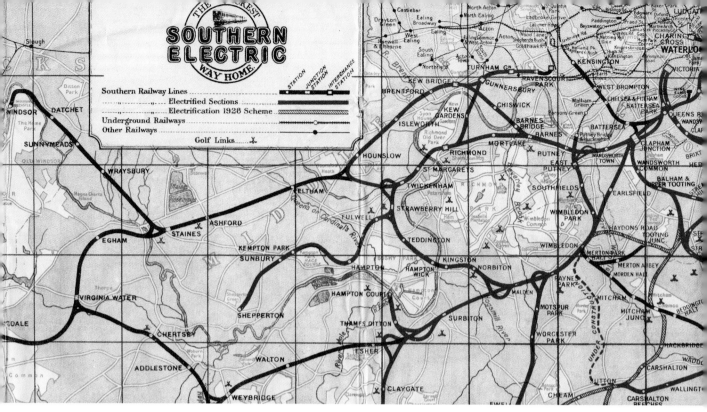

Figure 9.2. Southern Railway network around SW London in 1925. The GWR took over the job of conveying anglers to destinations upstream of Windsor.

But clearly this was not a poor-man's option for obtaining access to his sport. For him it was walking or nothing, so if you lived more than a few miles from accessible water, angling was not a realistic pastime.

Things really began to change with the arrival of the railway age. The first lines appeared in London about 1830, and over the next fifty years a comprehensive network built up so that it was possible to reach within a few miles of almost any fishing spot within thirty miles of London within a hour or so. Figure 9.2 shows the Southern Railway network around the Lower Thames in 1925.

While the fares were not cheap, the short journey times and frequent services did away with the need for expensive overnight accommodation, bringing increased areas of fishing within the reach of the average angler.

The following narrative of the era of cheap fares for anglers is summarised from Callcut's book written in 1924. In the early days of the railways, as already noted fares were not cheap, and rail travel was still beyond many poorer anglers. In 1841 a 19-year-old stationer called Dick Ghurney hit upon the idea of making a little extra money by arranging excursions for groups of anglers based upon horse-drawn transport. Early venues included the Thames at Teddington, the Lea, and the Colne at West Drayton. Some of these outings set out at 2 am from The Angel, Islington. Fares on Ghurney's excursions were significantly cheaper than individual travel by rail. Then in November 1871 there took place a very popular roach fishing match on the Lea at Rye House. Although the fishing was limited to just two teams battling for a £25 prize, many followers of both sides desired to watch the event. Once again Dick Ghurney rose to the occasion, and as Secretary of one of the clubs involved (called The Hoxton Brothers) he negotiated an excursion rail fare with the Great Eastern Railway. As this generated a profit for the railway company they asked Ghurney to discuss extending the scheme; in April 1872 cheap anglers' fares were made available by the GER for both individuals and parties. In order to manage the scheme a new association was formed, entitled "The United London Angling Association Central Committee"; this was eventually to evolve into the London Anglers Association. In the following years, similar concessions were negotiated with other rail companies, though this did not always go smoothly. There were squabbles between rival fishing organisations, and accusations of abuse of the privilege (people using the cheap excursion fares for purposes other than angling). In some cases this led to exasperation on the part of the rail companies, and new concessions had to be carefully negotiated from time to time. But by 1894 nine railway companies were participating in the scheme for anglers from the metropolis; Great Eastern, Great Western, South Eastern, South Western, Great Northern, London, Brighton and South Coast, Midland, North Western and Metropolitan[3]. The anglers privilege ticket scheme continued until WWI when it was dropped; but it was resurrected during the inter-war years.

Figure 9.3. A horse-drawn passenger carriage. Not an angler's outing this time (note ladies in smart hats), but such carriages would have been used for the purpose.

THE ANGLERS' REST INN,
BELL WEIR LOCK, EGHAM.

This Inn, pleasantly situated close to the River and Bell Weir Lock, offers great advantages as a stopping-place for Boating and Fishing Gentlemen and others.

Every Accommodation at Reasonable Charges.

BOATS TO LET, HOUSED, OR TAKEN CARE OF.

A Fisherman always in Attendance.

JOHN HYDE, Proprietor.

ANGEL HOTEL,
STAINES.

A First-class Hotel for Families and Gentlemen, where every comfort and the best Accommodation will be found by Oarsmen, Anglers, and Tourists.

WINES and SPIRITS of the best Quality.

H. BAKER, Proprietor.

In contrast to many more remote areas where trout and salmon fishing dominate, overnight accommodation has never really played a major part in the enjoyment of Thames angling. Having said that, many waterside hotels and inns did offer services for anglers including boat hire, arranging the services of professional fishermen, selling permits, provision of meals and liquid refreshment, and the occasional overnight stay. Many inns advertised as being angler friendly - though not all hostelries welcomed the muddy boots and often rough attire of the fisherman - and provided attractions such as mounted fish and other memorabilia on display. Some, especially those in and near London, also acted as the headquarters of local angling societies and provided services for meetings and match weigh-ins. A few, particularly those situated on islands, offered private fishing – examples include Taggs Island Hotel at Hampton, and the Monkey Island Hotel at Bray.

Contemporary advertisements for some of these hostelries appear throughout this book.

MONKEY ISLAND HOTEL
BRAY, BERKSHIRE.

UNDER ENTIRELY NEW MANAGEMENT. Redecorated and furnished. The finest fishing and boating on the River Thames, and recognised to be the most picturesque and historic places which river visitors should not fail to see. The Hotel is entirely alone on the Island, and the acreage is six and a half. The fishing rights belonging to the Hotel is about a mile and a half reach, and well stocked with all kinds of fresh water fish. Permission to fish these waters is free to resident visitors, and customers may avail themselves of the pleasant pastime by applying to the proprietor for a permit.

Professional Fishermen and Fishing Punts always in readiness. Steam Launches, Pleasure Punts, and Rowing Boats for Hire. Splendid accommodation for campers. Conveyance sent to meet all trains on receipt of wire.

DISTANCES.—Taplow Station, G.W.R., 1½ miles; Maidenhead Station, G.W.R., 2 miles; Windsor, S.W.R., 4 miles.

TELEGRAPHIC ADDRESS: Monkey, Bray, Berks.

THOS. WILTSHIRE, Proprietor.

Tackle dealers

In the days before the internet and mail order, the local tackle dealer was the main source for rods, reels, smaller tackle items and bait that are essential for the fisherman. In addition, they provided an invaluable source of information on where was fishing well, who had caught what, and advice on local venues, baits and tackle items. As Arthur Ransome said in his wonderful chapter on tackle shops in *Rod and Line* in 1929, the sight of rods in a window brings a fisherman to a full stop as surely as the sight of a bridge. Being a major city with good fishing nearby, London was well-supplied with tackle shops from the earliest days.

Hugh Sheringham penned a series of three articles in the Salmon and Trout Magazine in 1926[4], entitled *The early days of tackle dealing*. He had access to a scrap book apparently created in the early 19th century, which contained many references to early tackle dealers in London to which he adds many others from published works.

The earliest comes from the first edition of Walton's *Compleat Angler* dated 1653; Piscator promises Viator that he will:-
.....*go with him either to Charles Brandon's (near to the Swan in Golding Lane); or to Mr Fletcher's in the Court, which did once belong to Dr Nowell, the Dean of St Pauls, that I told you was a good man and a good fisher; they both be honest men and will fit an angler with what tackling he wants.*

Figure 9.4. An early 18th century advertisement for a London Tackle dealer; From Sheringham (1926)[4].

To all Lovers of Angling.

ONESIMUS USTONSON,

Succeſſor to the late Mr. John Herro, at the

No. 48, the Bottom of Bell-Yard, Temple-Bar, MAKES all Sorts of Fiſhing Rods, and all Manner of the beſt Fiſhing Tackle, Wholeſale and Retail, at the loweſt Rates; ſells the right Kirby's Hooks, being the beſt tempered of any made, which cannot be had at any other Shop; the beſt Sort of Artificial Flies, Menow-Tackle, Jack and Perch, and Artificial Menows; and all Sorts of Artificial Baits, &c. made upon the ſaid Hooks, in the neateſt Manner, for Pike, Salmon and Trout; Spring Snap Hooks; Live and Dead Snap, and Live Bait-Hooks, Trowling Hooks of various Sorts; the beſt Sort of Treble and Double Box, and Single Swivels; Gimp, both Silver and Gold; the beſt and freſheſt India Weed or Graſs, juſt come over; likewiſe a freſh Parcel of ſuperfine Silk Worm Gut, no better ever ſeen in England, as fine as a Hair, and as ſtrong as Six, the only Thing for Trout, Carp, and Salmon; the beſt Sort of Multiplying Braſs Winches, both ſtop and plain; Woved Hair and Silk Lines, and all other Sorts of Lines for Angling; various Sorts of Reels and Caſes; and all Sorts of Pocket Books for Tackle, Menow Kettles, and Nets to preſerve Live Bait; Fiſhing Paniers and Bags; Variety of Gentle-Boxes and Worm-Bags; Landing-Nets and Hooks; Fiſhing-Stools; Wicker and Leather Bottles; and many ther Curioſities, in the way of Angling. All Sorts of Trunks to ſhoot Darts and Pellets.

In the second edition (1655) reference is made to the hook maker and merchant Charles Kirby, in Harp Alley in Shoe Lane. In the edition of 1676 there is an advert for John Margrave stating that *he sold all sorts of the best tackle, at the sign of the three trouts in St Paul's Churchyard, on the North side.*

In the 18th century, London tackle dealers were concentrated on two sites; Crooked Lane, where 11 shops were based, and at Bell Yard[5]. Crooked Lane was just north of London Bridge, and was swept away in Victorian redevelopment. Bell Yard is still there, close to Chancery Lane and a few hundred metres from Embankment. There was one supplier on London Bridge itself; *"John Souch at the Golden Salmon and Spectacles was selling sailmaker's needles, fish hooks and other equipment for fishing in 1730"*[6].

The most complete directory of London tackle shops in the 19th century was provided by Hofland (1839, 1848). The first edition listed 34 such establishments, and the later edition, edited by Edward Jesse, no fewer than 41. The domination of Crooked Lane and Bell Yard had eased somewhat, with three at each location in the later list. Most were within a few hundred yards of the Thames or Lea throughout the city and beyond. The "Where to fish" guide for 1928 listed 22 tackle shops in Central London, including no less than eight in the postal area SW1. Every Thames-side town sported at least one dealer; in the 1928 guide, four were listed for Oxford and five for Reading.

Figure 9.5. The inside of John Forrest's tackle shop at 24, Thomas Street, London W1, in 1926[7]; this was the London branch of the well-known Forrest's of Kelso. Wouldn't you just love to be allowed to spend an hour here? This was one of 22 tackle shops in central London at that time.

In the early days most tackle dealers made all or most of the equipment they sold, but gradually specialist manufacturers evolved, at first locally and then as infrastructure improved, across the country.

Some contemporary advertisements for tackle businesses are reproduced throughout this book.

Chapter 9 footnotes

[1] The Graphic, Summer Number 1882. Drawn by J C Dollman.
[2] "Fishing excursions up the Thames, Illustrated London News, August 17 1850.
[3] Fishing Gazette, November 17 1894.
[4] Salmon and Trout Magazine 1926; No 43, pages 112-121; No 44, pages 209-220; No 45, pages 316-323
[5] Courtney Williams (1945).
[6] Gerhold (2019).
[7] Fishing Gazette, January 30 1926.

COOKHAM.

LLEWELLYN'S HOTEL.

CLOSE BELOW THE BRIDGE.

This Hotel having been extensively enlarged, offers superior accommodation to Anglers, Boating Parties, and others visiting this the finest part of the Thames.

Choice Wines and Spirits.

BOATS, PUNTS, & CANOES TO LET BY THE HOUR, DAY, WEEK, OR SEASON, ON REASONABLE TERMS.

JAMES LLEWELLYN, Proprietor.

CHAPTER 10

Barbel

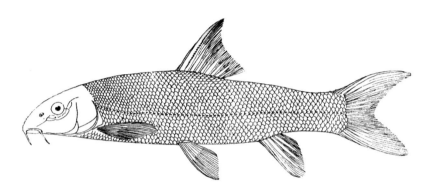

Barbel come first in the alphabetical list of major Thames fish and are thus addressed first. This is appropriate as this species perhaps more than any other represents the essence of Thames angling, being a highly popular quarry of anglers and one which has thrived in the river throughout recent history. From the tidal reaches upstream, barbel occur in good numbers to the upper reaches around Lechlade. In 1887 Taunt mentioned that they were plentiful between St John's Lock (the uppermost on the river) and Buscot Lock.

Barbel have been a major Thames species since the river was a tributary of the Rhine thousands of years ago. They like medium to large rivers (rarely being found in small streams) and steady to fast flows, and found the Thames and some of its tributaries very much to their liking. Even after the impoundment of most of the main river by weirs and locks (see Chapter 3) enough fast and steady-flowing water remained to keep them happy.

As a food species the barbel apparently borders on the unpleasant (I have never tried to eat one myself) but their large size and great strength has made them a very popular fish with anglers; Isaac Walton called them "a lusty and cunning fish".

Brookes, writing in 1781, stated that there were good barbel to be caught from Kingston upstream. Of the lower tributaries, he mentions only the largest, the Mole and Wey as holding these fish. They have occurred in fact, and still do occur, in good numbers well downstream of Kingston; Baddeley reported in 1834 that they are caught as far down as Brentford ("*at the back of the town, in a field called Old England*"), 8 km seawards of

Teddington Weir and 11 km downstream of Kingston. He also mentioned a favourite barbel swim at Isleworth, a little upstream of Brentford, known as "the Barbel Hole" or "Prideaux's Folly". Writing in 1960 Frank Murgett reported catching 14 barbel in a day near Popes Villa at Twickenham.

According to Smith, in 1860 the best places for ledgering for barbel were the deeps below Kingston Bridge and Sunbury Lock, Halliford, Weybridge, Chertsey Weir, all round the Penton Hook Reach, above Laleham, Maidenhead opposite Formosa Island, and the deeps at Bray; in this last place, a few years earlier, one hundred barbel weighing 256 lb had been caught in two days by two anglers; the following day 65 were caught weighing 154 lb. He also mentioned large individual fish such as one of 12½ lb caught by Mr Bigbee in 1823 at Hampton Deeps; the fish was landed on roach tackle. He also reported that a Mr W Croft had landed a barbel of 10½ lb at Chertsey Bridge.

Taunt stated that barbel were to be caught at Richmond and that there were eight professional fishermen at that place available to guide anglers. Teddington Weir has always been known as a good location for this species. Interestingly, John Bickerdyke[1] claimed in 1894 that barbel fishing on the upper Thames was not as good as further down, and cited the weirpools at Goring and Streatley, which appeared ideal for the species, as rarely if ever having produced one for the angler; certainly many of the tales of large catches during Victorian times came from the lower river.

In 1781 Brookes recorded interesting encounters with both large numbers and a large fish:-

On the morning of August 23 1771, Mr Warren, the perfumer, of Marylebone Street, began to angle in Walton Deeps, and found such sport, that he stopped before noon, tired with fatigue, and found that he had caught 280 lb weight of large size barbel. This gentleman usually has the deeps baited with worms overnight, and in the morning fishes from a well boat, with a perfumed paste for bait. In June 1772, when Mr Warren came to the usual fishing hole, a brother angler cried out, that he had had great sport, but that he had been devilish unlucky, for he had hooked a sturgeon who had carried away his line. Well (say Mr Warren) have a little patience and I'll catch the gentleman; which he did in about half an hour, and it proved to be one of his old acquaintances, a barbel, which weighed 11 lb, but being out of condition, Mr Warren had punched a hole in his tail and turned him again into the Thames. This fish had then the anglers hook sticking into his gills, and has been twice since caught by Mr Warren who as often has given him his liberty.

Although Mr Warren was clearly in the habit of releasing some of the barbel he landed, it was in fact common practice to kill all you caught well into the 20th century. In 1834 Baddeley described a day's fishing at a spot known as "Lady Young's Hole" at Hampton Court in which he and a friend caught more barbel than they could carry, and although helped by a third person they were very glad to be able to leave some of their catch at Brentford.

Killing barbel was a particularly regrettable action as they are not good to eat; most killed were either dumped directly, or given to others who probably tried eating them once and thereafter dumped any they were given. Binnell, writing in 1758 said of the barbel:-

The flesh is soft and flabby, and in no great esteem; the spawn is very unwholesome, especially in the month of May, purging both upwards and downwards, is surfeiting and dangerous, and those that eat thereof break out in blotches and red spots, and will loathe their meat, lose their appetites, and be extremely disordered.

Hardly a compelling advertisement for eating barbel!

Brookes provided a fascinating insight into the tackle in use for barbel fishing in 1781:-

Your rod must be very strong, with a tough whalebone at the end. You have no occasion for a float, but must put a large bullet on the line so that your bait may lie ledger. You must have ten hairs next the hook, but the remaining part of your line must be silk. If you make use of a wheel, as in trout fishing, it will be so much the better.

The quote above mentions using a "wheel" or reel for barbel fishing, but many a good fish has been hooked on gear with a fixed length of line such as a roach pole. In many such cases the fish won, leaving the shaken angler with an impression of unstoppable strength and a broken line. But sometimes the angler triumphed; one such encounter took place in about 1910 involving 19-year old Len Parker, later better-known as Captain Parker of the Downton Bull Hotel in Wiltshire. In an article on the use of the roach pole he wrote[2]:-

Figure 10.1. Float fishing for Thames barbel from a punt in 1814[3]. Note the usual arrangement of fixing the punt with two ryepecks, and the ubiquitous kitchen chairs for the anglers.

I fished at Richmond, from Messum's Raft, in the winter some years before the Great War: when numerous dace were there to be caught on pearl barley, and every now and then a good barbel. Week-end after week-end I fished here, hoping to get one of these barbel, and at last I did, and what a thrill, my first trip in an aeroplane was absolutely nothing in comparison. I struck and down went my rod top under water, I let it go – I'd got used to handling fish by now – still lower and lower it went until the third joint was almost submerged. The other anglers all started shouting good advice, but what could I do with my rod half under water and something on the end pulling like a dog? It eased up slightly, but down again the very next second, this time only the butt remained out of water. A fast stream was running, I got all hot and bothered, but I hung on and "gave rod" as I had been taught, but I'd precious little to give. Fortunately the rushes became weaker, I got the rod up slightly but the dead weight frightened me and I was tiring and beginning to think he would smash me. Another plunge or two and still I held him, then a sudden slackening, but I was quick and had him tight again; he was giving up the fight. So giving a little, taking a little, at last up to the surface he came, off came my butt and with a few more struggles he came to the net, a beautiful fish of just under 7 lb, my first barbel, the thrill of my life.

Mention has already been made of some remarkable catches of barbel in former times; the sort of numbers that we could only dream-of when I started fishing in the 1960s. Although by no means an everyday occurrence, some remarkable catches were taken well into the 20th Century. For example, 62 in a day by a Dr Mackintosh, 79 the next day by Mr Couchman, and 45 on a third day by Mr Couchman's brother, in about 1907; all these were fishing with professional fisherman Bert Cox of Marlow. A few years later, F H Amphlett and Arthur May, fishing with the same boatman, caught 30 barbel in two days as part of a larger mixed catch that included chub, dace and roach[4].

Although unremarkable in the context of large catches of barbel made around the time, the bag taken at Abingdon on August 25 1898 by two anglers is of interest because there is a photograph of the fish (Figure 10.2). One of the anglers (pen-name Piscator) described the catch in a letter to the Fishing Gazette:-

Having previously engaged George Brewerton, the Abingdon fisherman, we ground-baited a swim on Wednesday morning and evening, and again on Thursday morning, putting in at each baiting 500 worms, some loose and some in clay.

At 4.15 in the afternoon (Thursday) we (my friend, the fisherman and myself) arrived at the swim, and started leger fishing with two rods out. Almost immediately I had a knock, and after a few minutes landed our first a nice barbel of 4 lb; and by 7.45, when we stopped fishing, or after being on the swim only three and a half hours, we had twenty barbel in the punt, and they turned the scale at 80 lb (averaging 4 lb a fish), the two largest weighing 5½ lb each. I may mention that two fish broke our tackle, and five more were missed by being slightly hooked.[5]

Figure 10.2. A catch of twenty barbel weighing 80 lb by two anglers in less than four hours at Abingdon in 1898. The catch is described in the text. This is the only picture of a large catch of Thames barbel that I have seen, and was probably taken by professional photographer J Brewerton, brother of the fishing guide in the picture, George Brewerton. But what a terrible waste, barbel are not good to eat. Photograph reproduced by kind permission of Abingdon Area Archaeological and Historical Society, R J Faulkner collection.

Four possible factors spring to mind to explain the apparently better catches in Victorian times compared to most of the 20th Century. First, the stories of large catches probably represented exceptional good fortune even then, with the less successful trips forgotten or not recorded. Support for this suggestion comes from the writing of Arthur Ransome[6] (of Swallows and Amazon fame) who said:-

I have never fished for barbel. Fishing for barbel needs a greater expenditure of worms and faith than I have ever been in a position to afford. You enrich the river with a thousand lobworms daily for a week to induce the barbel to look at worms favourably. Then you fish for him. But you hardly ever catch a barbel, even after this prodigious baiting. It is a sorry business, persisted in because once or twice in a lifetime the angler finds barbel on the feed....

Second, the native crayfish, probably an important food item for barbel, were abundant; while there were some still to be found in the middle Thames in the 1960's they were by no means numerous (see Chapter 22). Third, the vast number of lobworms formerly used as groundbait may well have represented a major food source for the fish, and supported enhanced stock levels; rather in the way that artificial high-protein groundbaits can do today. And fourth, nearly all the great catches recorded were taken from a punt, and the anglers were guided by professional fishermen who undertook groundbaiting of the swim. These advantages became much less usual in the 20th Century. In 1960 Frank Murgett wrote *"If your mind turns to barbel then you must have a boat because Thames barbel swim in fast waters, usually well away from banks"*; but by then serious fishing from a boat was rare, and professional guides were effectively a thing of the past.

Baiting of swims often involved large numbers of lobworms, and supplying these became an industry in its own right. One of the biggest suppliers was a Mr Wells of Nottingham. He had a team of collectors who picked the worms up at night from local parks and meadows. Frank Buckland[7] described the business:-

The worms are sold by the thousand or by the quart. In a warm, moist night, from two to six thousand worms are brought in by the collectors. Some people can collect worms much better than others. The worms are very cunning, and are apt to pop back into their holes if the person treads heavily.

You sir, said Mr Wells to one of our party, you would make a capital worm catcher! I asked why. Says Wells, You see sir, the gentleman is so long on his pins, and has such a great reach with his arm, so that he could stand still in one place and catch the worms all around him without moving about much. A short gentleman like you sir, would never make a worm catcher; you haven't got reach enough in the arm, and you're too short in the leg. The worms are terrible artful things. This gentleman I'd back to catch worms against you any night, and I give you a thousand worms to start with.

Last year he sent to London the large number of 400,000 worms. The price varies much. They average 3s 6d (17.5 pence) per thousand. The worms are principally used for barbel fishing.

Although baiting with large numbers of worms appears to have been *de rigeur* for serious barbel anglers, it was by no means a formula for guaranteed success. Wheeldon (1878) recalled a day's barbel fishing at the "Halfway House" near Staines, involving the use of 2000 lobworms as groundbait. In the event only two small fish were caught. Wheeley in 1897 suggested that 500 to 1000 worms were the optimal level, with perhaps greater numbers satiating the fish before they had a chance to take the anglers bait

Wheeley also made the interesting observation that barbel in the Thames tended to be found in much deeper water than in the Trent, often 15 to 20 feet. He suggested that this may have been because of excessive disturbance by punting poles in any areas where such poles, typically twelve feet or so in length, could reach the river bed. One of the largest Thames barbel seen for many years was killed when a professional fisherman inadvertently impaled

Figure 10.3. Barbel fishing at Teddington in the 1830s[8]. An angler in each punt and the chap wading from the bank appear to have large fish in play. Behind the boat in the background are what appear to be eel bucks.

it through the head with his punt pole[9]. The 12 lb fish was killed in January 1894, and was kept to be set up by a taxidermist. I wonder if the circumstances of its downfall were always explained to those who admired this trophy in its final resting place!

Although great catches were made in the heyday of Thames barbel fishing, very large fish were rarely caught. In 1860 Smith stated that the largest barbel he ever saw was a fish of 7½ lb taken on roach tackle below Teddington Weir, though he had heard of a few much bigger fish being taken in the past. There are likely to be two factors contributing to this lack of large fish. First, the tackle being used in those days was crude in the extreme compared to modern-day hooks, lines, rods and reels, and the odds must have been firmly in the favour of any large fish hooked. Second, the widespread practice of killing all fish caught, despite the fact that barbel were poor to eat, meant that most were cropped before they had a chance to reach great size.

Neither of these factors can really explain why Thames barbel were also of generally modest size when I fished the river in the 1960s; and indeed did not appear to be anything like as abundant as 100 years earlier, when most fish were killed. We caught a fair few in the Windsor and Maidenhead areas but as far as I recall the largest was about 7½ lb. If we wanted a crack at a larger specimen or greater numbers we went to the Hampshire Avon or Dorset Stour. The modest size of Thames barbel in the mid 20th century is further borne out by the fact that the largest fish caught from the lower Thames by that great Thames angler, Frank Murgett, weighed only 8 lb[10] (a fish from Bell Weir, Map 8). This said, the odd larger specimen did occur, such as the 13 pounder caught by John Cadd at Godstow (Map 4) in 1973[11]. For many years the national rod-caught record was 14 lb 6 oz, shared by two fish from the Avon and one from the Thames – caught at Molesey in 1888 by T Wheeler[12].

However, much larger fish have been caught in recent years, and it is almost certain that such fish were not present in any numbers in the river until the last twenty years or so. The record for the river is 20 lb 12 oz caught by John Llewellyn in March 2019[13], followed by one of 20 lb 9 oz caught by Rob Phillips in March 2008. Other twenty pounders are fish of 20 lb 7 oz by Steven Birt in February 2020[14], and 20 lb 2 oz by Simon Cook in October 2008. For some reason these fish are not recognised as river records by the Thames Angler's Conservancy, who grant the laurels to a fish of 19 lb 8 oz caught by Dave Broady in January 2018. One other nineteen pounder is recorded, a fish of 19 lb 1 oz caught by Garry Tear in 2017. Several fish over 18 lb have been reported caught since 2005, with literally hundreds of fish in excess of the earlier record of 14 lb 6 oz. Perhaps the most remarkable catch was a bag of Thames barbel taken over several days by Rob Hawthorn in November 2012, which included fish of 17 lb 6 oz, 16 lb 10 oz, 15 lb 9 oz, 15 lb 4 oz, 14 lb 8 oz, 14 lb 1 oz, 13 lb 9 oz and 12 lb; no less than five fish that exceeded the weight of a previous national record that had stood for the best part of 100 years. The exact locations of all these catches are closely guarded secrets!

Why has there been a boom in large barbel in the past decade or two? The trend is matched in many other waterways, and no less than 27 rivers in England and Wales have produced, in the past twenty years, barbel in excess of the old 14 lb 6 oz national record. Likely contributing factors are climate change (barbel thrive in warm water), the use of high-protein groundbaits boosting the diet of the fish , and the increase in populations of alien species that are likely to represent a major food source, such as signal crayfish and Chinese mitten crabs. Whatever the reason, there appears to be a better chance of catching a Thames barbel over 15 lbs now that at any time in the past.

Chapter 10 footnotes

[1] Bickerdyke J (1894) Fish and fishing – VIII barbel and bream. Nottinghamshire Guardian, 21 April 1894.

[2] Parker L A (1939) The roach pole. In "The Anglers News and Sea Fishers Journal" issue 1756, January 21 1939.

[3] From Salter (1814).

[4] Fishing Gazette, August 20 1910.

[5] Fishing Gazette, September 3 1898.

[6] Ransome (1929).

[7] Land and Water, number 602, August 4 1877. Reproduced in Buckland (1880).

[8] New Sporting Magazine, 1837. Engraved by J W Archer, from a drawing by J Jackson.

[9] Amphlett (1894).

[10] Murgett (1960)

[11] Angling Times Yearbook 1976/77.

[12] These fish were removed from the record list by the British Record (rod-caught) Fish Committee in 1968 due to doubts regarding the reliability of the weights. However, they were soon to be eclipsed.

[13] Anglers Mail, April 1 2019.

[14] Angling Times, February 28 2020.

CHAPTER II

Bream

On the Thames the bream just occurs.* Patrick R Chalmers, *At the tail of the weir (1932).

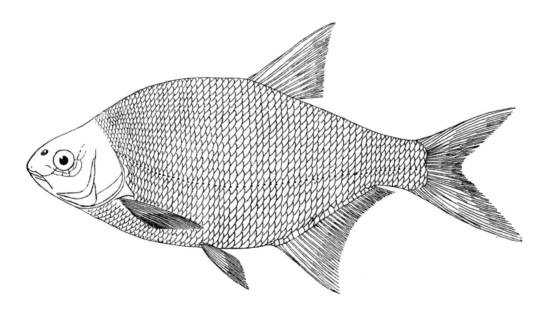

The rather quaintly-worded quote above from Chalmers delightful 1932 book typifies the general historic view of the distribution of the bream in the Thames. In the 1781 edition of the Art of Angling, Brookes reported "bream aplenty" in the Mole, but very few in the Thames. Salter in his book of Thames angling written in 1814 does not mention bream in his description of fishing stations between Staines and London. In 1834 Baddeley stated that bream were to be found in the Brent between Hanwell and Brentford, in the Mole and in the Wey at Weybridge, but very few in the Thames itself.

What was the reason for this lack of bream in the main river, and why have things clearly changed so radically in the last 150 years?

The answer almost certainly lies in the physical nature of the lower main river before the construction of the locks and weirs around 1820. As described in Chapter 2, the Thames would have been a fast-flowing gravel-bed river with extensive shallows and riffles, and few refuges from flood flows. It would not have been really suitable for bream, though any that did descend from the tributaries like the Mole and Wey would no doubt have clung on for a while in the deeper holes. The construction of the locks and associated weirs between Chertsey and Teddington between 1811 and 1813 would have created deeper slower reaches and, in the lock cuts, refuges from flood flows. Suddenly there was ideal habitat for the species and, with the abundant stocks in the lower tributaries, a ready source. In 1897 W H Brougham[1] recalled being told by an old fisherman, John Stains, that the river received a great injection of bream when the Wey "burst"; within days, he had a catch of three hundredweight where he had never caught one before. Unfortunately no date was recorded for this event.

As late as 1860 it was stated that the Thames:-

does not produce many bream, but they have been occasionally caught there of a large size, as is evinced by the drawing on the walls of the Bell at Hampton, of one taken in the Deep there, of 6¾ lb. I have fished the Thames for more than 20 years, and have only caught three.[2]

However, after that the species appears to have become more numerous in the lower river. In the course of the 1866 season a member of the Piscatorial Society, Mr John Johnstone,

caught a total of 549 lb at Walton[1]. The same source records that Mr Alfred Jardine and a friend caught 213 lb of bream, largest 6 ½ lb, from the Holliday Hole below Shepperton Weir. A catch with a total weight of 126 lb 2 oz, largest fish 4 lb 2 oz, was reported from Shepperton on September 2 1876[3], and another "good lot" of bream to 4½ lb was taken from the "Chalk Hole" at Halliford in August 1887[4]. The largest fish recorded from the lower river until recent times weighed 10 lb 3 oz, and was found floating downstream in a moribund condition in April 1923 (Figure 11.1)[5]. The fish was set up, and in 1926 was displayed in the King's Head, HQ of the Francis Francis Fishing Club in Twickenham[6]. Two fish of 8½ lb each were caught at Surbiton during the 1890-91 season[7].

Figure 11.1. Bream of 10 lb 3 oz found floating in the river at Twickenham in April 1923.

Figure 11.2. The weigh-in at a London angling club match in 1898[8]. Bream feature heavily in the catches, and there are several pike.

However, the very structures that are likely to have made the river more suitable for bream, the weirs and locks, will also have acted as barriers to slow their spread. The big catches thus far described were all from the four-mile reach which included the confluence with the Wey, between Shepperton and Sunbury locks (Map 9). No doubt some were flushed downstream and others may have made their way upstream via the locks. But much of the subsequent upstream spread of the species appears to have involved intentional transfers by angling interests. Brougham stated that bream first occurred in the Chertsey reach of the river in the 1850s; he recorded the recollection of a professional fisherman, William Galloway, that:-

Mr Heseltine, who was a great angler in those days, frequently caught large quantities of bream below Shepperton and always brought them in the well of his punt to Chertsey and turned them into the river.

In the summer of 1873, local professional fisherman James Haslett groundbaited Chertsey Weir and fished it for 21 consecutive days[9]. He caught a total of 496 lb of bream, an average of 24 lb per day. By 1876 the Chertsey area was one of the best parts of the Thames for the species[10]. Taunt (1887) stated that another of the best pitches for bream on the river was at Walton, *not far from the wooden bridge that carries the towing path over the entrance to the backwater*; he did not mention any presence of the species upstream of Chertsey Weir or downstream of Sunbury Weir. Almost none occurred in the river upstream of this stretch until a more extensive programme of restocking was initiated.

105

At a meeting of the Maidenhead, Cookham and Bray Thames Angling Association in 1876, discussion took place regarding approval by the Conservators of a proposal to catch bream in the lower reaches and transport them upstream[10]. However, before that could be arranged a gift of bream from the Great Ouse was made from the Bedford Angling Club in exchange for some barbel; the fish were stocked at Cliveden[11]. The transfer from the lower river took place about two years later, when Thames Conservancy keepers netted 113 bream from Walton Deep for transfer by boat to Marlow[12]. Many other transfers took place from the lower river and from various still waters. These included releases between Maidenhead and Bray in 1880[13], to the Reading and District AA part of the river in 1888, at Windsor in 1892[14], Henley in 1900[15], 1902[16] and 1903[17], and Abingdon in 1901[18] and doubtless many other initiatives.

The success of these transfers was soon apparent; examples of recaptures are fish of 7 lb 2 oz at Windsor in 1890[19], one of 8½ lb at Hambleden caught by Dr Eliot in 1898[20], and 3½ lb at Henley in 1900[21]. A good catch was taken at Henley by A E Hobbs in 1909, comprising 14 fish totalling 53 lb; the largest weighed 6½ lb and was set up[22]. This fish in its case is held by the River and Rowing Museum at Henley. However, as late as 1906 the Victoria County History of Berkshire recorded:-

Bream are occasionally taken in the upper Thames, where they have been introduced from Norfolk by various fishery associations, but their numbers are hardly sufficient to enable them to hold their own and stock the river to any appreciable extent. They are quite as rare in the Berkshire portion of the river as are carp.

The status of bream in about 1930, according to Chalmers (1932) has already been quoted at the head of the chapter. However, he described one reliable spot for catching them, in his usual style:-

Pole the punt into Hennerton Backwater, below Wargrave, and rejoin the main river at Beggat's Hole Ferry. On the Berkshire bank, just where the backwater ends, is a lawn shady with elms. And there is, or was, an ancient willow who leans out, mopping and mowing, to the Oxfordshire shore. Just upstream of that willow (yes, I see bubbles) you will find bream of a midsummer morning. Or else you will not, for, of course, I cannot be positive.

By this time the fish were clearly established further upstream too; in 1928, J Perkins caught a brace of bream weighing 10 lb 13½ oz and 9 lb 14½ oz between Eynsham Bridge (Map 3) and Carrot's Ham, upstream of Oxford (Figure 11.3)[23]. Other early large fish in the upper Thames include a 9 lb 8 oz fish from Eynsham by W Ashton in 1919, and 9 lb 4 oz from Godstow by W H Chivers in 1916[24].

RECORD BREAM.
Caught by J.J.PERKINS, at Eynsham, Sept 20th, 1928. Wgts. 10lbs 13¾ozs & 9lbs 14¾ozs.

Figure 11.3. Bream of 10 lb 13½ oz and 9 lb 14½ oz caught by J Perkins in 1928. © River and Rowing Museum, Henley on Thames, UK.

Peter Stone, in his fishing autobiography entitled "Old Father Thames" written in 1997, gives some fascinating and first-hand history of the increase in bream in the upper river. Despite the record of the two large bream near Eynsham in 1928, already mentioned, the species was very scarce in the Oxford area in the 1930s and 40s. Then small fish started to appear at Moulsford, about 25 river miles below Oxford; on hearing this, Stone visited there and caught his first ever bream, a fish of about a pound. The species soon spread upstream, and in 1949 he caught 16 weighing 22 lb at Kings Weir, upstream of Oxford. He predicted great bream fishing would develop in the area, and he was right. In the book he describes many subsequent catches of over 100 lb, with individual fish up to 7 lb. Another very successful angler in the area was Bill Taylor, who caught at least one bag of 100 lb plus every year from 1957 to 1965, when he moved away from the area, topped by a catch of 148½ lb taken in just four hours.[25] These huge catches generally comprised relatively large fish; the largest in the 148½ lb haul was over 7 lb, and the average was over 3½ lb. However, not all stretches contained such large fish; Taylor reported that the Sandford to Clifton Hampden reach swarmed with small bream; although he "often" made catches of more than 100 fish, he never saw one of more than 1½ lb.

Some even larger catches have been recorded in more recent times, including the Thames match record catch of over 203 lb taken at Medley in 2008, and 170 lb 11 oz, comprising 37 bream and a single perch, at Sunbury also in 2008. Another catch of almost 200 lb, taken in only three hours at Kingston in 2013, comprised just 33 bream and included several fish around 8 lb. The successful angler was Tony Curd[26]. But the biggest catch of which I am aware was taken in a night session in the 1970s by local angler John Cadd at Oxford. He landed 109 bream and 12 roach for an incredible 436 lb[27].

Although bream made their way downstream from Sunbury Weir, at first there were relatively few in the tidal reach below Teddington for the same reason that they were scarce upstream before the locks were built – rapid flows and lack of shelter from floods. The only place where they were described by Amphlett (1894) was in a deep hole opposite Pope's Villa about half a mile below Teddington Weir. However, the construction of the half-tide weir and lock at Richmond in 1890 changed that, and bream quickly colonised this "new" impounded reach. For some reason, numbers then declined in the tidal reach to virtually zero by about 1930; the Annual Report of the Thames Angling Preservation Society for 1933 [28], in discussing the tidal reach recorded:-

...but probably the most marked feature is the capture of a number of bream, a fish little seen here for a generation, though previously the tidal was well famed for it. These bream are probably largely the offspring of fish turned in by your Netting Committee below Teddington Weir and at Twickenham on November 8th and 14th, 1931.

John Burrett, writing in 1960, stated that bream were rarely heard-of in the Tidal Thames in his youth (perhaps before the restocking in 1931?) but that numbers were by then increasing, with bags of up to 20 lb of smaller bream being reported. He predicted that the fish would increase in size in the following five to ten years. In the second (renamed) edition of his book published in 1968 he reported increasing catches of the species including a specimen of 8 lb 14 oz caught below Teddington Lock in March 1962. Twenty years later, Wheeler (1979) stated that small numbers had been reported throughout the tideway when salinity levels allow, and suggested that a good population was established as far downstream as Wandsworth Bridge. In September 2014 the first "TideFest" match, fished at Strand on the Green, was won with a catch of more than 34 lb, mostly bream.[29]

When I fished the river in the 1960s there were almost no bream between Egham and Marlow – at least I never heard of anyone claiming to have caught one – but there were strong populations above and below this. I recall catching ten bream to 4½ lb upstream of Sonning one day in March 1966. Nowadays the species seems to be well spread throughout the river from well upstream of Oxford to Kew and below – including the 1960's "black hole" between Egham and Marlow. Fish of six or seven pounds are regularly taken and over 10 lb occasionally. The largest of which I have heard was 11 lb 8 oz caught by S Martin in February 1954[30] at Goring, but I suspect larger ones have in fact been caught. Murgett (1960) stated that he and his friends had caught five Thames bream over ten pounds; *one so big that I dare not tell the weight, for you'd only call me a liar.*

Bream generally feed on the river bed, and while they may be caught float fishing most large bags are caught ledgering. A very useful technique is to deploy a swim-feeder. This is a combined weight and container for a small volume of groundbait that is located on the line a foot or two above the hook, and is cast to the fishing spot. It is a relatively recent development, being first patented in 1948[31]. The swimfeeder precisely delivers groundbait immediately upstream of where the baited hook comes to rest. This, combined with general distribution of larger balls of groundbait, helps to keep a shoal of feeding bream in one spot. In this way some very large catches have been made.

Chapter 11 footnotes

[1] Thames Angling News, 1(8), June 1897.
[2] Smith (1860)
[3] Marston (1963)
[4] Wheeldon (1878)
[5] Fishing Gazette June 2 1923
[6] Young (1926)
[7] Fishing Gazette, March 28 1891
[8] The Graphic, September 2 1899
[9] Illustrated London News, June 17 1876
[10] Reading Mercury, May 6 1876
[11] Aldershot Military Gazette, May 27 1876
[12] Reading Mercury, May 18 1878
[13] Reading Mercury, September 4 1880
[14] Reading Mercury, December 24 1892
[15] Oxford Journal August 4 1900
[16] Surrey Mirror, December 19 1902
[17] Reading Mercury, August 15 1903
[18] Reading Mercury, March 23 1901
[19] Oxford Journal, March 22 1890
[20] Fishing Gazette, August 13 1898
[21] Reading Mercury, August 10 1901
[22] Fishing Gazette, July 16 1910.
[23] Taylor (1960)
[24] Sheringham 1928
[25] Taylor (1968)
[26] Angling Times, July 17 2013
[27] Angling Times Yearbook, 1976/77
[28] Thames Angling Preservation Society Blue Book, 1934
[29] Thames Anglers Conservancy website (www.rivertac.org/2014/10)
[30] Graham (1972), and Fishing Gazette, March 13 1954
[31] Maxtone Graham (1990).

110

CHAPTER 12

Carp

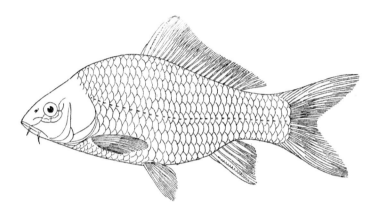

Carp have occurred in small numbers throughout the river for centuries, but it is only in recent years that their numbers have increased, and the methods of capture developed, to the extent that anyone would target them specifically. In the last thirty years the numbers and size of carp in the river have increased tremendously such that the river has become a first-class venue for the species.

There are many old records of captures of carp in the river, but mostly the fish were of modest size. There are probably three reasons for this. First, the carp in the Thames at that time were indeed of only limited maximum weight. The original "wild" carp in Britain was a fish of moderate weight, being long and lean in the body. The rotund monsters of today have arisen through programmes of selective breeding over hundreds of years. For more than twenty years from 1930 the British record was held by a fish of 26 lb, caught by Albert Buckley at Mapperly Reservoir. Then in 1951 the record was broken with a fish of 31 lb 4 oz, and a year later Richard Walker caught his 44 lb fish that was a record for many years. The era of modern carp fishing for large fish had well and truly arrived. The second reason why large carp were rarely reported was that the tackle in use at the time, especially that for roach and other smaller species that were then the usual quarry, was not up to landing a hard-fighting fish weighing in double figures without very great skill and not a little luck on the part of the angler. The third reason is that, until the 1970s, night fishing was not allowed upstream of the London Stone at Staines; fishing for large carp is generally much more productive by night.

While carp may thrive once at large in rivers, it seems that flowing water rarely offers suitable conditions for breeding of the species. Very small carp are virtually unknown in the river; indeed, in the recent explosion of carp numbers, fish weighing less than about 10 lb are extremely few. It seems probable that all Thames carp started life in still waters, and either escaped to the river from adjacent lakes and ponds during floods, or were intentionally stocked. Having said that, some of the more productive reaches of the river are nowadays connected to old gravel workings which are being used as marinas, and it is likely that some natural breeding takes place here to supply fish to the river itself.

One of the earliest records is of a fish of 13 lb taken at Hampton Court in 1739[1]. Most of the carp in earlier days would have escaped into the river from flooded adjacent still waters, but there were some intentional introductions; for example in 1892 *a number of fine carp, from 3 lb to 7 lb, have been placed in the Windsor district of the Thames by the local angling society*[2]. It is also likely that a number were purposely or inadvertently introduced among the large numbers of roach and bream stocked over the years by the Thames Angling Preservation Society (see Chapter 8).

Figure 12.1. A busy fishing scene at Teddington Weir in 1876[3]. At times in the previous thirty years fair catches of carp were taken here.

From the 1850s, and possibly earlier, there were several decades when the carp fishing around Teddington was really quite good on occasions. A correspondent in The Field in September 1858[4] reported that anglers fishing with local professional William Kemp caught 17 carp in two days; a change in the weather then spoiled the fishing. The reliability of this report was challenged in the correspondence columns but in a follow-up response the same correspondent claimed he could prove that at least 150 carp had been caught at Teddington so far that season; he suggested that the fish originated in an escape from a still water. This was before the TAPS started stocking carp into the area. Two "large" carp were reported caught there in October 1867[5], and in an editorial in "The Field" in January 1870[6] there is reference to a catch of six in a day the previous year. Interestingly, there is also a suggestion that carp fishing was only worthwhile here from October onwards. In October 1870 there was a report that at least 20 carp had been taken there in ten days[7]. A fish of 6½ lb was caught by a Mr Sinbaldi in September 1871[8]. However, by 1875 the numbers had dwindled; in reporting[9] some fish being caught in that year it was noted that *Mr W Hawkins, has, in his good old days of fishing, taken more carp in one day than are now caught in the whole season*. This is consistent with the hypothesis that the fish arrived as a result of episodic escapes from local still waters. Fennell (1870) suggested that the *disruption of the dam of the canal of Sion House* a few years earlier explained much of the surge in catches; Sion House lies about six km seawards of Teddington Weir. It is interesting to note that most of the reports failed to indicate the weight of the fish being caught; presumably they were of modest size.

During this time odd carp were reported from elsewhere in the river, for example fish of eight, five and four pounds in one day in July 1858 at Ham Point, Weybridge[10], an eight pounder at Walton in 1875[11] and a fish of 9½ lb at Windsor in 1877[12].

A discussion at the TAPS Annual Dinner in 1876 concerning the decline in carp captures in the river led Francis Francis and Mr W H Broughham to resolve to initiate a stocking programme[13]. The following spring a number of still waters were netted at Bushy Park, Hampton Court, Twickenham Common and Osterley Park. As a result, 177 carp were transferred to the Thames; 15 to Hampton Deep (largest 12 and 14 lb), 22 to Kingston (most about 10 lb), 16 to Thames Ditton, 24 to below Teddington Weir (3-5 lb), 30 to Sunbury and 70 to Walton Reach[14]. Several were reported caught in the ensuing months, and several large fish hooked and lost are likely to have been from these releases. However, the fish then apparently disappeared as very few carp were reported from the Thames for the next 20 years or so.

There was then a little more carp activity throughout the river, presumably arising from new escapes. In 1926 Young reported that an 18 pounder was the Thames record, a fish caught at Windsor in about 1895. Fishing at Teddington in 1899 Mr G Sinbaldi caught three in two days weighing 4 lb 4 oz, 5 lb and 5 lb 5 oz[15], and the following year the same location yielded a nine pounder for T V Denniford[16]. A fish of 15 lb was reported at Brentford in 1901, but was not captured by angling[17]. A splendid fish 14 lb 1 oz was caught in 1907 by Charles Cook in the tidal river at Twickenham Deeps [18]. Englefield (1912) reported having caught five carp in a sitting at Weybridge "some years" earlier; the fish weighed from 2 lb to 6¼ lb and were presumably the result of a local escape.

Even when few carp were being reported, it is likely that there were numbers of large fish scattered through the river. As already discussed these fish were difficult to catch (or at least difficult to land) and the periods of apparent activity probably coincided with new injections of smallish fish into the river; once the fish grew and dispersed they dropped

Figure 12.2. Carp of 11 lb 2 oz caught in 1916 at Windsor by J W Campbell[21].

from view. Occasional large fish were found stranded; for example one of more than 20 lb found live the in rushes at Benson in 1883[19]. About twenty years later a local angler, Edwin Gosling, located a shoal of large carp a mile or so upstream of Benson, but despite a concerted effort throughout a whole summer was unable to catch one. However, one of 12½ lb became stranded in a meadow during an October flood. Gosling also claimed that large carp were located around Sonning at that time, but again they remained uncaught[20].

The period from about 1910 to 1960 seems to have been a relatively quiet time for Thames carp, or at least for reports of them. Chalmers (1932) said that he had only ever seen one Thames carp. Captures during this period include fish of 11 lb 2 oz at Windsor in 1916[21] (Figure 12.2), 10 lb at Laleham in 1922[22], a fish 20 inches long at Twickenham in 1924[23], and one of 6 lb 3 oz at Petersham in 1926[24]. Burrett (1968) in his list of *large fish from the lower Thames; Staines to Isleworth 1950-1967* had four double-figure carp; 17 lb 8 oz at Chertsey caught by W J Graham in September 1960; two near the outfall from Kingston Power Station (17 lb 2 oz in October 1954 and 14 lb 6 oz in August 1959); and a ten pounder at Richmond in November 1956.

The Thames record list produced by the Federation of Thames Anglers in 1955 (See Chapter 6) listed a carp of 16 lb 15 oz as the largest from the river, but gave no details. Peter Stone stated that the Thames Conservancy stocked carp into the river in the 1950s, but I can find no other information on this. When I started fishing the river in the early 1960s there were some large carp around the warm-water outfalls from the coal-fired power stations at Earley (between Reading and Sonning) and Kingston, with odd fish to 20 lbs being occasionally caught.

A little after this time carp started appearing and increasing in number throughout the river. In 1970 Peter Stone wrote[25]:-

In 1968 a 15 lb carp was caught at Oxford. Shortly after, two small ones weighing a pound were caught several miles below at Clifton Hampden, followed by another 'Oxonian' weighing 12 lb. In February 1969 a friend took a 9lb fish in a match and two weeks later my friend Fred Towns took a nice fish from Godstow Weir on legered cheese-paste.

Last season saw an even greater number being taken from the Thames – mostly from the lower reaches. One huge fish weighed 26 lb, whilst several others topping 20 lb were also reported.

In 1968 a fourteen pounder was reported at Hampton Court[26], and a remarkable catch of eight carp averaging 6½ lb each was made by Sid Cragg at Clifton Hampden[27].

Carp were also increasing in the tidal reaches. Wheeler (1979) reported that between 1968 and 1973 eleven small carp were recorded in the fish samples from power-station intakes between Wandsworth and Dartford; others were reported by anglers in this area.

In 1972 Alan Campion caught a 30 lb 8 oz carp at Sonning, which was stated to be a Thames record[28]. In that report the previous record was said to have been caught by Major A Swayer in 1965, but I have been unable to locate details. The river record was again beaten in 1974 with a fish of 31 lb from Oxford by John Cadd[29].

The power stations at Earley and Kingston were decommissioned in 1976 and 1980 respectively, though neither was responsible for any significant generation, and thus warm water discharged to the river, after 1975. Their attendant carp appeared to spread out, and large fish started to appear throughout the river. A 22 pounder was caught at Windsor in 1976[30]. Peter Stone reported that, by the mid 1990's, *the river was full of carp.*

From 1973 the old ban on night fishing in the river upstream of Staines was abolished. This, coupled with the increase in numbers of large fish, encouraged a few anglers to target Thames carp seriously. One of the earliest specialists was John Wallace of Maidenhead. By 1997 he had caught more than 30 carp from the river, including a 24 pounder from Sonning[31]. Another early convert to Thames carping was Mike Wilson, who fished mainly in the reach between Clifton Hampden and Benson. A friend of his hooked six carp in a session while chub fishing in the early 1970s, only landing one, a ten pounder. A week later, Mike caught two of 9 lb and 14 lb. He caught seven over the next year.

A good picture of modern-day Thames carping is provided by the 2019 book edited by Rob Maylin, containing chapters by many of today's top specialists in this field. Some enthusiasts fish several days (or rather nights) a week, and catch of the order of thirty or so large carp each in a season. The fish are all large, with fish under ten pounds a rarity. Numbers seem roughly equally split between the fully-scaled commons, and mirror carp which have fewer often large scales and significant areas of skin not protected by scales. These variations have arisen through generations of selective breeding in fish farms and would have been unkown to our Victorian forebears. Carp occur throughout the river; Graham Stevens reports catching carp in seven out of the eight reaches (ie between locks) from downstream of Teddington to upstream of Old Windsor. Good catches have been reported upstream and downstream of Reading, in the Benson/Shillingford area, and around Oxford. Most successful carp anglers are understandably somewhat reticent to reveal their favourite locations, but carp are probably present, and caught, in every reach from upstream of Oxford to well into the tidal river. Some tremendous catches are recorded in the book. Over the years Dave Walker has caught nine fish over 30 lb, best 37 lb; Trevor Tull has landed six over 40 lb. Great sessions include eight in 12 hours by Zeth Christie, and a four fish catch totalling more than 130 lb for Ash Geden (44 lb 14 oz, 35 lb 10 oz, 28 lb 12 oz and 23 lb 12 oz).

There are other interesting points to be gleaned from the experience of this new band of specialists. First, in contrast to stillwater fishing for carp which is best in summer and autumn, the fishing is just as good in the winter as earlier in the season, in all but the most severe weather. Jason Smith reported that of 29 carp caught one season, 25 were taken from November onwards. This is consistent with the experience of their predecessors well over a century earlier at Teddington. The fish also seem to be quite happy in a fairly fast flow; in some cases several ounces of lead have been necessary to anchor the bait in the chosen spot. Finally, the unique scale patterns allow individual identification of the fish. Many anglers have made multiple recaptures; for example, the record fish of 50 lb 14 oz caught by Nick Helleur was also the previous record when it was caught at 48 lb 7 oz by Steve Shenfield in 2017; it was also caught at 45 lb (2015) and at least once more at around 30 lb. Aidan Savan recorded catching one fish on at least five occasions over three seasons, and Bobby Coote caught one he named "the friendly ghost" seven times in the London Docks.

Catching large Thames carp is a specialised business requiring considerable knowledge and skill for consistent success. Baits are typically manufactured high-protein pellets, often flavoured and scented and used in favourite combination, and groundbaiting with the same or similar material is considered essential. The sport has developed its own terminology for rigs and baits that sounds like a foreign language to non-aficionados. For example, Nick Helleur's river record fish was caught on a *snowman rig with heavily glugged Sticky Krill bottom bait with Signature Squid pop-up*, and the groundbait was *peanuts with salt and chilli powder, plus Sticky Krill boilies with Krill Liquid[32]*. And Ash Gedden's 130 lb catch was taken using *Dynamite Complex-T pop-ups fished over a pre-baited area of the same boillie heavily glugged in Sweet Tiger Liquid.[33]*

Although there are clearly good numbers of large carp nowadays throughout the river, the lack of small fish suggests that there is no natural reproduction in the Thames. It is thought that the river may have received a particularly good stock of escapees during the major summer floods of 2007. Future carp fishing is likely to be dependent upon continued escapes from adjacent still waters, or intentional releases.

Chapter 12 footnotes

[1] Brookes (1781 edition).
[2] Oxford Journal, December 3 1892.
[3] The Pictorial World, October 14 1876.
[4] The Field, September 18 1858.
[5] Sporting Life, November 2 1867.
[6] The Field, January 15 1870.
[7] Sporting Life, October 15 1870.
[8] The Field, September 14 1871.
[9] Sporting Gazette, September 18 1875.

[10] "Otter" (1864).

[11] Sporting Gazette, September 18 1875.

[12] Fishing Gazette, December 28 1877.

[13] Illustrated Sporting and Dramatic News, May 5 1877.

[14] Graphic, August 31 1878.

[15] Fishing Gazette, November 4 1899.

[16] Surrey Comet, October 13 1900.

[17] Acton Gazette, February 8 1901

[18] Fishing Gazette, July 13 1907.

[19] Field, September 22 1883.

[20] Fishing Gazette, June 30 1900.

[21] Fishing Gazette, July 29 1916.

[22] Oxfordshire Weekly News, October 18 1922.

[23] Westminster Gazette, September 11 1924.

[24] Fishing Gazette, June 19 1926.

[25] Article in "Shooting Times" reproduced in Stone (1997).

[26] Reading Evening Post, July 12 1968.

[27] Reading Evening Post, September 6 1968.

[28] Sports Argus, October 22 1972.

[29] People September 29 1974.

[30] People, August 22 1976.

[31] Reading Evening Post, November 12 1997.

[32] "Carp Feed" website.

[33] "Adventure" website.

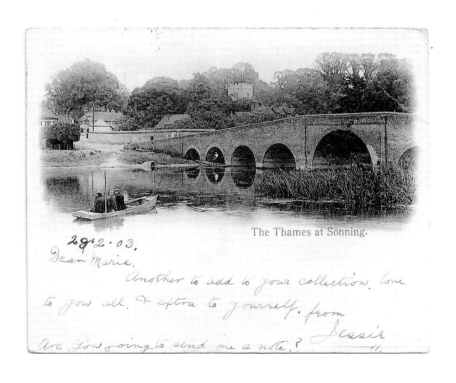

The Thames at Sonning.

29.2.03,
Dear Marie,
Another to add to your collection, love
to you all, & extra to yourself, from
Jessie
Are you going to send me a note?

From *The Pictorial World*, October 14 1876. Artist J Temple.

CHAPTER 13

Chub

As the chub is a coarse fish it is seldom cooked and eaten by any but the poorest people.
Alfred Williams, *Round about the Upper Thames* (1922).

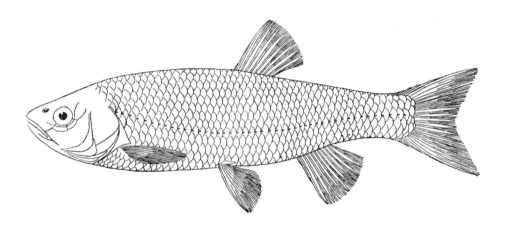

Chub are found throughout the length of the non-tidal river and its tributaries, but the species has never really thrived in the tidal reaches in contrast to roach, dace and barbel. The furthest downstream that chub were recorded in Amphlett's very thorough 1894 survey was in Strawberry Deeps, just below the point of the Island formed by Teddington lock cut. In 1968 Burrett also refered to few chub occurring at Teddington. In a detailed description of the fish recolonising the tidal river, Wheeler in 1979 recorded odd specimens in the London area but suggested that the species had never been abundant in the tideway. This is probably because of the lack of cover and habitat structure to which the species seems attracted.

Landwards of the tidal limit however the species does well, especially around islands and backwaters, and where trees line the banks. In 1860 Smith wrote:-

I have caught chub round the islands above and below Kingston Bridge; all along the kemp (sic) *sheathing at Halliford; in Chertsey Mead, adjoining the wharf, below the bridge; and on the Burway Field between Laleham and Chertsey Lock..... I especially recommend the island above Goring for chub, and the large island below Henley Bridge.*

Figure 13.1. Thames chub fishing under overhanging trees[1]. Chub are often found associated with some sort of cover.

The chub is one of the larger of the Thames coarse fish, and was a stern test of the early angler's skill and crude tackle:-

In August 1770, whilst Mr Warren of Marylebone Street, was fishing for gudgeons, after having raked the ground, in about three hours he hooked a fish which broke his hold; in a swimm or two he hooked another, which did the same; in a very few swims he hooked a third, which broke his tackle; on which he left off fishing; and next morning he returned to the same place, where he took eighty-three chubs, the least weighing two, and the largest six pounds. The second day he was broke three times, but catched a fish, having in his mouth one of the hooks and piece of line he had before lost.[2]

Chub often feed at or close to the surface, and dapping (or dibbing) was once a favoured fishing method on the Thames (Figure 13.2). Jesse (1836) described dapping on the river near Oxford:-

We dibbed for chub in deep holes, under the hollow banks in the river, sometimes with cadbaits (caddis larvae) which is a killing bait, and at others with a black beetle. In fishing with these, the bait should be kept gently on the move, and this causes the chub to come at it with the greater eagerness. It is, indeed, one of those baits that a chub delights in, but

120

Figure 13.2. "Dibbing" (dapping) for chub in the Thames. Note the evidence of success to the left of the anglers feet, and the anglers keeping out of sight of the fish. From Robertson (1875).

notwithstanding this, the angler should keep himself as much concealed from the view of the fish as possible. When this has not been properly attended to, I have seen chub swim round the bait over and over again, showing their eagerness to take it, but abstaining from doing so in consequence of the angler having exposed himself. The fish, after this disappointment, have disappeared from the spot, and it was sometime before they returned to it.

Cornish (1902) described successful "dibbing" for chub on the Thames:-

Drifting against a willow bush one day, the branches of which came right down over the water like a crinoline, I saw inside, and under the branches, a number of fair-sized chub of about 1 lb or 1½ lb. It struck me that they felt themselves absolutely safe there, and that if there was any way I could get a bait over them they might take it. Next morning when the sun was hot I got a stiff rod and caught a few grasshoppers. Overnight I had cut a bough or two out at the back of the willow bush, and there was just a chance that I might be able to poke my rod in and drop the grasshopper on the water. After that I must trust the strength of the gut, for the fish would be unplayable. It was almost like fishing in a faggot-stack. Peering through the willow leaves I could just see down into the water where a patch of sunlight about a yard square struck the surface. Under this skylight I saw the backs of several chub pass as they cruised slowly up and down. I twisted the last two feet of my line

121

Figure 13.3. Charles Cornish playing a large chub which he eventually lost because he had forgotten his landing net. Drawing by Lancelot Speed (1860-1931). From Cornish (1902).

round the rod-top, poked this into the bush with infinite bother and pluckings at my line between the rings, and managed to drop the hopper on to the little bit of sunny water. What a commotion there was. The chub thought they were all in a sanctuary and that no one was looking. The moment the grasshopper fell there was a regular rush to the place, very different from what their behaviour would have been outside the bush. There was a hustle and jostle to look at it, and then to get it.

One was hooked:-

....fast and flopping, and held quite tight by a very strong hook and gut, like a bull with a ring and pole fastened to his nose. I got him out too – not a big fish, but about 1½ lbs.

Another method of capture for chub close to the surface is dry fly fishing as described by Hofland (1848):-

The pleasantest way of fishing for chub is with an artificial fly, for this fish rises freely, and is not very nice in his choice of flies: but I have generally found the red and black hackle palmers, the red with gold, and the black with a silver twist, answer best. Most of the osier aits on the Thames afford a shelter for chub, and by casting your line from a boat, so that the flies shall fall under the overhanging osiers or willows, if done in an artist-like manner, you cannot fail to have sport.

Another favourite bait for large chub used to be a frog – presumably these form a part of the diet of chub throughout the river. For many years the largest Thames chub on record was a fish of 7 lb 1 oz caught by Stanley Mead near Wargrave in September 1897 - on a frog[3]. Instructions on how to handle and mount such a bait were offered by Chalmers (1932):-

122

Figure 13.4. This 1880 illustration[4] entitled "coaxing a chub" is meant to show a stealthy approach to fishing for this shy species. A present-day specimen hunter would probably be dressed in camouflage clothing, and crouching behind that bush.

The frog is killed first of course. A large bait hook is placed through the reptiles body so that the angle of the hook is out of the mouth, the shank protruding from the tail; the hind legs are tied to the gut This latter may be weighted with a small envelope lead, or a shot. The bait is fished on a fly-rod in the "sink and draw" style of the salmon fisher. I have never used a frog for bait because I am sentimental about frogs, who are pretty and yellow and hop-in-the-grass, and I scunner at killing them to amuse myself when an artificial fly is equally entertaining. And despondent frog prisoners in a bait box nearly break my heart.

For his compassion I can almost forgive Chalmers for referring to a frog as a reptile!

Almost catching a chub on a frog was described by Cornish (1902). He lost the fish after a protracted struggle because he had failed to bring a landing net with him (Figure 13.3). He put the fish in excess of 4 lb; *the biggest chub I shall ever not catch.*

A couple of other baits that were once popular for catching chub have fallen out of popular use, for reasons that may become obvious. The first is greaves, defined by the Shorter Oxford English Dictionary as *the fibrous matter or skin found in animal fat, which forms a sediment on melting and is pressed into cakes for dog's food, fish bait etc.* Wheeley (1897) instructed that the cake must be well scalded or stewed before use. The following recipe for the preparation of greaves was provided by Cholmondeley-Pennell in 1886:-

The greaves, after being broken up with a hammer, should be gently boiled for about half an hour, long enough before they are wanted for use to admit of their getting cold and hard. The whitest pieces are the best, and these can be most conveniently disposed of to hide the hook by being cut into broadish strips or slices; but as before observed the whole thing as a process is unattractive and as a bait beastly.

Hardly more appealing was the use of bullock's pith and brains as bait and groundbait respectively. Wheeley again has advice to offer:-

Pith, the spinal cord of the bullock, is the best winter bait for chub fishing. The outer skin must be snipped off the pith with scissors; all the streaks of blood must be washed away, and it is a good plan to scald the pith in boiling milk. The interior, or core, is too soft to stop on the hook by itself, so part of the skin must be left on to afford a hold. The point and barb must be run right through this skin. The brains are used simply as an attraction to the fish, and not as food for them. Scald the brains, a good quantity for days baiting. The brains are cut or squeezed up, and mixed with water in a tin or a wide-mouthed bottle; the whitish fluid is poured into the swim, and the hook, baited with pith, travels down with, or immediately after, it. The fish seize the pith greedily, the tempting morsel generally being irresistible after the white particles of brain have slipped by.

To further unsettle the squeamish there was a practice of chewing the brains being used for groundbait:-

The process of chewing ox-brains, whether cooked or raw, and sputtering them into the water all day long for ground bait is certainly (at least in our opinion) one which might raise an objection to the use of such a bait on the part of any angler troubled with the slightest feelings of delicacy in the following of his amusement.[5]

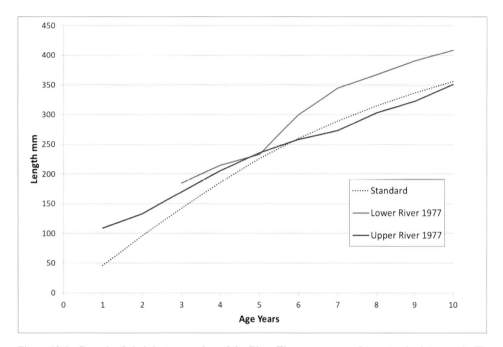

Figure 13.6. Growth of chub in two reaches of the River Thames, compared to a standard (see text). The "lower river" was between Hurley (Map 7) and Windsor (Map 8), and the "upper river" between Buscot Weir (Map 2) and Clifton Weir (Map 4).

The growth rate of chub in two zones of the river was investigated in 1977 by scale-reading.[6] The growth curves are shown in Figure 13.6, along with a standard for comparison. The standard was derived from calculating the average growth for chub from eight UK studies[7]. Upper-river fish exhibited a growth rate fairly close to the standard, whereas those from the lower river were growing rather faster.

The well-known Oxford angler Peter Stone, in his fishing autobiography "Old Father Thames" published in 1997, noted that chub were increasing in size in the Upper Thames. He suggested that this might be due to the spread of signal crayfish, which represent a rich food source for large fish. The increase in the size of chub has occurred throughout the river as indicated by the predominance of recent captures in the list of the ten largest chub from the river of which I am aware (Table 13.1); it is likely that there are others of which I have no record.

The well-known specimen hunter Frank Guttfield spent a lot of time fishing the Thames in his later years. Writing in "Classic Angling" soon after his father's death in 2015, Fred Guttfield reported that Frank had caught nine chub over 7 lb from the river, including one that just made it into the top-ten list in Table 13.1.

Table 13.1. List of the ten largest chub caught by anglers in the Thames.

Weight (lb-oz)	Date	Captor	Notes
9-04	Sep 2007	Dylan Docherty	
9-03	Sep 2012	Carl Welch	Chertsey[8]
9-00	Mar 2020	Robin Cave	[9]
8-10		Tom Hussey	Lower Sunbury[10]
8-05	Jan 2007	Danny Smith	
8-05	Mar 2019	Pete Cranstoun	[11]
8-04	Jul 1975	C Smith	
8-04	197?	John Arthur	Bray[12]
8-02	? 2012	Rob Hawthorn	[13]
8-02	? 2015	Frank Guttfield	[14]

Chapter 13 footnotes

[1] Illustrated Sporting and Dramatic News, August 24 1878.
[2] Brookes (1781).
[3] "Faddist" 1951.
[4] Illustrated Sporting and Dramatic News, July 17 1880.
[5] Comment from the editor of "The Field", quoted by Cholmondely-Pennel (1886).
[6] Banks (1979).
[7] Hickley and Dexter (1979).
[8] Angling Times, August 11 2012
[9] Drennan News, April 15 2020
[10] Anglers Mail
[11] Drennan News, June 13 2019
[12] Keith Elliott, pers. comm.
[13] Anglers Mail
[14] Classic Angling, No 96 July/August 2015, p16.

CHAPTER 14

Dace

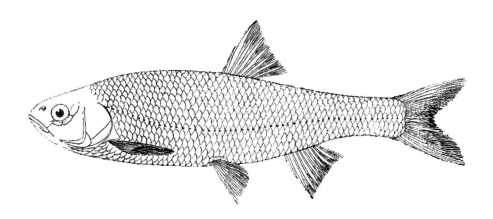

The dace is a small fish – the national record is only of the order of 1.5 lb (under one kg) – but is nonetheless very popular with anglers, not least on the Thames. This is probably down to their abundance, widespread distribution, willingness to feed under a wide range of conditions winter and summer, good fighting qualities, and perhaps their splendid appearance – they really do look like the archetypal fish.

Dace occur throughout the length of the river, from the highest reaches to well down the estuary – they were one of the first major species to recolonise the river through London as water quality improved in the 1960s. Early in the 19th Century they were said to caught "in great abundance" at Fulham, where their scales were sold "to the Jews" for the manufacture of artificial pearls[1]. The scales were reported to fetch between 12/- (60p) and a guinea (£1.05) per quart; see the section covering bleak in Chapter 22 for more details of this quaint business. In Victorian times punt anglers would count a day's catch of dace in dozens; for example in September 1867, one punt caught 20 dozen dace in a day, and two gentlemen fishing for two days at Twickenham caught 42½ dozen dace and roach[2]. And in September 1900, one angler caught nearly 200 dace in a day at Teddington[3]. These catches probably represent "red letter" days; a more reliable indication of average catches can be obtained from the following account[4] of fishing at Twickenham in 1883-4:-

I fished on fifteen days ranging from August 26, 1883, till February 10, 1884, my total take during that time being 107 lb 4½ oz, an average of 7 lb 2½ oz. The best take was on the first-mentioned date, viz 17 lb 10 oz, the whole being dace, with the exception of 13 oz of roach.... The lowest days take was on November 11, viz 1 lb 4 oz.

A commercial seine-netting trip at Chiswick in about 1900 was described by Cornish:-

Dace were our main catch – bright silvery fish , at about three to the pound, for they do not run very large in the tideway; but they were in perfect condition, and quite as good to eat, when cooked, as fresh herring. For some reason the Jews of London prefer these fresh-water fish; they eat them, not as the old Catholics did, on fasts, but for feasts. They will fetch 2d each at the times of the Jews holidays, so our fisherman told me, and find a ready sale at all times, though at low prices.

Figure 14.1. An angler at Battersea in 1744[5]. Dace were a popular quarry throughout the tidal Thames, and were one of the first species to recolonise the lower tidal reaches as water quality improved in the 1960s. The man in the centre foreground appears to have some sort of framed net over his shoulder.

Fly fishing (or "whipping") was a popular method of targetting dace. Sheringham (1910) devotes a whole chapter to using this method at Isleworth:-

But Isleworth is a simple, un-premeditated sort of matter. At luncheon-time one has a sudden conviction that too much work is telling on one's health, and that an afternoon off is the right medicine. A glance at the paper tells one that the tide was high at London Bridge at half-past nine; a simple calculation proves that, since it is an hour later at Richmond, the

128

Figure 14.2. A group of boys fishing on a busy day at Surbiton about 1910[6]. With all that boat traffic their likely catch is limited to dace and bleak.

Isleworth shallows will begin to be fishable at about two. A light ten-foot rod, a reel, fly box and basket take no time to collect; the rubber knee boots stand ready in the corner. One is equipped and away almost as soon as the idea is formed.

Sheringham considered that three dozen would be a fair basket on a good day, although catches of eight to ten dozen were taken "once in a way". The fish ran up to about six ounces, and averaged perhaps three.

This weight range appears to be about the norm throughout the river, and throughout the period of recorded catches. However, while commenting that a half-pounder is unusually large for the Thames, writing in 1867 Francis reported a catch of thirteen fish weighing 7 lb; an average of a little over the half pound. These fish were taken on the tail of a lobworm being fished for barbel.

Eighty years later a very experienced Thames angler, Frank Murgett, noted that he had never caught a dace over six ounces in the river[7]. Several dace over a pound appear in the record lists (Chapter 6) though there is always doubt over large dace due to their similarity to small chub. The recent record is a fish of 1 lb 3 oz caught by R Page in January 1964.

The possibility that some of the large dace reported from the river were in fact small chub was discussed in a note[8] penned by Greville Fennell, a Thames authority and author, in 1872. He wrote:-

I have two letters, both asking me what is the largest dace I ever knew or heard of having been taken in the Thames, as a local paper speaks of them this season as reaching ¾ lb

Figure 14.3. Anglers enjoying some sport at Isleworth, about 1920. The fish visible just above the chain looks like a dace, while the one on the right is more like a roach. Perhaps the catch is being kept in the watering can. The cats are watching with interest![9]

each. I or any of my friends, however, never saw a Thames dace approaching anything like this in weight, and therefore I may say such a standard is exceptional. Query, were they chub? More unlikely mistakes than this occur daily in punt and on the bank. The largest Thames dace I ever saw was taken by my man Harry Crystalle, while fishing near the railway arch at Richmond, and this, weighing 9½ oz, was considered by all the professional fishermen there as marvellous. I should in common with other lovers of fly fishing be glad indeed to hear that dace were increasing in size and numbers in the Thames; but almost all accounts lean to the contrary.

A study of the fish community in the reach of the river between Caversham and Sonning locks was undertaken in 1958-9[10] by the University of Reading. The relationship between fish length and age (determined by scale reading) showed that the dace in this reach were very slow growing. The age/length relationship is shown ("Reading 1959") in Figure 14.4, along with a standard growth curve, reflecting an average growth rate from 11 studies (including this one) throughout the UK[11]. In the report of the Reading study it was suggested that the low growth rate indicated overcrowding (especially of roach, which have a similar diet to dace), relative to the limited food supply.

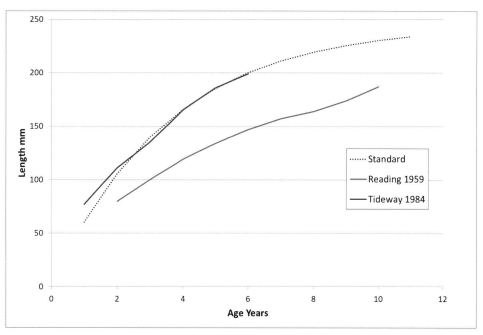

Figure 14.4. Relationship between age and length of dace from the Thames near Reading in 1958-9, and for the tideway in 1984. Also shown is a standard growth curve, representing average growth rate from 11 studies throughout the UK.

Also shown in Figure 14.4 is the age/length relationship for dace sampled in the tidal Thames in 1984[12]. In this case the growth is close to the standard curve. In both these cases the results are only valid for the reach and period of the observations; the situation may well have changed since they were made.

Chapter 14 footnotes

[1] Faulkner (1813), page 4. Faulkner also recorded that roach scales were also used for the same
     purpose, and I have many times heard the same story about bleak eg MacMahon (1946)
[2] Surrey Advertiser, September 9 1867.
[3] Reading Mercury, September 8 1900.
[4] Cholmondely-Pennell (1886), citing R A Banfield of the Clapham Junction Angling Society.
[5] View of Chelsea by J Maurer, 1744.
[6] Postcard postmarked 1911.
[7] Murgett (1960).
[8] The Field, September 7 1872.
[9] Postcard, publisher unknown.
[10] Williams (1967)
[11] Hickley and Dexter (1979).
[12] Pilcher (1989)

Hardy's "Eureka" Reel

The most popular reel for general fishing or trotting ever made. You have only to handle the "Eureka" to instantly realize its many good points and advantages.   In 2 sizes 30/- and 35/- FROM YOUR DEALER or HARDY'S BRANCHES

GET A CATALOGUE OF
HARDY'S SUPER BOTTOM FISHING TACKLE FREE
From your DEALER, or Free and Post Free from HARDY'S

LONDON BRANCHES:
(West End) 61, Pall Mall.   (City) 12, Royal Exchange

HARDY'S — ALNWICK — ENGLAND

132

CHAPTER 15

Eels

The history of eels in the Thames has been something of a roller-coaster, with periods of abundance and periods of great scarcity. Before humans had much influence upon the river and its inhabitants the species abounded throughout the catchment from the estuary to the highest headwaters and tributaries, as indicated by the eel rents paid by many fisheries and mills at the time of Domesday (1086). These are shown in Table 15.1.

This overall abundance persisted until the 19th Century, as witnessed by the widespread distribution of historic eel traps. Permanent eel traps and wicker-work bucks were used to trap adult eels during their seawards migration. Naismith and Knights (1993) noted evidence of 22 sets of eel bucks, and 23 other fixed traps at mills and weirs in the Thames catchment, but suggested that there were likely to have been many others. The location of more than 30 sets of bucks is detailed in Appendix 2; again, this is likely to be an incomplete inventory, as virtually all traces have gone. The most upstream fixed trap at a mill may have been at Inglesham, upstream of Lechlade[1].

Figure 15.1. Eel bucks upstream of Caversham Bridge. These are in the raised position; when fishing, they are lowered below the surface.

Table 15.1 Annual eel render (rent) paid by fisheries (F) and mills (M) in the Thames catchment, as recorded by Domesday (1086).

	Eel rent	Notes
Lechlade (F)	175	
Shifford (F)	250	
Taynton (M)	62	R Windrush
Eynsham (M)	450	
Bladon (M)	125	R Evenlode
Cassington (F)	175	
Deddington (M)	100	R Cherwell
Thrupp (M)	125	R Cherwell
Somerton (M)	400	R Cherwell
Dorchester (2 F)	975	R Thame
L. Wychendon (M)	80	R Thame
Shabbington (M)	100	R Thame
South Stoke (F)	300	
Shinfield (5 x F)	550	R Loddon
Shinfield (M)	150	R Loddon
Whistley (F)	300	R Loddon
Whistley (M)	250	R Loddon
Wargrave (3 F)	300	
Remenham (M)	1000	
Hambleden (F)	1000	
Medmenham (F)	1000	
Marlow (F)	1000	
Wooburn (F)	300	R Wick
W.Wycombe (F)	1000	R Wick
Hitcham (F)	500	
Taplow (F)	1000	
Dorney (F)	500	
Eton (F)	1000	
Upton (F)	1000	
Datchet	2000	
Iver (4 x F)	1500	R Colne
Harefield (4 F)	1000	R Colne
Harmondsworth (F)	1000	R Colne
Harmondsworth (3 M)	500	R Colne
Stanwell (3 F)	1000	R Colne
Stanwell (4 M)	375	R Colne
Byfleet (F)	325	R Wey
Kingston (F)	125	
Petersham (F)	1000	
Total	**22992**	

A full description of the methods used for the capture of eels is given in Chapter 5.

European eels are a single stock that breeds in the Sargasso Sea, to which area mature adults return from throughout Europe. After hatching, the young fish adopt a planktonic lifestyle and drift in the upper layers of the ocean on the Gulf Stream. As they approach the coast they morph into elvers, at first transparent and termed "glass eels", and then become pigmented elvers and enter the rivers in the spring and early summer. A major upstream migration of elvers is a memorable sight, with tens of thousands of them moving in a continuous "rope" along the margins of the river. It generally takes place over a very few days at any one spot, and the event at Kingston was such a local spectacle that it was named "eel fair". In 1834 Jesse made two independent calculations of the numbers involved at the peak of migration, of 1600 and 1800 per minute. He recorded notes on the phenomenon in the year 1832 at Kingston Bridge. Elvers first appeared in the afternoon of April 30, increasing in numbers and continuing all night. The next morning numbers were still very high until about 4 pm, when migration stopped. The next day (May 2) large numbers were passing until noon, when again migration stopped. On May 3 much smaller numbers were seen, with only a very few stragglers being seen on May 4. Some elvers had been seen downstream at Twickenham some three weeks earlier, but it is likely that they needed very high tides to pass Teddington Weir. April 30 was the peak of the spring/neap cycle in that year, with very high tides. It is likely that the downstream water level was close to equalisation with the upstream water level at high tide on April 30 and May 1; Kingston Bridge is only about two kilometres upstream of the weir.

Numbers of elvers fell sharply over the next 20 years. Venables (published in 1874 but written in 1858), stated that there had been no "eel fair" for the past 16 years, ie since about 1842. This is likely to have been due to water quality, which had deteriorated during this period, rather than problems with obstructions, which had not changed significantly.

Varying numbers of elvers entered the tidal Thames over the next few decades, depending upon water quality at the time. As they were part of a pan-European stock and not descended from eels that had grown up in the Thames, there were always good numbers of elvers available to "have a go" at the river each year throughout this time. Some managed to pass through the estuary and into the river in 1912[2], and good numbers were seen at Teddington in 1914[3] . These, however, were unusual years with coincidentally better water quality probably due to high freshwater flow. In most years, none or a few made it through the tidal reaches until the general recovery of the estuary from pollution in the 1960s and 70s. I found good numbers of elvers in the intertidal zone at Hammersmith Bridge in 1972, one of the first recent-year observations of the species this far up the tidal zone[4].

There was thus a period of the almost 50 years when few if any elvers made it from the sea and into the Thames. The river was not without eels during this period, however, as large numbers of elvers were brought from the Severn Estuary and stocked into the river on many occasions and at many locations. Many of these initiatives were poorly reported, and most are known only through contemporary press releases rather than through any official record. Examples of releases of which some details are available include 100,000 in 1918 at Hampton Court, Windsor and Henley[5]; 25,000 in 1919 at Maidenhead[6]; 25,000 in 1920 at Abingdon; 400,000 in 1943 between Lechlade and Oxford[7]; 1,000,000 in 1944 between Lechlade and Abingdon[8], and a further 1,000,000 in 1946 between Oxford and Lechlade[9]. There is also anecdotal evidence of many other releases of elvers up until the 1970s.

As female eels may remain growing in the river for twenty or more years post-elver (males usually only half of that), the sporadic introductions of elvers meant that adult eels were present, albeit at relatively low densities, throughout the 20th Century. When I fished the river extensively in the 1960s we caught the occasional eel; I recall one of about 2 lb at the warm-water outfall from Earley Power Station downstream of Reading in 1963.

The status of Thames eel populations in the 1980s was reported in detail by Naismith and Knights (1993). They noted a large estuarine stock, but more limited numbers and distribution throughout the non-tidal catchment. They trapped for eels at 235 sites throughout the Thames Basin. While most lower-river sites yielded eels, only 22% of sites upstream of Goring (Map 5) did so, and there was a complete absence from many of the major tributaries such as the Kennet, Thame, Cherwell and Evenlode. This poorer than pre-pollution population of eels they put down to obstruction by weirs, and a decline in elver numbers throughout Europe.

While there have been no further systematic surveys of eels throughout the catchment, it is clear that elver numbers have declined considerably in the past 30 years. Comparison of populations at three sites on the Thames, Roding and Darent between 2005 and 2009, with those observed in the 1980s, led a team of researchers from the Zoological Society of

London[10] to suggest that numbers of elvers entering the estuary had dropped by over 99% over a couple of decades. A similar decline is reported throughout the Eastern Atlantic basin. So, once more eels are becoming very scarce in the Thames, though this time not due to local factors.

Because they are rarely directly targeted by anglers there are relatively few descriptions of the capture of eels in the literature. Writing in 1912 Englefield recorded the capture of seven silver eels weighing together 7½ lb near Maidenhead over three evenings in July. A trap catch at Dorchester Abbey Mill on the Thame included some eels over 5 lb in weight, and a nine-pounder had once been caught; even bigger was a 15 pounder from a buck near Newbury on the Kennet[11]. The same writer witnessed a catch of 16 eels in a net one night around 1900 at Chiswick – the best that the fisherman concerned had experienced.

The record Thames eel in the Thames Anglers Conservancy list was caught in August 2016 by Matthew Kendall and weighed 8 lb 5 oz. The previous best was 5 lb 2 oz.

Eels are well-known for seeking out nooks and crannies, and for entering intake and outlet pipes. In 1886, poor quality drinking water was traced to dead eels in the mains of the East London Waterworks Company. The Company stated that there had been "only" seven cases of stoppage of mains from eels in the course of a fortnight; as a contemporary press report[12] suggested, the actions of the company would have inspired more confidence if they had appeared to regard this occurrence in a more serious light.

IN THE NAME OF THE PROPHET—EELS!
WHAT MAY BE EXPECTED WHEN THE MAINS OF THE EAST LONDON WATERWORKS COMPANY ARE OPENED.

Figure 15.2. Cartoon lampooning the East London Waterworks Company when eels were found in their supply mains in 1886. Origin of cartoon unknown.

Figure 15.3. Eel grigs being set at Eton, about 1890. [13]

Chapter 15 footnotes

[1] Williams (1922).
[2] Gloucester Chronicle, August 8 1912; Fishing Gazette 30 November 1912; Fishing Gazette 25 January 1913..
[3] Fishing Gazette, May 15 1943.
[4] Solomon (1975); Wheeler (1979).
[5] Uxbridge and West Drayton Gazette, May 3 1918; Sheffield Weekly Telegraph, June 29 1918; Western Times, April 23 1918.
[6] The Sportsman, April 17 1919.
[7] Daily Telegraph, May 13 1943.
[8] Gloucester Chronicle, June 24 1944.
[9] Western Morning News October 25 1946.
[10] Gollock *et al* (2011).
[11] Cornish (1902).
[12] Morning Post, October 15 1886.
[13] From Manning and Green (1890).

CHAPTER 16

Gudgeon

There appears to be a fascination in gudgeon fishing which is not easy to account for, and it still exists. **Alfred Jardine (1908)[1].**

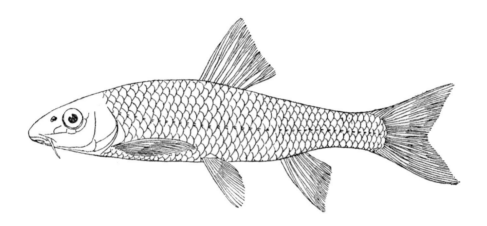

The gudgeon is a small, one might say almost insignificant member of the carp family, rarely exceeding about 16 cm in length. For many years the angling record stood at a mighty 4 oz 4 dr (about 120 g), shared by three fish of the same size, one of which was from the Thames; this fish was taken at Datchet in 1933 by one George Cedric. But what it lacked in size the species makes up for in numbers, often being abundant and free-biting. These properties made it popular with anglers, especially beginners and casual sportsmen. Many a potential angler has had his lifelong commitment to the sport assured by the capture of one of these feisty little beasts – including myself. It was also a favoured bait for angling for trout and pike, and for baiting eel traps. Add to this the fact that it is one of the tastiest of the freshwater fish, and one can begin to see why the humble gudgeon has played a significant part in the history of Thames fishing.

A favourite method of fishing for gudgeon was to moor a punt in a likely spot, and then to drag the river bed with a long-handled rake. The muddying of the water quickly attracted "gudgings" (as Holinshed[2] termed them) to the area to feed avidly on the insects and other small creatures disturbed by the rake. This was popular sport for families, as illustrated in

Figure 16.1. A Victorian party gudgeon fishing from a punt on the Thames[3]. Note the rake lying across the centre of the vessel, the flower-pot of worms, and the use of kitchen chairs for comfort. As is usual for punt fishing the boat is fixed by two ryepecks driven into the river bed. The gent in the middle looks like he may be finding the excitement underwhelming , and has nodded off.

Figure 16.1. Robertson (1875), from which this illustration is taken, describes the fishing thus:-

The "man" habitually sits astride the well of the punt with a flower-pot before him, in which are the worms for bait. He is thus ready to detach the fish from the hooks as soon as they are caught, dropping them into the well, and rebaiting the hook, if necessary. As many as twenty dozen of these little fish are occasionally taken in a day. They are considerably in request for the breakfast-table at the hotels on the river-banks, and are purchased from the fisherman at sixpence the dozen.

Frank Buckland (1871) describes the ethos of this sort of fishing:-

We well remember, one fine day in August last, going out on a gudgeon fishing expedition. A luxurious dog-cart carried us quickly to Surley Hall, well-known to Etonians. There we found the Charon[4] of this part of the river, Finmore by name, waiting for us in his punt. The old man's family has had the fishing of the water for more than a hundred years; and the old man himself knows every hole and patch of weeds in the river just about Windsor as well as a Londoner does the shops of Regent Street. In the punt were placed three chairs and three fishing-rods, two punt poles with sharp iron spikes on their ends, called in these parts "ryepecks"; why and wherefore they have received this name we cannot ascertain; lastly, an enormous iron rake. Three anglers occupied the three chairs; two of them were great salmon fishers, who, but a few weeks ago, thought a fish under 20 pounds nothing; they were now pleased with catching little gudgeon not a quarter of an ounce in weight. The laziness of gudgeon fishing is indeed laziness. If you exert yourself in the least, the whole thing is spoiled. It is quite contrary to the rules to put on one's own bait, to alter one's own float, to take captured fish off the hook; all this is done by Charon, who not infrequently has quite enough to do.

Francis Francis also valued the enjoyment of an appropriately-conducted gudgeon party:-

To the angler of mature years, gudgeon-fishing on the bosom of Old Thames with a chosen friend, who is lively, philosophical, contemplative, or convivial as the humour changes, a cold pigeon-pie, a bottle of sparkling sherry, unlimited seltzer cooling in the well, a fine warm day, and a case of fragrant Cabanas, is not to be despised by any means[5].

Sport could be fast and furious. Otter (1864) reported catching 100 Thames gudgeon in an hour in 1858; up to a dozen could be taken, without rebaiting, on a single worm bait threaded carefully onto the hook. One local expert in the Henley area, Mr Bell, was known to take up to 60 dozen gudgeon in a day in the 1860s, but one must doubt his true sporting credentials as he fished with two hooks![6] But the prize for the greatest catch of gudgeon in modern times must surely go to Simon Willsmore while fishing in the Lower Thames Championship competition in 2010. In the five-hour match he caught an astonishing total of over 700 gudgeon, along with three perch and a single roach to take third place with a total weight of 19 lb 10 oz. His catch rate averaged more than two fish a minute throughout the five hour match – and, unlike Mr Bell, he only used one hook! And, I am sure that he did indeed exert himself, contrary to Buckland's philosophy. Allowing for the perch and roach, the average weight of Simon's gudgeon would have been a little under half an ounce.

The effectiveness of stirring up the bed to attract gudgeon is confirmed by a snippet from Wheeley (1897) describing gudgeon fishing not in the Thames itself, but in the lowermost reaches of a tributary, a couple of hundred yards from the main river:-

When fishing the Mole, near Hampton Court, I have caught lots of gudgeon at the spot where the carts are taken into the water, the grinding of the wheels and the splashing of the horses thoroughly disturbing the water, and sending plenty of thick water down stream. So accustomed are the fish to the disturbance, that they feed close to the carts, coming into the muddy water to search for worms and other food.

Because gudgeon fishing apparently appealed to young ladies and was considered a respectable pastime, it was often considered as a romantic opportunity (Figure 16.3). Courtney Williams in his delightful anthology "Angling Diversions" written in 1945 sums it up well:-

Figure 16.2. A young angler at the gudgeon-fishing spot at Molesey described by Wheeley (1897), in about 1910[7]. It is now submerged within a flood-relief channel.

The Thames gudgeon party, which must now be regarded as a Victorian period piece, comes rather into the same category, although it attracted a different class of society. Normally, it was made up of a number of young people of both sexes, who would hire the requisite number of punts, each boat being in charge of a professional fisherman. It was his duty to bait the ladies hooks, and to stir up the river-bed with a long rake in order to collect together the shoals of gudgeon. Sometimes the sport was fast and furious and fish were caught every minute; the ladies took to it enthusiastically, although perhaps, not seriously. At a time when the emancipation of women was in its infancy (and hardly that), it is certain that younger members of the fair sex welcomed the gudgeon party as an excuse to get away from their daily occupations of arranging flowers, doing needlework, and awaiting upon Mama. Besides, it offered wonderful opportunities for romance, since after all, the fishing was but a secondary consideration, and as soon as it could be decently concluded, without offending the susceptibilities of the shyest members of the party, a move was usually made to one of the more fashionable river-side hotels, there to make merry......It was all, of course, very respectable, but very romantic and great fun. The youth of the present day carries on the tradition – but since we live in a more practical age, it dispenses with the fishing.

142

Figure 16.3. One of a series of 1879 drawings entitled "Gudgeon fishing on the Thames with my cousin", by J Temple[8].

Henry Cholmondeley-Pennell (1886) described a day of light-hearted fishing with his cousin and another couple. He concluded with:-

But there! What's the good of talking and making myself melancholy, a fellow can't eat his cake and keep it; it's all over and done with, and here I am back at my venerable Coach's again - Homer, Horace, Livy – Livy, Horace, Homer – the old grind. Adieu to gudgeon and gudgeon fishing, Hurley Bucks, Harleyford Woods, and pretty cousin Julia – until the next long vacation.

However, the contribution of gudgeon fishing towards romantic harmony was not always positive; in 1836 Edward Jesse wrote:-

It is mentioned as fact, that the clergyman of a parish in the neighbourhood of Hampton Court, who was engaged to be married to the daughter of a bishop, enjoyed his gudgeon fishing so much, that arrived too late to be married, and the lady, offended by his neglect, refused to be united to one who appeared to prefer his rod to herself.

When gudgeon were needed for bait for either angling or setting eel traps, the usual method of capture was using a small cast net. Such a net, not exceeding 13 feet in circumference, was the only type allowed after most netting was banned upstream of Richmond Bridge in 1860.

Mention has been made of the culinary properties of the species. Mrs Beeton[9] gives a simple recipe:-

143

Ingredients:- Egg and bread crumbs sufficient for the quantity of fish; hot lard.
Mode:- Do not scrape off the scales, but take out the gills and inside, and cleanse thoroughly; wipe them dry, flour and dip them into egg, and sprinkle over with bread crumbs. Fry of a nice brown. Time:- 3 or 4 minutes.

A gudgeon from the Thames was the first fish I ever caught, at the age of eight, and I have retained a great fondness for them ever since. They are embedded in the development of fishing on the river and occupy a place in the history of Thames fisheries out of all proportion to their modest physical dimensions.

Figure 16.4. A delightful sketch of children fishing at Datchet, published as a postcard in about 1920. These wooden jetties were constructed in the 19th Century, and were replaced at some later date by almost identical structures made from tubular metal with planked decks. It was from one of these latter structures that the I caught my first ever fish, a gudgeon, in about 1955. I wonder how many other youngsters caught their first fish here?

Chapter 16 footnotes

[1] Fishing Gazette, August 29 1908, p 202.

[2] Holinshed's Chronicle, 1587.

[3] Figure entitled "Gudgeon Fishing" from Robertson 1875

[4] A somewhat morbid allusion; in mythology, Charon is the boatman who ferries the spirits of the dead across the River Styx.

[5] Francis (1876).

[6] Fennell (1867a).

[7] Postcard, publisher, and exact date not known.

[8] Illustrated Sporting and Dramatic News, October 11, 1879, p 96.

[9] The book of household management, by Isabella Beeton (1861).

CHAPTER 17

Perch

Our friend the perch is one of the most beautiful fish it has pleased Providence to place in our waters. No lady's dress was ever made so beautiful as the perch's when he is in full season. **Buckland (1883)**

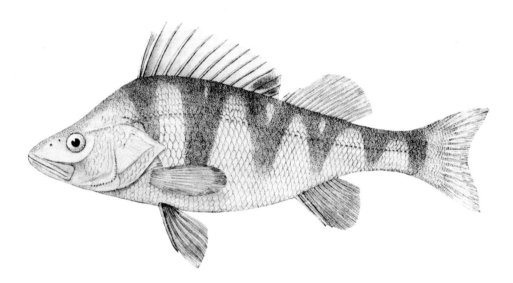

The perch is a splendid looking fish and deservedly popular with anglers. Not only does it look good, but it grows to a fair size (the national record is in excess of six pounds) and puts up a lively fight when hooked. The history of perch in the Thames is a very interesting tale, and there are much larger fish in the river now than, quite possibly, any time in the past.

Perch are native to the Thames and occur throughout the non-tidal river, and the tidal reaches to well seawards of London Bridge. Holinshed listed "pearches" as one of the fish abounding in the river in the 16th Century , and Fennell recalled that, as a boy around 1825, he enjoyed perch fishing by hiring a boat at Tower Stairs, and fishing with live shrimps while drifting with the ebb tide. Englefield, fishing in the Maidenhead area in the 1870s, developed a method of perch fishing involving a sort of paternoster tackle with a very short hook length which could be lowered into holes between overhanging branches. He described many catches of 50 to more than 100 perch in a day, averaging of the order of a pound each. Virtually all were killed, and at the end of one day's sport he complained that the catch *made ones creel heavy and its strap to cut into ones shoulder*.

Figure 17.1. Landing a perch at Hampton Court in 1882[1]. The guide is Tom Whatford of Hampton.

Although fair-size perch were clearly abundant at that time, the largest Englefield caught were two fish of 2 lb 4 oz, caught at the same time on a two-hook paternoster fished in the Bray reach of the river. Another angler, pen name Piscator Senex, reported a similar situation in the 1870s, including a catch of about 240 perch on live minnows over two days; the three largest fish totalled 8 lb[2]. The lack of larger fish among the thousands landed may have been down to the ubiquitous practice of killing almost all fish caught – especially a species as tasty as perch. But this cannot explain the lack of very large perch when I fished the river in the early 1960s, long after releasing virtually all fish caught had become the norm. I fished a lot for perch, usually with small live fish as bait, but caught very few over 2 lb. One of the best spots was where the Boveney Ditch entered the river, a mile or two upstream from Windsor. This stream carried the treated effluent from Slough Sewage Treatment Works, which earned the confluence the local name of "the sewer hole". Small fry clearly found something in the effluent attractive for large numbers gathered around the spot, and this in turn attracted the predators. We developed a good method of locating them, by scattering dry groundbait onto the surface of the ditch, to be carried out into the main stream. The small fry would swarm in to eat the powder from the surface, and generally within a few minutes there would be showers of fry erupting from the water as the predators took advantage of the concentration of potential prey. By casting out a livebait into the centre of action, a "take" was almost guaranteed. These were mostly perch, with a fair smattering of chub to about 4 lbs and small pike, which usually bit through the line. But despite catching possibly hundreds of perch here, the largest was only a little over 2 lb; a similar situation to that reported 90 years before. The largest perch I caught elsewhere in the river was a fish of 2 lb 11 oz at the warm water outfall from Earley Power Station, downstream of Reading, on a small roach livebait. For several years around that time I was an avid reader of "Angling Times", but I cannot recall a three pound perch being caught anywhere in the river in the early 1960s. Murgett (1960) also commented on the lack of large Thames perch, adding that he had caught a few two-pounders here and there. He put this down to the murky water, observing that all the good perch waters he knew had very clear water. Occasional larger fish had occurred in the past; the river record stood at 4 lb for many years, shared by fish from Sunbury taken in 1870 and one from an unknown location in 1908; however, the exact weight of 4 lb indicates that the actual size of these fish is uncertain. A fish of 4 lb 5¼ oz replaced these fish as the largest from the Thames; it was taken on livebait by G B Irons in December 1953.

In the late 1960s perch of all sizes became very scarce on the Thames and indeed in many other waters, apparently afflicted by a mystery disease. In 1968 I started research for a PhD at the University of London, exploring the physiology of growth in perch. As this was intended to follow on from the work undertaken some years earlier on fish populations in the Thames at Reading, I planned to use fish from the river; I even obtained a very formal-looking document from the Thames Conservancy granting me permission to take small numbers of fish below the legal size limit of nine inches. But I was unable to catch any perch from the Thames, and had instead to obtain fish from a lake which was apparently unaffected by the ailment. This may have been the same affliction that greatly reduced perch in the Thames in the 1880s[3].

Figure 17.2. "Perch fishing", from Robertson (1875).

Figure 17.3. A perch being played having been hooked on a paternostered livebait. The professional boatman is James Haslett of Chertsey. From Jardine (1904a).

Figure 17.4. An Edwardian lady angler with a Thames perch, clearly being admired by more than one generation of what was presumably her family.

The species started to recover during the 1970s, and has built back into strong populations throughout the river – and indeed has achieved astonishing top weights compared to earlier years. Three-pounders started to appear in the 1990s, four-pounders after the year 2000, and there have been a dozen or more five-pounders since 2008. The river record is a fish of 6 lb 4 oz, taken in October 2014 at Ditton Marina by an angler known only as "Bill"; he caught a second fish of 5 lb 8 oz on the same day! Some good catches involving numbers of fish have also been taken; for example a catch of 120 lb including eight four-pounders by two anglers in 2007[4]. Although the exact location of most of the catches is a closely guarded secret, several of the largest fish have come from the tidal section. The recovery is not limited to the lower reaches, with a match catch of 59 lb 10 oz taken on the Medley Stretch at Oxford[5]. The average weight was just under two pounds, and the catch included four three-pounders.

The most likely explanation for the great increase in numbers of large perch is a shift in food availability. Perch are opportunistic predators and will eat any animal food that is available to them. The introduction and spread of signal crayfish throughout the river, and of Chinese mitten crabs in the tidal and lowermost non-tidal reaches, are likely to represent a huge boost in feeding opportunities for perch.

Figure 17.5. David Solomon with a 2 lb 11 oz perch from the warm water outfall from Earley Power Station, between Reading and Sonning, in December 1963. A large fish for the river in those days, it made the front page of "Angling Times" in what was admittedly a quiet week; it would be thoroughly unremarkable nowadays.

Chapter 17 footnotes

[1] From Illustrated Sporting and Dramatic News, December 2 1882. Artist J Temple.
[2] Letter to Fishing Gazette, February 17 1917.
[3] Editor's footnote to letter in Fishing Gazette, February 17 1917.
[4] Angling Times, November 27 2007.
[5] Midland Angler, January 2014.

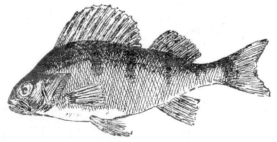

CHAPTER 18

Pike

More lies have been told about the pike than any other fish in the world.
(Buckland, 1883).

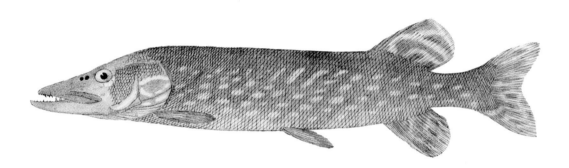

The pike is the largest of the native Thames freshwater fish, and a justifiably popular quarry for anglers and, in former times, professional fishermen. It is to be found throughout the river from the highest reaches to the tidal section. Being a predator on other species (and indeed on its smaller close relatives), it is fished-for using live and dead fish for bait, and with a variety of artificial lures constructed to imitate smaller fish. Being both a good fighter when hooked, and good to eat, it has been a popular target for fishermen throughout the ages.

Fishing for pike from punts was popular in Victorian times, generally with a "man" to provide the livebaits (or fish for killing for use as spinning baits), locate the best spots, bait the hooks, unhook the catch and of course to do all the hard work of propelling the boat. The punt allowed significant reaches of river to be fished in comfort, a real advantage as pike are generally well-spread throughout the river. James Englefield described such a day of fishing around Maidenhead in February 1864. The river had been in flood for several weeks, but as it began to fall and clear conditions were deemed to be good. "Andrews" was instructed to ensure a good supply of fresh bleak for bait and to pick up the angler from his riverside house at 10 o'clock on the appointed day. Fishing commenced just downstream of the road bridge, and between there and Surley Hall, four miles downstream, a total of 18 pike between 2½ and 8 lb were caught and killed in lay-byes and eddies out of the main stream. Not everyone approved of the slaughter, however. His neighbour and fellow angler, on seeing the catch laid out proudly on the lawn, said in a low but audible voice to his wife *if he goes on like this there will soon be no jack left in the river*. I do not know what he did with the fish, as he said of his household *we never ate jack*. The terminal gear used that day comprised four treble hooks and a single hook to pass through the lip of the bait, twelve inches of gimp (wire), and five or six swivels. It is not surprising that the angler was able to report that not a fish was lost!

Figure 18.1. A catch of 17 pike weighing 82 lb taken by Frederick and Hilda Slade in 1902 at Wargrave. The largest fish weighed 8½ lb. Picture from Jardine 1904b.

In January 1875 similar conditions caused Alfred Jardine take his punt out of the main stream, which had the thickness of pea soup, into a quiet eddy at Sonning. He ledgered with a livebait hard on the bed and in an hour caught six pike up to 13 lb in the one spot[1]. Many years later the exact location was revealed in an article in Fishing Gazette[2]; it was in the eddy at the downstream end of Long Eyot, about 1500 m downstream of Sonning Bridge and 400 m upstream of where the Patrick Stream deviates from the main river. The same article also told of a catch of 27 pike weighing 190 lb taken by Jardine and T W Reilly over two days in January 1877. These were taken at Sonning and Shiplake, and the largest fish weighed 21 lb.

Figure 18.2. Pike fishing at on St Stephens Island, Kingston, in 1881[3]. The guide is local fisherman John Johnson Snr.

While the practice of killing all the pike caught undoubtedly led to a profusion of small fish and a scarcity of large, some good fish were indeed reported. As suggested by the quote from Buckland at the head of this chapter not all tales about large pike are to be believed, and they tend to grow with each retelling of the story. One capture in 1907 however was very well recorded[4] and can, it is suggested, be taken at face value. In January of that year a fish of 29½ lb was caught at Oxford by E J Bowles, a clerk from Christ Church College.

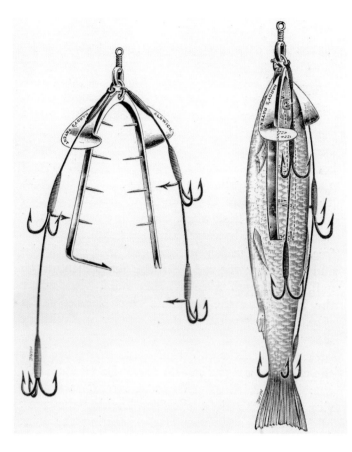

Figure 18.3. An example of some of the serious ironmongery used for fishing a spun deadbait in former times; a Hardy "Crocodile" flight.

It was caught in a backwater off the main river known as the Pot Stream. The bait was a live roach about 10 cm in length, fished about three feet below a float. The fish was taken to a coal merchant nearby to be weighed, where it was witnessed at 29 ½ lb; three hours later it went 29 lb on scales in the kitchen at Christ Church College. The fish was said to have been set-up by Coopers, but I am not aware if the trophy has survived to the present time. Reference is made in various books and articles to pike of thirty pounds caught at Marlow and Windsor many years ago, but little credence can be given to such anecdotes in the absence of details. But there is good evidence of a number of twenty-pounders caught in days of yore. Alfred Jardine (1904b) listed a total of 81 pike over 20 lb caught in England between 1874 and 1903; of these, nine were caught from the Thames and are included in Table 18.1, together with other 20-pound plus fish reported in Fishing Gazette and other journals between 1875 and 1909.

Other twenty pound plus pike reported at other times include fish of 21 lb at Abingdon in 1833[5], 20 ¼ lb at Henley in 1870[6], 24 lb at Yarnton in 1914[7], 21½ lb at Tilehurst in 1929, 29 lb 12 oz, location unknown, September 1919[8], and two of 24 lb 6 oz and 20 lb 2 oz taken at Cookham on the same day in February 1925 by Mr L C Parsons (Figure 18.4).

There are some earlier "records" of large pike from the river, but generally details are too vague for the stories to be taken at face value. One such tale of some interest was apparently reported in The Times in 1851, as reported in the Fishing Gazette in 1917[9]:

Mr William Barry, of Abney House, Little Marlow, killed on Saturday last, a pike, in the River Thames, fronting his residence, which weighed nearly 35 lb. It was a female fish and rather out of condition. Had it been taken a little earlier in the season it must have weighed upwards of 40 lb. Mr Barry, after three-quarters of an hour's sport in an ineffectual attempt to land it, was compelled to shoot it. The fish has been stuffed by Mr Fisher, of Eton, and inspected by hundreds of the Waltonian fraternity. It was unfair on the pike to shoot it after so good a fight – Ed.

Table 18.1. List of twenty-pound plus pike caught from the Thames between 1875 and 1909. From Jardine (1904b), contemporary issues of Fishing Gazette, and other newspapers.

Date	Weight	Location	Captor and notes
January 1875	26½ lb	Hampton	
1876	22 lb	Nuneham	[10]
January 1877	21½ lb	Sonning	Alfred Jardine
1877	27½ lb	Hampton	Client of Milbourne . Wheeldon (1878)
January 1878	20½ lb	Sonning	Alfred Jardine
January 1878	27½ lb	Hampton	
August 1881	24 lb	Walton	[11]
March 1883	22 lb	Shiplake	Mr Sharp, client of Tom Neale[12]
July 1883	24 lb	Marlow	
December 1895	20½ lb	Henley	A E Hobbs
January 1898	26 lb	Bablock Hythe	Dr W J Turrell.
February 1898	28 lb	Radcot Bridge	Mr Page [13]
February 1898	25 lb	Lechlade	
November 1898	20 lb	Lechlade	
December 1899	22 lb	Lechlade	
March 1900	21 lb	Lechlade	
November 1901	22½ lb	Marlow	
November 1901	27¼ lb	Henley	
December 1901	27 lb	Oxfordshire	
October 1902	20½ lb	Buscott	Alfred Jardine
October 1902	20 ½ lb	Buscott	Alfred Jardine
February 1903	21½ lb	Lechlade	
October 1903	20½ lb	Buscott	
March 1905	25½ lb	Teddington	Alfred Bilton
January 1906	21 lb	Caversham	
January 1907	29 ½ lb	Oxford	E J Bowles.
February 1908	26 lb	Caversham	

Peter Stone, in his lovely autobiography[14], described the pike fishing in the Oxford area from the 1930s onwards. During the war he caught many pike and distributed them among his neighbours. The fish averaged four or five pounds, with a fourteen pounder being considered a big one for the river. The largest he heard of at that time were 18 and 19 lb. In the river below the Toll Bridge at Wolvercote he would expect to catch at least six pike in an afternoon's fishing; his largest catch was 22 fish up to 8 lb. It seems that all pike caught at that time were still being killed. Stone records how a friend Fred Smith caught eight pike between 11 and 18 lb in the nearby River Cherwell; he said that he could have caught more but there was no point as he couldn't get any more on the handlebars of his bike!

Figure 18.4. Two pike weighing 24 lb 6 oz and 20 lb 2 oz taken at Cookham on February 15 1925. Above, on the day of capture[15], the captor L C Parsons is on the right. Below, after setting-up by W F Homer[16]

Figure 18.5. Two good Thames pike. Left: a fish of 27½ lb Caught by Jack Collins, son of the lock-keeper at Shifford, on December 31 1933[17]. Right: an 18 pounder caught by E Harris from his back garden in Oxford in December 1938[18].

In later years, larger pike started to appear. A thirty pounder was reported from the Medley reach in 1970, caught by John Cadd[19]. Stone put this down to the developing stocks of bream providing rich feeding, but the trend towards catch and release almost certainly explains much of the increase. Up to the early 1990s Peter had never caught a twenty pounder in the river, but by the time he was writing in 1997 he said that there were "plenty" fish of that size.

Frank Murgett told a similar story of pike being of limited size in the 1940s and 50s in the lower Thames[20]. He noted many fish up to about six pounds, but said it was difficult to find anything much bigger; his own best fish was only 10 lb. And in his book on the Lower Thames, John Burrett listed only two pike in double figures in his list of large fish taken below Staines between 1950 and 1967. I do not recall any of my fishing pals catching, or seeing caught, a pike of much more than 10 lb in the middle Thames during the 1960's, though we caught plenty up to that weight. But, as in the upper river, better things were to come.

Over the past 20 years some huge pike have been caught in the Thames. On February 24 1987, West London school teacher Bill Rushmer caught a monster of 33 lb 6 oz in the tidal river below Teddington Weir. This was the culmination of a targetted campaign by Bill, seeking large pike that he was sure inhabited the area. This fish was a Thames record until Colin House beat it with a fish of 34 lb 2 oz in December 2011. This has in turn been beaten by a fish of 36 lb 3 oz taken in the Castle Stream in Oxford in December 2014.

A live fish has been the most popular bait for large pike throughout most of the history of pike fishing. While many anglers would catch their own live bait, this was sometimes difficult and time-consuming. Many fishermen preferred to have them supplied by a professional fisherman, or to purchase them from a tackle dealer. At the end of the 19th century several dealers in London offered live baits for sale; dace were the most popular because they were about the right size, and were tough and survived well impaled on a hook. The Fishing Gazette carried many advertisements for supply of live bait. Livebaiting was still widespread when I started fishing in the 1960s, but this somewhat barbaric practice has fallen from favour with artificial lures and dead baits (often sea fish purchased from a fishmonger) proving just as effective.

Chapter 18 footnotes

[1] Senior (1885).

[2] Fishing Gazette December 21 1901.

[3] Illustrated Sporting and Dramatic News, January 22 1881.

[4] Oxford Times, January 19 1907.

[5] Berkshire Chronicle, June 1 1833

[6] Buckinghamshire Herald, November 5 1870

[7] Fishing Gazette 27 November 1917

[8] Cased mounted fish offered for sale on eBay in October 2019. Inscription on case read "PIKE caught by J Farmer in the River Thames, Sept 7th 1919. Weight 29 lb 12 oz."

[9] Fishing Gazette September 15 1917.

[10] Reading Mercury, January 15 1876

[11] Aberdeen Evening Express, September 2 1881,

[12] Berkshire Chronicle, March 17 1883

[13] Dundee Evening Telegraph, February 9 1898.

[14] Stone (1997).

[15] Fishing Gazette, March 14 1925

[16] Fishing Gazette July 11 1925

[17] The Sketch, January 17 1934.

[18] The Sketch, December 21 1938.

[19] Angling Times Yearbook, 1976/77.

[20] Murgett (1960).

CHAPTER 19

Roach

The roach is perhaps the most popular quarry for the pleasure angler on the Thames, by virtue of its abundance and willingness to feed, its good potential size, and its beautiful appearance. It has also been responsible for many a match-winning weight when the bream were not in a feeding mood. They occur throughout the river from the highest reaches to the tidal zone, often being found well seawards of London Bridge when conditions allow. Indeed, Walton said of Thames roach that they were *the largest and fattest in this nation, especially below London Bridge*[1].

Figure 19.1. A roach, from Houghton's 1879 work "British freshwater fishes". The species is considered by many to be the handsomest of our freshwater fish, and it is justifiably popular with anglers.

Roach were netted for both food and for their scales, as recorded in a history of Fulham written in 1813[3]:-

The season for blennetting for roach and dace begins on the first of July. They are caught here in great abundance, especially after heavy rain. Their scales are sold to the Jews for the purpose of making false pearls, and are worth from twelve shillings to a guinea a quart.

The process of making artificial pearls using fish scales is described in the section covering bleak (Chapter 22), the main species used for this purpose.

Shortly after Walton described the large roach below London Bridge, Cox (1686) reiterated the fact *the Thames below bridge abounds with very large fat roach, such as I may confidently affirm exceed in magnitude all others either in ponds or rivers.* One might suspect that he was merely plagiarising the earlier writer except that he adds details of a quaint, if not terribly sporting, method of catching these fish thus:-

The way of fishing for roach at London Bridge is after this manner; In the months of June and July, there is a great resort of those fish to that place, where those that make a trade of it take a strong cord, at the end whereof is fastened a three-pound weight; a foot above the lead they fasten a pack-thread of twelve foot long to the cord, and unto the packthread at convenient distances they add a dozen strong links of hair with roach-hooks at them, baited with a white snail or perriwinkle; then holding the cord in their hands, the biting of the fish draweth the packthread, and the packthread the cord, which admonishes them what to do; whereby sometimes thay draw up half a dozen, sometimes less, but commonly two or three at one draught.

In 1781 Brookes described roach fishing in the tidal Thames:-

In August the roach fishery affords much pleasure about London, where it is thus practised; any waterman will provide a boat with rip hooks, to fix it in the middle of the stream; and prepare your groundbait, which is of bran and stale bread, mixed in balls, and thrown in upstream, with clay and small stones within, sufficient to sink it speedily, and lodge it at the bottom. Not more than three can conveniently fish in one boat, which is usually hired at

Figure 19.3. Fishing at London Bridge in about 1750[4]. At times the roach fishing here was very good.

the rate of three pence per hour. Your tackle must be strong, your float large, and heavy-leaded, to sink the quicker. The constant bait is a well-scoured gentle, three at least on your hook, which must swim ten or twelve inches at most, from the bottom. The best times are; from half-ebb tide, to within two hours of high water: and the best places are, the whole sand-bank in the middle, facing the Tower; that opposite the Temple; before Whitehall; and against Chelsea Church. At these places you will find plenty of sport. Some, with very good success, pick out some stand against the shore, among the chalk stones at the bank of the Isle of Dogs, near Limehouse, under the wind-mills, and fish there in the same manner, from dead ebb, and within an hour or more of high water, retiring backwards as the tide comes in. As the soil is oozy and slippery, care must be taken chuse such a place as you may securely retreat as the tide advances.

There is another highly approved method of this diversion below the bridge, called stern-fishing, by fastening the boat to the stern of any collier, or vessel that has lately been on a voyage, and has her bottom foul, which contains insects and foods for the fish; use about two joints of your rod at most, and a line no longer than four feet, you float fixed within twelve inches of the top of it. Angle three or four gentles on your hook at a time, and lay in as close to the ship's stern as you can, letting it swim about three yards. In this you use no groundbait. You must begin when the tide first ebbs, and for two hours, at least, you will not fail of catching many fish (roach and dace) and those very large ones.

The deteriorating water quality in the lower tidal reaches in the 19th Century destroyed this interesting fishing, though fish sometimes penetrated the area when freshwater flows were high. In Dickens' Dictionary of the River Thames (1887) it is recorded:-

Very many handsome trays of roach were got in the lower districts as far down as Putney during the season of 1879[5]. The fish ran very large for the Thames, 1 lb and 1½ lb fish not being uncommon. These fish travel down stream with the up-country floods; as soon as these subside, and the "bad water" from below assumes its supremacy of volume, these fish head back again into Richmond and Twickenham districts out of reach of the nets, which are unceasingly at work to the east of Isleworth.

Figure 19.4. A good roach being landed near Henley in about 1925[6].

162

Figure 19.5. A roach weighing 2 lb 13½ oz taken from the Thames at Pinkhill by F Humphris on Christmas Day 1945. © River and Rowing Museum, Henley on Thames, UK

Figure 19.6. A good catch of roach taken at Henley in March 1925, by Stanley Mead[7]. The fish were all taken in a three-hour spell. The best weighed 1 lb 11¼ oz, and the fish averaged one pound each.

A scientific study of the fish stocks in the Thames between Caversham and Sonning in the 1960s concluded that the roach were overcrowded and stunted, and took on average 11 years to reach the Thames Conservancy size limit of eight inches in total length[8] (Figure 19.7). A reduction in the population was recommended, along with actions to encourage sizeable pike and perch. A similar study of roach in the tidal Thames more than 20 years later found that roach were achieving a length of eight inches in about seven years[9]. Another investigation of roach in the upper river (Hart's Weir to Clifton Weir) in 1977 showed a rate of growth intermediate between the other two studies[10].

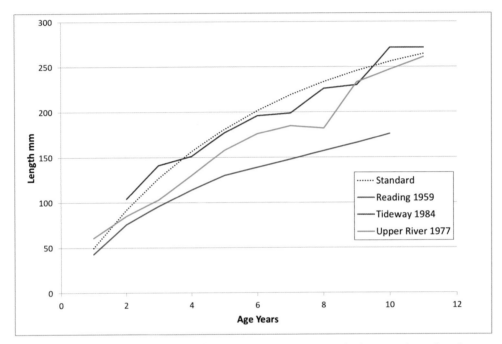

Figure 19.7. Growth of Thames roach in three studies, compared to a standard; see text for explanation.

Another observation on the good growth of roach in the tidal river was made by angling writer Peter Mead in 1965[11]. He reported good catches of large roach in this zone, and put their size down to feeding on the beds of small freshwater mussels and pearl mussels that abounded here. A small whole mussel, removed from its shell, proved an excellent bait.

Although not renowned for big catches of large roach, at times the Thames has produced very good catches of good size fish, and the occasional real monster. Fennell (1870) recorded a catch of 87 lb of roach taken by Messrs Raphael and Hart close to where the Thame joins the Thames at Dorchester. The fish were all between 4 oz and 1 lb 2 oz and were taken in six hours; the fish were still feeding well when the anglers stopped fishing. The Fishing Gazette for March 14 1925 recorded some excellent catches at Pangbourne; a group of anglers took 77 roach for a total weight of over 110 lb over a weekend. The best weighed 2 lb 1 oz, and several others were over 1¾ lb.

A list of the largest Thames roach for which I can find records is shown in Table 19.1, topped by a fish of over 3½ lb. Murgett (1960) describes a remarkable catch of five Thames roach over 2 lbs taken in less than 45 minutes in unusual circumstances. He was fishing in a weirpool on the lower Thames when the lock keeper shut down the weir hatches and reduced the flow to a trickle. He caught the roach on large lumps of silkweed (see below), along with two large barbel. When the flow was resumed three quarters of an hour later, all bites stopped. The roach represented five of only six two-pounders that this very experienced Thames fisherman caught in many years of fishing the river.

Table 19.1. Details of Thames roach in excess of 2¾ pounds.

Weight	Captor	Location	Date	Source
3-9-12	T G Player	Sonning	June 1949	Eaton (1956)
3-6-0	J Adams		Aug 1969	Graham (1972)
3-5-0*	David Booth	Staines	Nov1927	TAC website
3-1-0	Matt Davies	"Around Oxford"	Sep 2012	Anglers Mail
3-0-0*	David Booth	Staines	Nov 1927	Sheringham (1928)
2-13-8	F Humphris	Pinkhill	Dec 1945	See Figure 19.5.
2-13-8	G Edmonds	Old Windsor	1903	Sheringham (1928)

*These two entries are almost certainly the same fish capture but its real weight is unresolved.

One incredible fish not on this list was caught in a tributary, the Hogsmill River, just a few hundred yards from the confluence at Kingston; I would guess that this fish spent much of its time in the main river. The fish weighed 3 lb 13 oz and was caught by local angler Aaron Winter in early 2013.

Although most Thames roach are caught on the ubiquitous maggot bait, there are two other baits that can account for both good catches and large fish. The first is silkweed, the green alga that grows in short filaments on most Thames weirs, sills and aprons. Fish downstream happily feed on strands of silkweed that become detached from these structures, and when all is quiet will graze actively on the attached weed. Anglers have learned to bait their hook by dragging it through the attached weed, and immediately trotting it with the current downstream. This method is most effective when the flow allows the angler to wade onto the weir cill to fish directly downstream. The anglers shuffled feet dislodge strands of silkweed, acting as groundbait. Roach and dace are particularly susceptible to this ploy, though most other species are taken at times – reference has already been made to a couple of good barbel taken on this bait. This bait has been used for many years; an article on its use was published in 1894[12].

The second very effective bait is boiled hemp seed. This is the seed of the cannabis plant, and is readily available from seed merchants for use in animal feeds – though I think it may be heat sterilised to prevent it being grown on! Frank Murgett devoted a whole chapter to fishing hemp in his book on fishing the lower Thames[13]. He referred to anecdotal evidence that the bait was introduced to the river by Belgian refugees during WWI, and suggested that the fish needed to be "educated" into recognising hemp as food. It peaked in popularity between the wars, but was still very-much in vogue when I first fished the river in the early 1960s, and is still extensively used especially as ground-bait. Other popular baits for roach include bread in various forms, cheese and stewed wheat.

Figure 19.8. Two good Thames roach being landed in a single net. Location and date unknown.

Chapter 19 footnotes

[1] Walton (1676)
[2] Fishing Gazette February 25 1961.
[3] Faulkner (1813)
[4] Stonegate, London Bridge, image ©London Metropolitan Archives (City of London).
[5] *The year 1879, though not especially wet as a whole, included one of the wettest summers on record* (Brooks and Glasspool 1928).
[6] "Haunts and hints for anglers – fresh water angling" published by the Great Western Railway Company, 1925.
[7] Fishing Gazette, 4 April 1924.
[8] Williams (1963).
[9] Pilcher (1989).
[10] Banks (1979).
[11] Mead P (1965) "Big roach from the tidal Thames", Fishing Magazine, January 29 1965.
[12] Fishing Gazette, 1 September 1894.
[13] Murgett (1960)

CHAPTER 20

Salmon

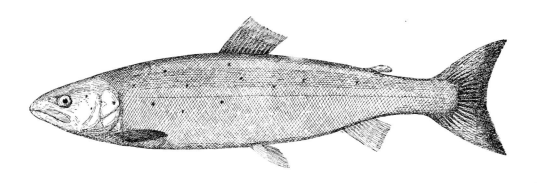

The Thames was historically a productive salmon river, supporting good net and trap catches of fish of high average weight. Before the construction of mills, weirs and locks it is likely that much of the river was well provided with potential spawning and rearing areas from the tidal limit through to the upper reaches and tributaries. The overall gradient of the bed was of the order of 0.37m/km between Lechlade and the tidal limit, with good gravel beds, shoals and shallows; good potential salmon habitat. However, obstructions to migration and other human impacts on the potential salmon environment of the river eroded the suitable and accessible habitat to the extent that the species was extirpated from the river by the early 1830s. Several attempts to re-introduce salmon since then have all failed, but the saga of decline and false dawns is very interesting and worthy of revisiting.

Holinshed's Chronicle, written in 1587, talked of the *fat and sweet salmon, dailie taken in this streame, and that is such plentie after the time of the smelt be passed, and no river in Europe able to exceed it.* Records tell of *seven score* (140) salmon taken in a single week at Wandsworth in 1580[1]. One fisherman at Chelsea reported catching nine salmon in a week in May 1664. The fish averaged more than 19 lb each and fetched between 14d and 18d per pound. On June 7, 1749, 47 fish were caught in a day below Richmond Bridge. In 1766 over 130 Thames salmon were sent to Billingsgate in a single day, and the price fell to 6d per pound. As late as 1816, 90 salmon were netted in a single morning, and the price at Billingsgate fell to 3d per pound.

The old story about apprentices in London (and in many other places) having a clause in their contracts stating that they will not be required to eat salmon more than three times a week has already been discussed in Chapter 5.

Some very large individual fish occurred. Large specimens reported included fish of 72½ lb at Twickenham in 1820[2], and 70 lb at Laleham in 1789[3].

A detailed picture of a particular fishery and the decline in catches was provided by Richard Lovegrove, a witness at the 1861 Salmon Commissioners Inquiry[4]. Lovegrove was a professional fisherman whose family commercially fished the area around Maidenhead and Cliveden, and had access to a record book started by his grandfather in 1794. The record book is delightfully entitled "*An account of all the salmon caught at Boulter's Lock and the contiguous part of the Thames, from 1794 to 1821, both years included, that is to say, twenty eight years or seasons*". They fished in two ways; with a conventional seine net, and with bucks. The bucks were effectively eel bucks (see Chapter 5), set to catch fish moving downstream, and indeed both species, and lampreys and indeed probably many others, were caught at different seasons. The salmon, having overcome the fall represented by the weir in which the bucks were set, allowed themselves to be carried, probably tail first, back into the baskets. The narrowing passageway prevented effective use of the tail to swim back out. The rank of nine bucks appears to have been set within its own channel parallel to the main weir (termed the lock as it contained a flash-lock until the pound lock was built in its own channel in 1772); both the buck pool (immediately downstream of the bucks) and the lock (weir) pool were seine-netted. Of the 29 salmon caught in 1800, for example, 16 were caught in the bucks, three were netted in the buck pool, ten in the lock pool. The fish averaged over 13 lb, and were all caught between June and August. Available details of the catches are shown in Table 20.1.

Lovegrove mentioned that, had the journal been started 20 years earlier, bigger catches would have been shown. About the year 1780 his father caught more than 50 salmon above the weir, opposite Cliveden Spring, and other fishermen had similar catches. In 1793 they caught a fish of 42 lb in the lock pool. The very last fish to be caught at Boulter's was in 1823 or 1824, taken above the weir.

There are other similar records of catches, having been declining for some years, falling rapidly to zero at about this time. Another witness at the 1861 Inquiry was Thomas Milburn, a retired professional fisherman from Hampton who recalled the river over a period of seventy years. In the early years of the 19th century he was involved in the netting of many salmon, the largest 41 lb. The larger fish came in the spring, with smaller fish averaging 8 to 10 lb in the summer. He typically caught 18 to 20 a year, but spent most of his time taking gentlemen angling rather than netting. The adult salmon and the salmon fry (smolts) disappeared at about the same time in the early 1820s. A third witness was Henry Farnell, secretary of the Thames Angling Preservation Society. He said that he had lived at Isleworth for many years, and had regularly seen up to sixteen salmon caught in a single haul of the net, but had not seen a single fish for 36 years (ie since about 1825).

Table 20.1. Catches of salmon around Boulter's weir, 1794 to 1821, as reported by R Lovegrove to the 1861 Salmon Commissioners Inquiry.

Year	Number	Weight lb	Average weight lb	Notes
1794	15	248.5	16.6	Largest 25, smallest 11.5 lb. 14 caught in bucks.
1795	19	168	8.8	Largest 21, smallest 4 lb. 16 caught in bucks
1796	18	328	18.2	Largest 37, smallest 12 lb. 10 caught in bucks.
1797	37	670.5	18.1	Largest 31, smallest 12 lb. 33 caught in the bucks.
1798	16	317	19.8	Largest 28, smallest 19 lb. 10 caught in the bucks.
1799	36	507	14.1	Largest 28 lb. 35 caught in the bucks.
1800	29	388	13.4	Largest 23 lb. 16 caught in the bucks.
1801	66	1124	17.0	Largest 37, smallest 6 lb. 47 caught in the bucks.
1802	18	297	16.5	Largest 25 lb.
1803	20	374	18.7	Largest 31 lb. 240 lb of fish sold at 5/-.
1804	62	943	15.2	Largest 32 lb. 44 caught in the bucks.
1805	7	117	16.7	Largest 21 lb.
1806	12	245	20.4	Largest 33 lb, 6/- per pound. 9 caught in the bucks.
1807	16	253	15.8	Largest 30 lb. 15 caught in the bucks.
1808	5	88	17.6	Largest 20 lb. All caught in the bucks.
1809	8	116	14.5	Largest 32 lb.
1810	4	70	17.5	Largest 18 lb. All caught in the bucks.
1811	16	181.75	11.4	Largest 16, smallest 4.5 lb.
1812	18	224	12.4	Largest 19.5, smallest 6 lb. 9 caught in the bucks.
1813	14	220	15.7	Largest 22, smallest 6 lb. 13 caught in the bucks.
1814	13	97.5	7.5	Largest 12 lb. 12 caught in the bucks.
1815	4	52	13.0	Largest 14 lb. One caught in the bucks.
1816	14	179	12.8	Largest 29, smallest 3.5 lb. 8 caught in the bucks.
1817	5	76.25	15.3	Largest 29 , smallest 4.75 lb. 4 caught in the bucks.
1818	4	48.5	12.1	Largest 16.5, smallest 9.5 lb. 0 caught in the bucks.
1819	5	84	16.8	Largest 23, smallest 10 lb. 3 caught in the bucks.
1820	0	0		None taken within several miles of Boulter's.
1821	2	31	15.5	Larger 18, smaller 13 lb. Both caught in the bucks.
Total	**483**	**7448**	**15.4**	

The ancestors of a Mr Newman of Datchet left a record of the salmon they had netted in the area between 1796 and 1802 (Table 20.2)[5]. The largest weighed 34½ lb and was sold in May 1801 for 2 shillings and 9 pence per pound. The highest price achieved was seven shillings a pound (for a fish of 23½ lb in March 1802) and the lowest price, 10 pence.

The last record of a capture of a native Thames salmon may have been in 1830, when one was caught near Monkey Island by a Mr Wilder[6]. However, there is some uncertainty as to whether this was the same fish as described thus in a newspaper article in 1889[7]:-

It was in the early summer of 1832 that Si (Simon) Wilder was attending Captain Johnson, an old Waterloo officer, when the latter hooked, off monkey Island, spinning for trout, and the puntsman safely secured, a salmon of 32 lb weight. This fish, said to be the last salmon ever caught in the Thames, was given to Si by his patron, and sold by him to a Mr Tibbutt, then an upholsterer at Windsor castle, who then presented it to the King.

There are surprisingly few records of native Thames salmon caught by rod and line. The 32 lb fish caught by Captain Johnson is described above. The Lovegrove record book, already discussed, mentioned a fish of 17 lb caught at Boulter's by Major Jefferson in June 1797. The bait was a bleak, probably being used to try and tempt a trout. Courteney Williams (1945) refers to a fish of 24½ lb being caught at Shepperton on October 3 1812. It was caught by Mr George Marshall of Brewer Street, London, on "a single gut". Fennell (1867a) recorded that a Mr Rolls once caught a salmon fishing from the top of Marlow weir, but gives no further details.

Table 20.2 Details of salmon caught by the ancestors of a Mr Newman at Datchet.

Year	Number	Weight (lb)	Average wt. (lb)
1796	43	744	17.3
1797	14	286	20.4
1798	12	183	15.3
1799	7	113	16.1
1800	No record		
1801	7	168	24.0
1802	4	105	26.3

So what was responsible for the demise of the native Thames salmon? There is no doubt that the stocks had been under pressure for some time from a number of factors, but two in particular are likely to have been dominant. First, water quality throughout the lower river, and in particular the tidal reaches, had been deteriorating for some time and dipped particularly sharply in the early 19th Century. Second, the construction of the weirs for the navigation locks not only greatly restricted access by adult salmon (the concept of fish passes was virtually unknown at that time), it also drowned-out much of the spawning and nursery area in the main river. Spawning salmon, developing eggs and fry, and juvenile parr have rather specific requirements in terms of water velocity, water depth, and quality of gravel substrate, and the weirs would have compromised all of these. The construction of the eight locks and weirs between Old Windsor and Teddington in the period 1811 to 1822 fits closely the period of terminal decline in the catches at Boulters already described. About 1860 there was a huge upsurge of interest in hatchery production of fish for restocking. This was both a response to a perception of stocks and catches falling nationally, and because the technology and know-how were becoming available. Trout

Figure 20.1. Salmon and trout hatchery in a specially-designed building in the garden of Francis Francis at Twickenham.[8]

hatcheries were springing up across the country, both as commercial ventures and as facilities developed by angling organisations. Inevitably salmon were involved in this frenzy, and a group of enthusiastic fisheries managers, including the Inspector of Salmon Fisheries Frank Buckland, the angling author Francis Francis, and Stephen Ponder, developed and encouraged hatchery rearing for the species in the Thames. Quite sophisticated hatcheries were developed at the homes of Francis Francis in Twickenham (Figure 20.1) and Stephen Ponder in Hampton, but the numbers of fish involved were very small; about 48,000 fry were released to the river between 1862 and 1866[9]. More details of the efforts of Francis Francis are provided by Francis and Urwin (1991). While the stocking of trout developed into a highly successful fisheries management technique for the river (see Chapter 21), the salmon initiative was basically doomed to failure because of the small numbers of fish released and the fact that nothing had been done to address the fundamental problems that had been responsible for the eradication of stocks forty years earlier. In the face of the lack of evidence of any returning adults, the project fizzled out.

Figure 20.2. Cartoon from Punch Magazine, May 1 1901. The caption read *"WELCOME, LITTLE STRANGERS"* (Delight of Father Thames on seeing how the samlets arrived, having sustained a trying journey from Uxbridge without showing any signs of fatigue" – "Times", April 24).

The next initiative developed around the turn of the 20th Century in response to a temporary improvement in estuary water quality (see Chapter 4). The Thames Salmon Association was formed in 1899 with the aim of restoring a run of salmon to the Thames. Experience with the earlier restoration attempt and the trout stocking programme suggested that the fish should be stocked out as large as possible rather than as fry – ie as smolts in the case of salmon.

The following were some activities associated with this initiative:-

> April 1901. Six hundred smolts released at Teddington. More were to be stocked higher up the river, held at Mr Crosbie Gilbey's trout hatchery on the Colne at Denham, where all the smolts had been reared. *Tuesday's consignment was conveyed by road from Uxbridge in a number of large fish-carriers, and were in splendid condition and ready to run to sea.*[10]
>
> February 1902. 1000 smolts being reared at Mr Gilbey's trout hatchery.[11]
>
> August 1903. Nearly 2,000 young salmon stocked into the Thames at Teddington.[12]
>
> December 1904. Two hundred 1-2 year old salmon from the Shannon stocked into the Thames at Maidenhead.[13]

The only evidence of success of this programme was the reported capture of a grilse weighing just under six pounds at Molesey in May 1902[14]. Unfortunately the catch was consumed by the captor before expert identification could be confirmed!

The most recent programme of restocking ran from the mid 1970s to recent years. Again the stimulus was an improvement in the water quality of the lower river and estuary, and the natural recolonisation of the area by a large number of freshwater, marine and brackish water fish. The first confirmed record of a salmon in the Thames for more than 100 years was of a fish found on the intake screens of West Thurrock Power Station (about 35 km seawards of London Bridge) in November 1974. Its origin was unknown as no stocking of juveniles had taken place up to that time. Restocking commenced in 1975, and then took place each year up to 2008; details of the numbers of various life-history stages stocked are shown in Table 20.3. The fish were obtained from a wide range of sources throughout the British Isles, and in many years returning fish were stripped to provide fish for stocking. Smolts were generally released in the lower reaches of the river from Sunbury downstream, but the fry and parr were stocked into various tributaries where suitable nursery areas had been identified. These included the Ash, Chess, Clandon, Churn, Coln, Cray, Darent, Dikler, Eye, Grantsbourne, Halebourne, Kennet, Leach, Lee, Loddon, Lyde, Pang, Rib, Sherbourne Brook, Tillingbourne, Wandle, Wey, Windrush, and Winterbourne.

Numbers of adult fish reported in the river started to build about 1980 and are shown in Table 20.3; these records are taken from various sources including being found dead or moribund, capture by rod and line, and electric fishing. A salmon trap was commissioned at Molesey Weir in August 1983 and from then on this was the main source of records of returning adults. Some fish were reported caught by anglers from 1983 onwards – these are also shown in Table 20.3.

Table 20.3. Summary of numbers of juvenile salmon stocked to the Thames, adult returns, and rod catch, 1974-2010

Year	Fry	Parr	Smolts	Adult return	Rod catch
1974	0	0	0	1	
1975	9,300	0	0	2	
1976	48,000	0	466	1	
1977	5,000	3,000	0	0	
1978	2,000	3,000	0	1	
1979	0	47,560	668	1	
1980	0	48,904	0	4	
1981	5,000	45,500	5,000	8	
1982	0	35,900	2,800	128	
1983	7,300	85,937	38,688	91	10
1984	24,500	73,334	9,561	106	6
1985	0	70,565	29,194	75	11
1986	0	79,342	24,360	176	9
1987	0	100,703	28,063	58	5
1988	0	108,925	35,165	323	12
1989	36,000	120,611	53,521	133	8
1990	0	91,650	37,782	154	9
1991	0	79,574	78,023	59	1
1992	12,265	127,613	72,815	283	10
1993	53,825	28,327	99,161	338	16
1994	266,443	8,819	68,541	238	11
1995	135,710	0	79,524	190	13
1996	167,614	0	37,309	162	34
1997	107,341	29	65,452	29	2
1998	194,089	0	58,497	6	0
1999	182,479	0	57,586	36	1
2000	157,734	0	54,929	56	0
2001	193,728	0	66,436	11	0
2002	154,811	0	69,832	24	0
2003	82,108	0	67,967	18	0
2004	59,517	0	62,383	7	0
2005	16,000	0	68,758	0	0
2006	0	0	42,938	2	0
2007	6287	0	25,758	7	0
2008	0	5377	25,025	9	0
2009					0
2010					2

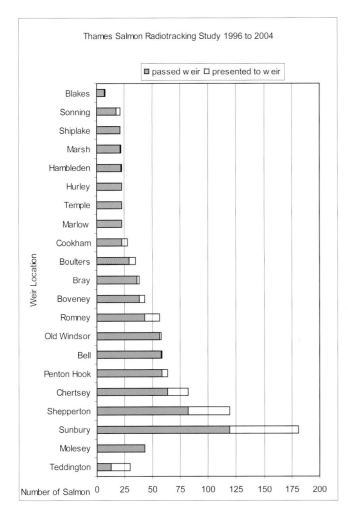

Thames Salmon Radiotracking Study 1996 to 2004

passed weir ☐ presented to weir

Figure 20.3. Numbers of radio-tagged salmon reaching (whole of histogram bar) and succeeding in passing (coloured part of histogram bar) weirs on the Thames, 1996-2004. Graph courtesy of the Environment Agency.

Following a review in 1994 the stocking strategy changed. From 1995 all stocking, including smolts, was concentrated in the Kennet and its tributaries, and virtually all stocking was undertaken as fry (target 200,000 per year) or smolts (target 70,000 per year) rather than parr. The targets were changed again following a review in 2004, to zero fry and parr, and 20,000 smolts. Recent small releases of fry and parr have been for experimental purposes, or utilising fish that were surplus to requirements for the smolt programme.

In parallel with the restocking has been a programme of installation of fish passes at all the weirs between the estuary and the likely spawning and nursery areas on the River Kennet. An investigation of the problems represented by each weir was conducted between 1996 and 2004 by radio tracking of individual returning adult fish[15]. Fish captured in the trap at Molesey were fitted with a miniature radio transmitter which allowed recognition of individual fish and allowed their progress to be followed by a series of listening stations located at each weir. The delay at each obstruction, between first arrival and last departure upstream, gave an assessment of any losses below each weir, and a measure of the delay at each location. The proportion of fish which succeeded in passing each weir is shown in Figure 20.3.

Underlying the changes in the conduct of the rehabilitation project was the realisation and disappointment that, so far, salmon had failed to complete a life-cycle "in the wild". There was some evidence of spawning activity, but none of successful production of smolts form fry and parr from such activity. What are the reasons for this apparent failure? There are probably several contributory factors.

First, the latter part of the programme has coincided with a significant drop in marine survival of salmon throughout most of its range. For example, the decline in return rate of hatchery smolts to the River Shannon in Ireland (the source of much of the Thames restocking material) is shown in Figure 20.4. Climate change may be a contributory factor here. Second, the water quality of the Thames tideway, especially during the third quarter of the year which is critical for the return of adult fish to the river, continues to be poor.

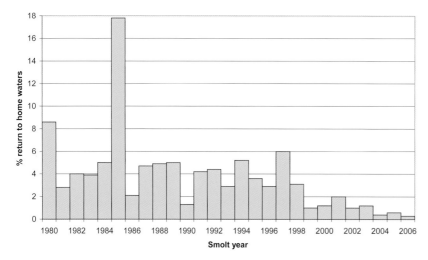

Figure 20.4. Rate of return to home waters of hatchery smolts released in the River Shannon in 1980 to 2006.[16] Data from 2008 Report of the ICES WG on North Atlantic Salmon.

It appears that in bad years virtually the whole run can be lost due to this factor alone. Third, we may have been optimistic in our assessment of the extent to which rehabilitation may have been possible. When salmon were native to the river, the stock may have been largely restricted to the main stem, with little evidence of significant utilisation of the tributaries. The factor that appears to have been the immediate cause of the final loss of the original stock, construction of the navigation weirs, still remains today. We have successfully overcome the issue of obstruction to migration by the construction of fish passes. However, the potentially more intractable problem, the loss of long reaches of fast flowing open river with extensive shallows and clean gravels, still applies. Perhaps with the rehabilitation scheme we were trying to push too big a rock up too steep a slope.

Chapter 20 footnotes

[1] Courtney Williams (1945)
[2] Courtney Williams (1945)
[3] Wright (1858).
[4] Anon 1861.
[5] Osborn (1896)
[6] Day (1887).
[7] Maidenhead Advertiser, December 24 1889.
[8] Illustrated London News, March 19 1864.
[9] Maxwell (1904).
[10] Western Times, April 226 1901.
[11] Manchester Evening News, February 20 1902.
[12] Yorkshire Evening Post, August 7 1903.
[13] Exeter and Plymouth Gazette, December 1 1904.
[14] South Bucks Standard, May 30 1902.
[15] Data provided by Environment Agency.
[16] Date from the 2008 Report of the Working Group on North Atlantic Salmon, International Council for Exploration of the Sea, Copenhagen.

176

CHAPTER 21

Trout

Thames trouting is a kind of high fever – that is to say to the enthusiast – and a regularly recurring fever year after year at that. It does not respond readily to treatment, and the only certain and complete cure is change of venue for the patient – this word may be used in more than one sense – from Thames to Styx. **Arthur Edward Hobbs,** *Trout of the Thames* **(1947).**

Thames trout and the fishery they supported had a long, rich and well-recorded history. A recent anthology of this one species in this one river (Below the Weir, by Peter Rogers 2008) was able to draw on the writings of no less than twenty angling authors for its content. But overall it is a strange tale, with most of the fish caught during the heyday of Thames trouting, 1850 to 1940, probably not originating from the Thames at all.

Before the construction of weirs for navigation, milling and fishing, the Thames would have been a magnificent fast stream with clear water and abundant weed growth. It would have been a good trout river, with many large fish supported by the productive environment. While there would doubtless have been sea trout entering the river, brown trout would have predominated. Where they occur together, brown trout and sea trout are freely interbreeding fractions of the same population. Females tend to be migratory (ie go to sea) as there is an advantage to them in attaining large size, as they can produce more eggs. However, where conditions are good for growth in the river there is less advantage in a migratory habit, and large productive rivers such as the Exe, Wye and Usk tend to have relatively few sea trout. For a discussion of the factors influencing the balance between brown and sea trout see Solomon (2006).

Holinshed (1587) included "trouts" in his list of abundant Thames fish, and they were taken throughout the river from the uppermost reaches of the tributaries down into tidal water. Up until the middle of the 19th Century all trout taken were wild fish produced naturally in the river and its tributaries. Very large fish were frequent and several of the largest specimens recorded were from this era before restocking programmes commenced.

The trout achieved fast growth and large size through adopting a diet of small fish rather than the invertebrates normally associated with smaller trout. The swarms of bleak, dace, roach, gudgeon and minnows that abounded in the Thames provided a ready source of food, and large trout often gave away their presence through the characteristic "skipping" across the surface by a bleak or other small fish that has been singled out by the trout for its next meal. The great majority of trout that did succumb to angling were caught by spinning (usually with a dead gudgeon or other small fish) or by livebaiting; few were caught fly fishing.

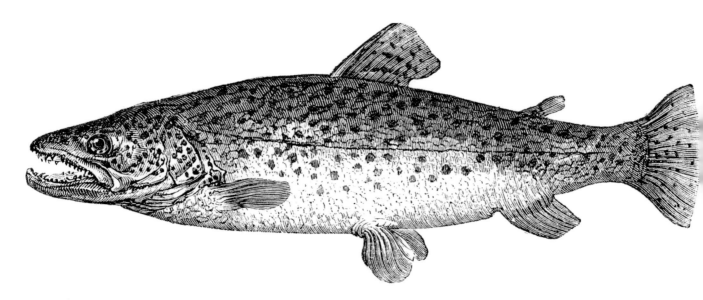

Figure 21.1. Drawing of a trout of 11 lb from the Thames in 1836. From Yarrell (1859)

Jesse (1836) gives details of some large trout captures including two caught on June 25 1818 by Mr D'Amaine at Hampton Deep; the fish weighed 8½ and 7 lb. A fish of 16 lb was caught by Mr G Marshall of Brewer Street, London. A Mr Cox was in the habit of drifting his boat down river from Maidenhead or Windsor to Hampton, trailling a bait or lure all the way. On May 20 1834 he landed from such an expedition with 14 trout "some of them large". Jesse reported that *a large trout may be seen feeding daily at this time* (June 1835) *opposite the water gallery of Hampton Court, which has denied every endeavour to capture it.*

After the construction of the navigation weirs, the weirpools became favourite locations for trout fishing. The trout liked such spots because of the fast flow, and the lack of disturbance by passing boat traffic. Jesse describes the fishing thus:-

The art of fishing for trout from the tops of the weirs of the river Thames is, I may venture to say, confined to very few, and to those in the habit of practising it for a considerable length of time. It requires good tackle, great skill, and some nerve. A bungler would even find it difficult to put a bleak properly on a set of the hooks which are used for Thames trout fishing, so as to make it spin as it ought to do. The angler sits or stands on the top of the piles of the weir, the foaming water rushing through them with great force and noise.

178

Figure 21.2. Trout fishing from a weir beam[1].

The torrent then forms eddies, and little whirlpools in the basin below, and from which as the water expands itself it again resumes its calm and stately movement. In the position I have described, the angler has to cast his line into the foaming basin, and this a skilful practitioner will do to a distance of thirty to forty yards. The great art, however, is in gathering the line properly in the hand for the second cast, so that it may not become tangled, or checked in its progress. When the position of the angler is considered, this is no easy task, especially as the loss of his balance might precipitate him into the torrent below. I do not mean to say that all Thames trout are taken by anglers in this position, as some persons troll from boats or the banks of an ait, but the best, and generally the most successful fishing, is from the tops of the weirs.

A graphic description of taking a tremendous fish in this manner was given by Francis (1880). He had spotted a good fish feeding below Sunbury Weir, and he and his "man" Tim set out a 5 am to try and catch it, knowing that others too had seen the fish and had designs upon it. Tim fixed the punt at the side of the weir and instructed Francis to wait while he tried to hook the fish. He wriggled out onto the weir beam on his belly, and spun the 3-ounce dace in and out of the current. He soon hooked the fish, and slipped along the weir towards the punt, and dropped the butt of the rod to his angler to fight the fish. After a long struggle the fish was netted and turned out to be 13½ lb in weight. *Worth getting up for* was the verdict of the fisherman; and a rival for the attentions of the fish clearly thought so too, as he arrived as the fish was being landed. Tim commented that the rival *don't get up early enuff* and that *the sight o'this'll be galls and wormholes and wuss than toothache to him.*

The precarious business of fishing from weir beams is well illustrated by Figures 21.2 and 21.3, drawn some 50 years after Jesse's graphic description was published. Fishing around many of the Thames weirs is still allowed subject to holding a permit from the Environment Agency. It is now a much safer and easier pastime as the weirs from which fishing is

Figure 21.3. Netting a trout hooked from the weir at Sunbury in 1884[2].

allowed have walkways with railings – and there are of, course, more rules. The only area now permitted for fishing at Sunbury Weir (the scene of the capture of the 13 ½ pounder and Figure 21.3) is a length of bank below the weir, on the lock island; clambering on the weir structure is strictly forbidden!

Despite the good catches mentioned by Jesse, all was not well on the river; he wrote *I regret to say that the good old times for Thames fishing are on the decline.* The reasons were severalfold, including the construction of the navigation weirs, increases in boat traffic, declining water quality, and over-fishing. The setting up of the Thames Angling Preservation Society as a reaction to these pressures is detailed in Chapter 7 . And one of the first species to receive specific attention was the trout.

However, the first organisation to address the declining stocks of trout by restocking appears to have been the Great Marlow Thames Angling Association. Between their formation in 1850 and the year 1880, they released on average more than 150 adult trout per year of one to three pounds in weight per year into the river. Many of these fish were sourced from a fish farm on the River Wick (or Wye) near High Wycombe, so were fairly local stock. In the early days the fish were purchased as eggs and reared in a hatchery in the greenhouse of the Rev. Florence Wethered of Hurley, until large enough to be placed into a rearing pond fed with water from a small stream at Bisham[3]. They were released to the Thames a year or two later. These fish did well but the process was expensive and time-consuming, and subsequently part-grown fish were purchased from trout farms on the Wick and further afield[4].

180

Table 21.1. Some very large Thames trout, taken by fair means and foul. The fish asterisked is that considered by A E Hobbs to be the largest authenticated rod-caught Thames trout[5].

Weight	Location	Date	Details	Source
23 lb 5 oz	Weybridge	1862	Found dead. Seen by Buckland	[6]
22 lb	Windsor	1834	Sir Samuel Hawker	Courtney Williams 1945
17 lb 3 oz	Radcot	1898	Nightline set for catching eels.	Hobbs 1947
17 lb	Tideway	1897	Net caught	Hobbs 1947
16 lb 15 oz	Reading	1880	Caught on a wagtail lure. R. Kennet, April 19	Buckland 1883
16 lb		1835	Caught by Mr Marshall	Jesse 1836
16 lb	Chertsey		Caught spinning by Mr Forbes.	Buckland 1883
16 lb	Marlow		In glass case in pub near Marlow Weir in 1877	[6]
15 lb*	Marlow		Caught by Bob Shaw	Hobbs 1947
15 lb		1835	Net caught on March 21	Yarrell (1859)
14 lb 10 oz	Hampton Ct	1883	Weight given as 14 lb 2 oz by Whymper 1883	Courtney Williams 1945
14 lb 9½ oz	Chertsey		Caught by Mr Forbes	Hobbs 1947
14 lb	Richmond	1834	Lt General Sir Samuel Hawker, May 31.	[6]
14 lb	Penton Hook	1962	Alan Pearson. Doubtful record – see text	[7]

Soon after this the Thames Angling Preservation Society started to stock trout into the lower river. Between 1860 and 1863 they stocked 804 adult trout, but some of these may have been American brook trout. Various stocking strategies were tried, including direct release of fry to the river, placing eggs into hatching boxes into the stream that ran from Christian Springs (Hampton) to the Thames, rearing fry on to larger size in a side-stream at Sunbury, and purchase and release of adult fish. Between 1861 and 1866, TAPS released of the order of 137,000 trout into the river. Many were reared in a hatchery constructed by Frank Buckland and Stephen Ponder in a greenhouse belonging to the latter at Hampton; the first batch of 30,000 fry from this facility in 1865 were reared-on in the side-stream at Sunbury; it had been concluded that stocking sizeable trout was far more effective than releasing fry. Evidence of the immediate effectiveness of the restocking programme was reported in 1864 :-

A few days since a gentleman, fly-fishing at Sunbury, hooked a handsome trout of 9½ lb, and the same evening one of 7 lb was taken in the same place spinning. At Penton Hook, Weybridge, Walton, Moulsey, and Teddington, a considerable number of trout, from 6 lb to 10 lb, have been recently captured; one of 9½ lb was caught with a spoon bait at Penton Hook. The weir at Sunbury was never known to be so full of trout of about 6 lb, and throughout the river considerable quantities of this fish, of one and two years old, have been seen, thus exhibiting a manifest increase by means of fish hatching.[8]

When TAPS decided that they could no longer justify the costs of rearing trout, Buckland and Ponder continued under their own steam. They were joined by Francis Francis, who also constructed a hatchery in his garden at Twickenham. After Buckland's death in 1880 the work was continued by James Forbes and Thomas Spreckley. Few records exist but it is known that one year Spreckley released nearly 300 trout of 10 inches in length.

Reading and District Angling Association also embarked on an active rearing and stocking programme. In 1878, Mr Frank Buckland made a donation to the R&DAA of 20,000 young trout which were released into the Thames. The 1879 accounts included a sum of £27/1/0 for construction of a trout nursery, and £15/3/6 for the *purchase and carriage of young trout*. The 1882 annual report records that 100 trout of about ¾ lb each were released into the Thames having been reared in the nursery at Caversham. The fish had been purchased as fingerlings from Wycombe. By 1883 it was claimed that a total of 60,000 trout had been released to the Thames by the R&DAA[9]. In 1877 trout were said to be *very few and far between* in this area, but in 1883 at least 150 had been caught, between two and nine pounds.

Table 21.2. A list of large trout taken from the Thames in one week in May 1883. From Whymper (1883).

Weight	Location	Angler	Notes
7 lb	Kingston	Mr Burningham	
7 lb 2 oz	Thames Ditton	Mr Loveland	
14 lb 2 oz		J Ross Faulkner	Another of 2 lb
7 lb	Hampton Court Weir	Mr Wild	
4 lb	Hampton Court Weir	G Woods	
10 lb	Hampton	Mr Kent	
7 lb	Sunbury Weir	E Lukyn	
4 lb 8 oz	Sunbury Weir	Mr Morton	
10 lb	Shepperton	Mr Lidney	
5 lb 4 oz	Shepperton		Client of George Rosewall
4 lb 8 oz	Shepperton		Client of George Rosewall
3 lb 12 oz	Shepperton		Client of George Rosewall
2 lb	Shepperton		Client of George Rosewall
7 lb 12 oz	Chertsey Weir	R L Pugh	
4 lb 14 oz	Chertsey Weir	R L Pugh	
5 lb	Chertsey Weir	T R Dyer	
3 lb 8 oz	Chertsey weir	T R Dyer	

Other organisations were also involved in stocking trout. The 1876-77 annual report of the Maidenhead, Cookham and Bray Thames Angling Association reported that more than 300 Wycombe trout had been stocked to the Thames, of which a large number were between two and three pounds. Private initiatives were also adding to the numbers of trout released; for example, a Mr Burrows was reported as having released 200 small trout to "the backwater" at Weybridge in 1897[10].

Figure 21.4. Churns of trout being stocked into the river by Henley Bridge. Date unknown. © River and Rowing Museum, Henley on Thames, UK..

Figure 21.5. Members of the Windsor and Eton Angling Preservation Society about to release a consignment of a thousand yearling Loch Leven strain brown trout into the river in 1891[11]. The fish had been supplied by Howietoun Hatchery at Stirling, and had made the 400 mile journey by train in these special containers with only one fish dying and three being considered poorly. The fish were conveyed by punt to be released between Monkey Island and Romney Weir stream.

The result of all this activity was that a considerable length of the river became well stocked with large trout. A list of large Thames trout taken in just over a week in May 1883 between Kingston and Chertsey was presented by Whymper (1883) and is displayed in Table 21.2. A fish of 12 lb 11 oz was taken at Hambleden in April of the same year.

John Bickerdyke wrote in 1894:-

Thames trouting has vastly improved of late years. A quarter of a century ago the man who caught a Thames trout was a sort of piscatorial hero. Now, as I have said, almost every weir between Pangbourne and Teddington yields several fish weekly.

A list of 73 trout caught between April and early June 1897, between Pangbourne and Twickenham, gave details of 73 fish up to more than ten pounds[10]. A Mr T W Gomm was responsible for the downfall of 13 of these fish, largest 9¾ lb and 9 pounds.

Table 21.3. Catches and average weights of large trout taken in the Thames, and the largest fish of each season, 1896-1909. Information from Amphlett (1901) and gleaned from the Fishing Gazette covering the later years.

Year	Total number	Total wt.	Average wt.	Largest	Venue
1896	118	436 lb	3.7 lb	9 lb 8 oz	Windsor
1897	147	674 lb	4.6 lb	10 lb 2 oz	Shepperton
1898	133	577 lb	4.3 lb	11 lb 8 oz	Marlow Weir
1899	127	533 lb	4.2 lb	10 lb 8 oz	Sonning
1900	90	400+ lb	4.4 lb	10 lb 0 oz	Boveney Weir
1901				8 lb 8 oz	Molesey Weir
1902				10 lb 4 oz	Henley
1903				10 lb 2 oz	Sonning
1904	45	210 lb	4.7 lb	8 lb 4 oz	Halliford
1905	60	255 lb	4.25 lb	9 lb 10½ oz	Pangbourne
1906	74	322 lb	4.35 lb	9 lb 1 oz	Henley
1907	72	319 lb	4.43 lb	8 lb 3 oz	Chertsey Weir
1908	54	221 lb	4.17 lb	8 lb 8 oz	Caversham
1909	48	242 lb	5.0 lb	10 lb 10 oz	Mapledurham Weir

A E Hobbs, in his lovely book *Trout of the Thames* published at the end of his fishing career in 1947, describes how the Henley Preservation and Restocking Society had stocked more than 12,000 trout, ranging from yearlings to fish of 4 lb, into the river since 1883. He listed sources as fish farms in Scotland, Norfolk and on the Rivers Exe, Kennet, Severn and Wick. A letter from Hobbs to the *Thames Angling News* in 1897 reported that the Society had released 400 two-year-old trout, 7 to 12 inches in length, into the river on January 29. These fish were from Colonel Constance's Weston Fishery in Norfolk.

Figure 21.6. A magnificent brace of Thames trout taken by A E Hobbs in 1902 and 1903, weights 10 lb 2 oz and 10 lb 6 oz. © River and Rowing Museum, Henley on Thames, UK.

In 1905-6, 250 of the trout released at Henley were marked with silver tags. Recaptures were reported as far afield as Bell Weir (28 miles downstream) and Tilehurst (11 miles upstream).

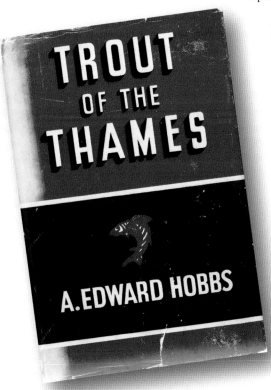

Hobbs himself was one of the most successful and prolific Thames trout fishers. In the 55 years between 1890 and 1945 he caught 878 trout of over 3 lb from the river; he released all fish of less than three pounds, and quite a number of larger ones too. The ten largest averaged 9¾ lb, and another 56 weighed over six pounds. His best days were eight fish (twice) at Mapledurham between 17" (measured and released) and 5 lb (killed and weighed), and six fish between Whitchurch and Mapledurham, best 8½ lb. Although there were many fishers who spent much time in pursuit of Thames trout no-one else can have come close to this incredible total.

There is an interesting tale[12] regarding the incredible case of two trout of over ten pounds caught by Hobbs (Figure 21.6), A while after Hobbs died, his daughter asked the brewery for which her father had worked as an architect if she could dump some rubbish that included a quantity of glass in their broken bottle pit; this turned out to be Hobbs' collection of cased fish! Fortunately the brewery (Brakspear's) recognised their importance, retrieved them and preserved them in their storeroom. When the brewery closed in 2003 the fish were acquired by the River and Rowing Museum, where of course their importance is fully recognised

Numbers of large trout were present in the river for the first half of the 20th century, as witnessed by the catches of Hobbs (he caught 11 between 2 lb 8 oz and 8 lb 13 oz in 1945). In his strange little book *The monarch of the Thames* published in 1955, Warren Hastings states that he had caught 25-30 Thames trout a year *some years ago*; however, as he had by then fished for more than half a century the lack of dates, and absence of any description in the decline in numbers, is frustrating. It seems that most stocking of trout into the main river ended with WWII, and Thames trout became scarce in the post-war years though some large fish were still occasionally being caught in the 1950s and 1960s. In the 1968 edition of his book entitled *Freshwater fishing in the Lower Thames*, John Burrett lists five trout over 6 lb in weight caught downstream of Staines between 1954 and 1958. The North Berkshire Herald presented a prize for the largest Thames trout each year for a few years; some winners are shown in the Table 21.4[13].

The 1966 winner, Joe Stallard, was probably the last of the specialist Thames trout fishermen. He caught numbers of good fish during the 1960's, including specimens of 9 lb 4½ oz from Busccot Weir, and 8 lb 14 oz from Radcot Weir in 1964.

Table 21.4. Largest Thames trout reported, 1966-8. From Howes (1969).

Year	Weight	Captor	Location	Bait
1966	7 lb 9 oz	J Stallard	Radcot Weir	Minnow
1967	2 lb 4 oz	P Maisey	Abingdon Weir	Bread flake
1968	9 lb	S Hills	Mapledurham Weir	Brandling worms

Figure 21.7. A hooked trout on the Thames. How are they going to land that one?![14]

What was probably the largest trout taken from the river since the war is surrounded by uncertainty. It is said to have weighed over 14 lb, and was reported caught in August 1962 by angling writer Alan Pearson. The catch was accepted at face value by Angling Times, but unfortunately the picture that they published of the fish proved to be a fake. Pearson immediately owned-up to the picture having been a practical joke, but was adamant that the catch and all other details were true. It is a shame that a silly jape undermined confidence in what was otherwise a tremendous catch.

Although some of the largest Thames trout were captured by dubious means, they nevertheless showed what consistently huge fish the river could produce. No other river in Britain comes close with regard to such a string of monster brown trout – even if most of them were not spawned in the river itself!

Chapter 21 footnotes

[1] Illustrated Sporting and Dramatic News, May 15 1882.
[2] Illustrated Sporting and Dramatic News, April 5 1884.
[3] Reading Mercury, October 23 1880.
[4] Englefield (1912)
[5] Letter to Fishing Gazette, May 28 1955.

[6] London Standard, April 4 1877.

[7] Angling Times, August 24, August 31 and September 7 1962.

[8] Northampton Mercury, May 28 1864.

[9] Wheeldon (1883)

[10] Thames Angling News, Vol 1(8), June 1897.

[11] Fishing Gazette, February 28 1891.

[12] Recorded by Jon Beer in the Telegraph Weekend, February 5 2005.

[13] Howes (1969).

[14] Illustrated Sporting and Dramatic News, August 3 1878.

CHAPTER 22

Other freshwater species

Pope or Ruffe

It may be angled for in the same way as perch; but by the scientific sportsman it is looked upon as an annoyance rather than a desideratum. **Smith (1860)**

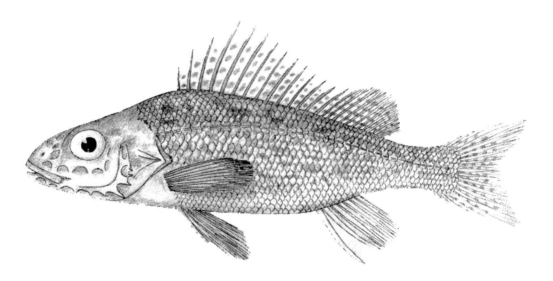

This is a small relative of the perch, and rarely grows to more than 17 cm in length. It is distributed throughout the Thames but, as indicated from the above quote, is of little interest to anglers, though Isaak Walton claimed that *no fish that swims is of a pleasanter taste.*

There was once a widespread practice among so-called anglers on the Thames of pushing a wine cork onto the spines of the dorsal fin of a ruffe, and releasing it to be henceforth firmly trapped just beneath the surface of the water, presumably to suffer a lingering death; Buckland (1883) suggests that it may in some way be connected with catholic persecution, though this seems a little unlikely. Although he refers to this as a cruel habit, Buckland goes on to say that *it is a very funny sight to see the surface for so many miles covered by these unfortunate popes.*

Writing in 1887 Armstrong clearly considered Thames pope to be unworthy of the attention of serious anglers:-

The pope is found in great abundance in many parts of the river; it bites greedily, and it is a common practice to take ladies to a "pope pitch" inasmuch as there is sure to be plenty of sport, the pope biting like a perch, and with a certainty of being hooked by a very small effort of skill.

This disdain for this blameless species (and indeed the female sex!) persisted until recent times. In his otherwise delightful autobiography, that great Thames angler Peter Stone confessed to having stamped on pope whenever he caught them in his younger days.

The Thames record, according to the Thames Angler's Conservancy list, weighed 6 oz and was caught in August 2011 by Paul Sullivan. This is a truly monstrous specimen; I do not think I have ever seen one in excess of about 2 oz.

Bleak

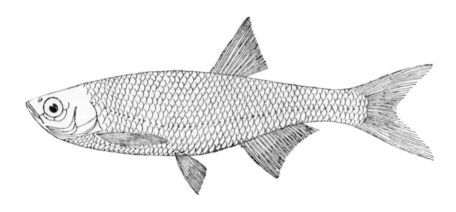

The bleak is a small fish of the carp family, rarely exceeding seven inches (17.5 cm) in length. The Thames angling record is a fish of 5 ½ oz, caught more than 50 years ago[1].

The fish abounds throughout the river, including the tidal reaches. Bleak dominated catches in the early years of the experimental fishing matches through London; for example, in the 1972 event fished between Vauxhall and Tower Bridge, 339 of the 352 fish caught were bleak; the others were ten dace, two roach and an eel[2]. In summer their presence is generally obvious as the fish tend to occupy the uppermost few inches of the water column, feeding on the surface. Bread scattered on the surface will usually attract a horde of bleak within a minute or two – if the swans and ducks don't beat them to it. They do not count in most fishing matches, and their main angling interest is as a target for beginners, and in the past as a bait for trout and pike fishing.

There is a perception among anglers of wide fluctuations in the bleak population numbers between years, with the species almost disappearing from some reaches. Considerable variation is to be expected in such a short-lived species, with one bad yearclass, or even more so with two bad yearclasses back to back, dominating the population. There is supporting evidence for this sort of fluctuation from the Environment Agency fisheries surveys. These show that there was a peak in numbers in the late 1990s/early 2000s, a dip in the 2000s into the second decade of this century, followed by a recent strong recovery[3].

However, perhaps the most interesting part of their history was the use of their scales in the manufacture of artificial pearls, along with to a lesser extent those of roach and dace. Details of the process were presented in an article in Land and Water in 1878[4]. The pearls were made from tiny hollow glass spheres, the colour being provided by an internal coating of suitable material. The article explained how bleak scales came to be used:-

At first the glass balls were filled with various materials, generally with a base of mercury. But in the year 1680 a rosary maker, named Jaquin, conceived the idea of using, in the place of the mercurial mixture, a harmless substance that produced an infinitely more perfect colour. This substance, the essence of orient, is formed from the scales of bleak, or ablette, a little white fish that abounds in the seine, the Marne, and the Loiret. The fishes are rubbed rather roughly in pure water contained in a large basin; the whole is then strained through a linen cloth, and left for several days to settle, when the water is drawn off. The sediment forms the essence of orient. It requires from 17,000 to 18,000 fish to obtain a pound of the substance. The scaly substance is liable to decompose quickly, and numerous chemical agents are employed by different manufacturers to preserve it. These means are kept a secret, but it is known that liquid ammonia, or the volatile alkali, is one of the substances most commonly used. The process of colouring the pearl is commenced by lining the interior of the ball with a delicate layer of perfectly limpid and colourless parchment glue, and before it is quite dry the essence of orient is introduced by a slender blow-pipe. It is then allowed to dry; the pearl is then filled with wax, and, if intended for a necklace, is pierced through the wax with a red-hot needle.

Buckland (1883) recorded that, fifty years earlier, the French had been large purchasers of bleak scales from Thames fishermen, but that they now obtained their supplies from more local sources.

Crucian carp and Rudd

The Crucian carp and rudd are members of the carp family and are residents of still waters, but occasionally turn up in the Thames presumably as a escapees from adjacent lakes and ponds. Very few have recorded in the Environment Agency fish surveys in the past 15 years. The rod record crucian carp for the river is 4 lb 2 oz, which is close to the national record.

Grayling

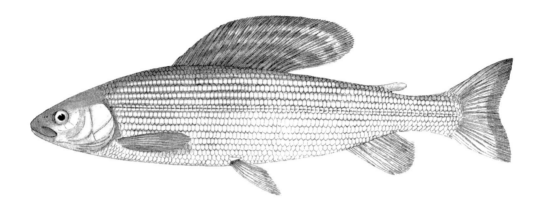

This beautiful fish abounds in some of the Thames tributaries (for example the Kennet), generally sharing trout habitat. However, it is rarely encountered on the main river. Attempts were made to restock the lower river with grayling in Victorian times, but few were ever seen again.

Tench

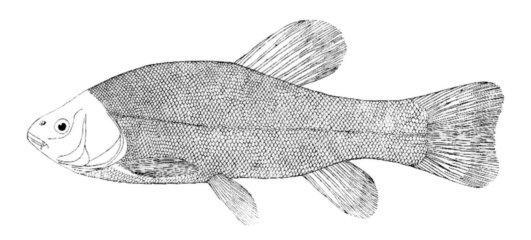

Tench have occurred in small numbers throughout the Thames since fishing records began. Being predominantly a fish of still waters it is likely that most in the river arrived there from adjacent lakes and ponds during floods, or by deliberate transfer. Usually occurring as single fish, sizeable catches are sometimes made presumably immediately following a mass escape in a flood. In 1912 James Englefield recorded catching no less than 17 tench between 1¼ and 2½ lb in deep, slow-flowing water *at the back of Hurley Mills*. It transpired that a flood during the cleaning-out of a pond at nearby Ladye Place had allowed much of the stock of tench to escape to the river. Englefield also caught tench here on subsequent occasions, but never more than two in a session as the fish dissipated into the surrounding river. Coincidentally, another catch of 17 tench, from 2 to 2½ lb, was taken by *some well-known Thames anglers* at Teddington in 1926[5]. Well-known Henley angler A E Hobbs caught two or more tench in the river on a number of occasions, up to 5 lb 5 oz; a group of four he had mounted by Coopers of London are held in the collection at the River and Rowing Museum at Henley. Several of the fish caught by Hobbs were golden tench, an ornamental variety that were almost certainly recent escapes from a riverside pond. The record for the river is a fish of 8 lb 11 oz taken by Duncan Green in June 2013.

Silver Bream

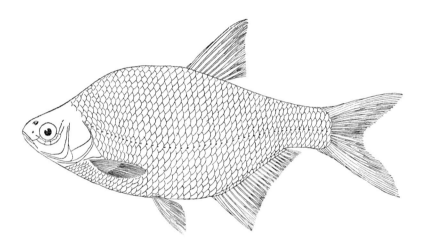

This smaller relative of the common bream is sporadically distributed throughout the Thames main river and tributaries. Fisheries surveys undertaken by the Environment Agency suggest it is most abundant in the upper river between Reading and Oxford. It grow to about 2 lb in weight, and is rarely a target species for anglers. One of the problems with establishing the extent to which it appears in anglers catches is uncertain identity due to the similarity to small common bream, and even more so to hybrids between roach and common bream. For this reason many of the old records must be considered unreliable. The current Thames record is a fish of 1 lb 14 oz caught by Stuart Manwaring in 2015. This is one silver bream record whose correct identification we can be sure of, as Stuart is an Environment Agency fisheries officer!

Wels Catfish

Wels catfish is a mainland European species that has been introduced to a few still waters in the UK. In recent years several have been caught in the Thames, but how they arrived there is a mystery. The largest weighed 64 lb and was caught by Jamie Drylie in August 2010[6].

Grass carp

Grass carp are an Asian species that has been introduced to the UK for experimental control of water weeds in enclosed still waters. The exacting requirements for development and hatching of the eggs means that it cannot breed in the wild in this country. A single fish weighing 30 lb 1 oz has been caught in the Thames, by Tim Hughes in August 2009. Its origin is a mystery.

Zander

The zander is another introduction from Europe. Originally introduced into the Great Ouse system they have gradually been spread, often illegally, into other waters. Numbers in the Thames are building steadily. The largest reported is a fish of 20 lb 9 oz caught by Warwick Salzer, but for some reason this fish does not feature in the Thames Anglers Conservancy record list; their largest is listed at 13 lb 12 oz, caught by Ashley Stockbridge in November 2009.

Huchen

This is another introduction from Europe. The huchen, or Danubian salmon, is a large non-migratory species that is held in high regard as a sport fish in SE Europe. It can grow to more than 50 lb in weight, and young fish, reared from eggs imported from Austria, were released to the Thames on a number of occasions between 1905 and 1914.

Alan Pearson, writing in 1961 in Burrett and Pearson, stated that *large numbers* of huchen "fry" were released into the Thames at Hedsor, Taplow and Teddington in 1905 and 1914, but I have been unable to find any further details of such releases. However, huchen were also being reared at the hatchery of Mr Crosbie Gilbey at Denham on the Colne, initially at least under the auspices of the Thames Salmon Association. One batch, hatched in May 1905, had reached about 15 cm in length by October[7], and on October 13 400 were released in Lord Boston's water at Hedsor, and on October 31 another 400 were released in Lord Desborough's water at Taplow Court[8]. A further batch of 150 young fish was released at Nuneham in late 1907 by Mr Lewis Harcort MP[9].

Little more was seen of these fish. It was reported that a number of small fish were recaught above Boulters Lock soon after releases at Hedsor and Taplow[10]. There was a single-line press report that a "Fine specimen of the huchen" had been caught above Weybridge in 1907.[11] A more reliable report was of a three pounder caught on a gudgeon livebait at Old Windsor in 1909[12]. The captor was Philip Geen, President of the London Anglers Association, fishing with professional fisherman Lumsden of Datchet, but as the fish was released there is no confirmation of the identity. It appears that some fish had been released or had escaped into the Colne from the Denham hatchery; a small fish, about 23 cm in length, was reported caught in an eel trap being operated by the Piscatorial Society water at Uxbridge, a mile or two downstream of the hatchery, in 1906[13].

194

Around 1913 anglers reported seeing "huchen-like" fish in the Thames at Nuneham, and an unsuccessful attempt was made to net the fish[14]. There was flurry of interest in 1933 when Lord Desborough, Chairman of the Thames Conservancy, announced that large huchen were present in the river near Abingdon. This was based upon sightings of "strange fish", and anglers hooking and having their tackle broken by large fish. All attempts to catch the fish were unsuccessful. Pearson discussed the possibility of there still being a small breeding population in the river at that time, but added no new evidence.

Small fry

There are several other species of fish native to the Thames that are of little direct interest to fisheries by virtue of their very small size. These are the bullhead, minnow, stone loach, three spined stickleback, ten spined stickleback and brook lamprey. All have a maximum length of just a few inches and they do not feature in anglers catches. All are widely if discontinuously distributed in the main river and tributaries and connected wetlands. They are occasionally trapped or netted for use as bait.

Crayfish

Native white-clawed crayfish once abounded throughout the Thames catchment from Staines to the uppermost tributaries. They were trapped for food in small pots resembling eel grigs and made from very fine withy rods. Trapping was particularly prevalent in the Binsey area upstream of Oxford[15], and most cottages near the upper river had one or two such pots[16]. However, around 1892, the native crayfish were struck by a virulent disease. Cornish recorded that the disease first appeared around Staines, and worked its way upstream right to the uppermost reaches. The crayfish turned bright red, emerged from their burrows and died. An investigation[17] of crayfish in the Thames tributaries around Oxford about 40 years after this mortality noted periodic violent fluctuations in numbers, with a particularly widespread event in the early 1890's.

Clearly the disease failed to completely eradicate the species as crayfish were widespread in the Thames during much of the 20th century, even if not as abundant as in former times. I recall collection several specimens from the river near Bray in the mid 1960s, almost under the newly-constructed M4 crossing.

What the 19th century epidemic failed to do, however, events in the latter part of the 20th Century did more thoroughly. North American signal crayfish were introduced to the UK for aquaculture, and soon escaped and spread rapidly. They first appeared in the Thames in about 1976 and quickly made themselves at home. What was not realised at the time of introduction was that the new species was a carrier for the crayfish plague, a fungal disease to which they themselves appeared immune. It was lethal to the native species however, and as quickly as the invader spread, the white-clawed species disappeared. Nowadays the distribution of native crayfish in the catchment is restricted to a very few uppermost reaches of tributaries where the signals have not yet succeeded in spreading.

The signal crayfish has become very abundant in the river, and this has led to the development of a fishery of its own. Roger Sellars and Dale Oram set traps throughout the reach from Reading to Oxford, and in 2015 landed more than 7.5 tonnes from the reach[18]. They grow much larger than the native species, reaching 200 mm in body-length and more than 300 g in weight. In addition to leading to the eradication of the native species, signals make extensive burrows which can lead to collapse of the river bank. They are also believed to consume large quantities of fish spawn.

There may be an incidental benefit to the introduction of signals to the Thames, however. Since they have become abundant, several predatory species of fish have grown much faster than before, leading to much larger individuals of barbel, perch and chub. The direct link is not proven, but the coincidence is very suggestive. Needless to say Thames anglers have been quick to take advantage of the surge in large fish, as described in earlier chapters.

Otters

Few things seemed to have angered our Victorian forebears more than having to share the river's bounty with otters. They were pursued relentlessly by trapping and shooting, and many clubs offered a reward for each one killed; for example the Thames Angling Preservation Society (one guinea), Maidenhead, Cookham and Bray Thames Angling Association (one guinea), Reading and District Angling Association (one pound), Windsor and Eton Angling Preservation Association (one pound), and Marlow Thames Angling Association (ten shillings).

In 1907 the Thames Conservancy considered making a byelaw to protect otters and to ban their molestation. This prompted Philip Geen, the president of the London Anglers association, to pen a furious letter to the Fishing Gazette[19], which included the following:-

Are there now no descendents of the robust sportsmen who knew what vermin were and how to treat them, or is it that they are frightened by the stupid sentimental fogies who for ever cry that taking cry "Live and let live" and of those others ever ready to say that it is unwise to interfere with "Nature's balance"? Reflections of those two glorious-sounding maxims have led me to wonder what place on earth man would now be holding had such mottoes been the guiding spirit of our forefathers' existence through the centuries back.

Surely there must be a few amongst the scores I personally know who are as cognisant of what is being done that tends to ruin the fisheries of the Thames as I and will presently offer a protest.

...the only reason that I have seen put forward for the protection of this cruel animal that eats its living victim until it dies, and then seeks a fresh one, is that it adds to the attractiveness of the river.

From time immemorial efforts have been made to keep them down on the Thames, but they remain more numerous than ever, and it is impossible for an observant eye to miss their cruel doings, and as for exterminating them that is equally impossible, for they breed like rats.

The Editor added a footnote:-

I have no wish to see the otter exterminated, but there is no fear of that, and I feel sure the good sportsmen of the Thames Conservancy will take a reasonable view, and at any rate, take evidence before protecting the Thames otter. It is certain that the Wild Birds Protection Act has done great harm to our fisheries, and to protect otters would be madness – Ed.

Not everyone, even those with an interest in fishing, had such strong otterphobic views. Robertson (1875) wrote:-

Without at all disputing the fact that a good many fish fall victims to the voracity of each otter which is suffered to survive, we cannot help putting in a mild plea on behalf of the species. There are now so very few of the tribe left near the river, their enemies have had such constant success, that from the victors we would now petition for a cessation of hostilities. The difference which the few remaining otters can make to the total quantity of fish in the river must be but a minute fraction, surely not enough to justify the complete extermination of "so interesting a native". The fact of the presence of an otter being detected anywhere seems to call for immediate notice in the Field, usually accompanied with talk of rewards for its destruction. The animal is generally alluded to in more vituperative language than would have been thought to exist in the vocabulary of the "gentle" angler; and should the death of the poor beast be compassed, the glory supposed to attach to the exploit is ludicrously out of proportion to the occasion.

And Church (1890) added:-

This, I knew, now more than forty years ago, as the haunt of an otter, and it suggests a word of protest, useless I fear, as such words almost always are, against the barbarous Philistinism which is banishing, if it has not already banished, this beautiful creature from the Thames. It is ruthlessly trapped and shot because the Angling Societies grudge it its tribute out of the multitude of coarse fish with which, though they are increasingly difficult to catch, the river still abounds. I should gladly see an Act which would give an absolute protection to what may still be left of the once abundant fauna of the Thames, the otter first of all, and with him to the kingfisher, the grebe, and the moor-hen, now made the victims of useless massacre, butchered to make a Cockney's holiday.

One odd feature of reports of otters trapped or shot is the tendency to give the length and weight of the victim. Perhaps this is all part of the "big game trophy" atmosphere of the culling of otters alluded to by Robertson (above). The largest otters were around 28 lb in weight, and four feet long from nose to tip of tail.

Press reports giving the locations of the otters killed gives some indication of their distribution throughout the Thames area. Of the dozens of reports that I have seen, none are upstream of Oxford. There are a number of feasible explanations including the possibility that otters were few that far upstream; however, it is known that otters occurred throughout the Upper Thames and that they were sometimes hunted with hounds (Williams 1922). Most press reports of trapping and shooting were from the Reading area, and from Windsor downstream to Molesey.

Although mostly residing in the vicinity of the main river, otters were known to make forays up smaller tributaries[20]:-

One reason for the fewness of Thames trout may be found, "Country Life" suggests, in the abundance of Thames otters. Not that these otters catch these trout in the Thames. They kill them long before they become Thames trout at all, in the tributary streams and brooks, whence the normal supply of trout is derived as the larger fish drop down to the big river. Otters, as most people know, prefer if possible to hunt up a tributary, going up it by night, and returning in the morning, or else sleeping in a hollow willow, and coming back the next night. In some Thames tributaries they seem to clear out all the fish.

An example of this behaviour was highlit when an otter appeared (and was shot) in February 1950 in the Kings Pool in Ewelme, at the source of the tiny Ewelme Stream[21]. This flows two miles to join the Thames at Benson, and supports a population of trout, but is not large enough to hide an otter for any length of time.

Chapter 22 footnotes

[1] Letter in Fishing Gazette, May 7 1955.
[2] Angling Times, August 3 1972.
[3] Stuart Manwaring, Environment Agency, pers. Comm.
[4] Land and Water, August 10 1878, No 655.
[5] Young (1926)
[6] Thames record list on website of the Thames Angling Conservancy.
[7] London Daily News, October 6
[8] Oxfordshire Weekly News, October 24 1906
[9] Oxfordshire Weekly News, January 8 1908
[10] London Daily News, October 6 1906
[11] Fraserburgh Herald and northern Counties Gazette, May 7 1907
[12] Cannock Chase Courier, July 3 1909; The Field, June 23 1909.
[13] Sportsman, October 10 1906.
[14] The Sportsman, July 16 1913.
[15] Hall and Hall (1859).
[16] Cornish (1902).
[17] Duffield (1933).
[18] Daily Express, June 9 2016.
[19] Fishing Gazette, May 25 1907.
[20] Falkirk Herald, October 8 1902.
[21] Diary of Fred Greenway, Ewelme resident; held by D Solomon.

CHAPTER 23

Other migratory and estuarine fish

Flounder

The flounder is a marine flatfish that is abundant in estuaries. Young fish may ascend some distance into fresh water. They were abundant throughout the Thames tideway until well into the 19th Century, and formed an important part of the catch of fishermen operating there. Deterioration of water quality reduced the numbers and range of the species. As described in Chapter 4 there was an improvement in water quality and distribution around 1875, allowing commercial exploitation of flounders from Westminster Bridge (Figure 23.1) upstream to Kew. However things again deteriorated for a decade or more, followed by a recovery from about 1895; in that year flounders were seen at Chiswick for the first time in more than a decade. The major deterioration from about 1910 saw the long-term disappearance of the species from the estuary. Now once again they are present throughout the tidal reaches.

Figure 23.1. Seine netting for flounders at Waterloo Bridge in 1880[1].

Lampreys

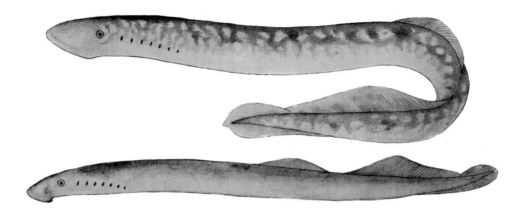

All three British species of lamprey have occurred in the Thames at some time. The picture above shows a sea lamprey (top) and a river lamprey (which are migratory); the third species, the brook lamprey, is a freshwater species.

The largest of the three is the sea lamprey. These spawn in the river and migrate to sea as juveniles after living for several years within silt banks at the edge of the river. As adults they are parasitic on large fish. They return to the river to spawn in the spring, and may ascend quite long distances into fresh water. Returning adults are typically 60-80 cm in length and may weigh up to 2 kg.

Sea lampreys occurred in small numbers in the Thames until about 1900, but never in large enough numbers to attract the interest of a targeted fishery. There are few recent records. One was recorded in an eel buck at Maidenhead in 1877[2], which was said to be "*a most unusual occurrence of late years*" even in the tidal reaches; this far upstream was said to be unprecedented.

River lampreys, or lamperns, are smaller than sea lampreys but have a somewhat similar life cycle. They return to the river to spawn in the winter at about 30 cm in length. Historically they occurred in very large numbers in the Thames, and the returning adults sustained a valuable fishery. Although they are considered a delicacy in Scandinavia they have not generally been valued as a food species in Britain, and the main value of the Thames catch was as bait for long-lines set for sea fish, especially cod and turbot. The Dutch in particular valued them and contracted Thames fishermen to supply them live. At Richmond in 1751 weirs built to catch lamperns were considered a real danger to the passage of boats, especially at night, and there were calls for them to be removed[3]. In 1790 Pennant reported that the catch for the river was of the order of 450,000 per year around 1776, and the price was about £2 per thousand. Before the navigation weirs were built the lamperns would penetrate well into the river; in 1861, a fisherman at Maidenhead reported[4] that his grandfather was reputed to have caught 120,000 in his eel bucks one winter, and his father still sold a catch of them as late as 1820, after which numbers fell rapidly. From that time onwards the main catch was taken at Teddington and Molesey, in wicker-work traps (called weels) set expressly to catch them. In 1860, in one day the Teddington fishermen sold 60,000 at £3 per thousand, but this catch may have been made over a number of days as the catch was stored live in special well-boats. A witness at the 1860 Salmon Inquiry stated that there had been no real diminution in the runs of lamperns, though there was considerable fluctuation between years. In dry years most of the fish were caught at Teddington Weir, but in wet years they were able to get past and the large catches were taken at Hampton Court (Molesey Weir). The Hampton Court fishermen would then sell them to the Teddington men, as it was only they who had the contract to supply the Dutch. The fish were kept alive in wicker baskets or well boats and taken down to Billingsgate where they were sold live. The contract price at that time ranged from £3 to £5 per thousand, and one fisherman alone was reported to have made £400 in about 1858.

Although the lamprey runs carried on at a good level long after the salmon disappeared, they too started to diminish later in the 19th Century. By 1879 Henry Taunt reported that while lampreys were still to be caught at Teddington Weir, they were *not present in such number as formerly.* Teddington weir was rebuilt and raised in 1882, and the following winter the catch there was very good, but disastrous upstream. In about 1891 it was reported that *the great body of migrating lamperns were all poisoned by the river, and lay in tens of thousands in the mud at Blackwall Point,* and by about 1900 *were almost forgotten.* However, temporary improvements in water quality in 1901 were associated with lamperns spawning in the gravel at Hammersmith[5]. As water quality temporarily improved, their numbers increased for several years; in 1909 about 6000 were caught at Hampton Court, one night yielding 1500[6]. A professional fisherman, Walter McBride, reported that numbers were greatly diminished, and that he only caught about 600 in 1912[7]. Soon after this they completely disappeared from the river for sixty years. Sea and river lampreys have reappeared in small numbers in recent years, and both have spawned .

Figure 23.2. Lamprey weels at Teddington Weir in about 1882[8]

Twaite shad

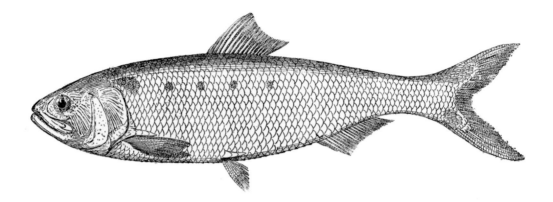

There is good evidence of a strong population of twaite shad in the lower reaches of the Thames in former times. This fish spawns in the lower reaches of rivers, often within the tidal freshwater reaches, and migrates to sea at about one year of age. The adults return to spawn in the spring, typically in May. They are not an esteemed food species but have at times been commercially exploited.

Yarrell (1859) described the twaite shad run in the Thames thus:-

Twaite-Shads appear during these three months (May to July) in abundance in the Thames, from the first point of land below Greenwich, opposite the Isle of Dogs, to the distance of a mile below; and great numbers are taken every season. These fish produce, however, but a small price to the fishermen, having little repute as food, their muscles being exceedingly full of bones and dry. Formerly great quantities of Twaite-Shad were caught with nets in that part of the Thames opposite the present penitentiary at Millbank, Westminster. Above Putney Bridge was a favourite spot for them; but the state of the water, it is believed, prevents the fish from ascending the river in the same manner as former years, and comparatively few are taken. The ordinary size of the adult fish of this species is from twelve to sixteen inches.

Shad are not allowed to be caught in the Thames after the 30th of June, that the remaining fish may cast their spawn without interruption from the nets.

The principal spawning time of the Twaite-Shad in the Thames is about the second week of July, when numbers may be seen and heard frisking at or near the surface. In the language of fishermen, the Shad are said to thrash the water with their tails; they appear to disencumber themselves of the matured roe by violent muscular action; and on a calm still evening the noise that they make may be heard at some distance.

While shad have sometimes been recorded in the tidal reaches in recent times, there is no evidence of local spawning.

Smelt

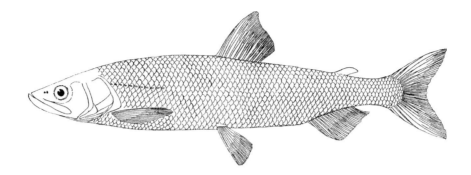

The smelt is a small, little-known migratory species which has nevertheless played a significant role in Thames fisheries history. It is a distant relative of the salmon and trout, and enters estuaries and the lower reaches of rivers in the spring to spawn. They may also re-enter estuaries to over-winter. The very largest fish may be 300 mm in length and weigh up to 200 g, but most are much smaller.

Until the 19th Century smelt were abundant in the tidal Thames and supported an important fishery. Up to 50,000 per year were caught in the late 18th Century[9]. They were caught in small-meshed nets and the season ran from August 28 until the following Good Friday. Up to 40 boats were engaged in the fishery at the peak of the season, working between Wandsworth and the tidal limit. However, by the time Yarrell recorded the above in 1859, the species had become much less abundant and widespread in the tidal Thames. They virtually disappeared from the middle and upper estuary soon after that, but remained present in the lower estuary area and the Medway. Along with a temporary improvement in water quality, Cornish (1902) reported:-

In August (1900) the delicate smelts suddenly reappeared at Putney, where they had not been seen in any numbers for years. Later, in September, another migration of smelts passed right up the river. Many were caught at Isleworth and Kew, and finally they penetrated to the limit of the tideway at Teddington, and good baskets were made at Teddington Lock.

However, as water quality deteriorated once more in the early 20th Century, smelts along with many other species disappeared from the upper and middle estuary for several decades. Smelts were among the first fish to re-appear when water quality improved in the 1960s[10], and have been fairly abundant since.

Sturgeon

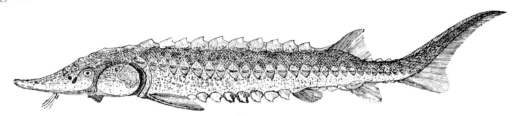

The European Sturgeon (*Acipenser sturio*) once had breeding populations in several of the larger rivers of Western Europe, but is now endangered having a viable breeding population only in the Gironde in France (plus a possible population in the Black Sea). It occurred as a vagrant in the Thames estuary in former times, occasionally penetrating well into fresh water, but none has been recorded for several decades. There is no evidence that there was ever a breeding population in the Thames.

Records identified for the Thames and adjacent tidal waters landwards of the Yantlet Line are listed in Table 23.1. A number of fish have been reported seawards of this, including a number in the tidal reaches of the Medway.

Table 23.1. Records of sturgeon taken from the river and estuary of the Thames

Date	Location	Details	Source
1717, June	Limehouse	"16 feet"	11
Early 1800's	Boulters Weir	Over a hundredweight	12
1820-1830	Clewer Point, Windsor	56 lb	13
1824	Windsor	150 lb, 7' 4"	14
1825, May	Gravesend	150 lb?	15
1832, July	"Thames"		16
1835, May	Wapping	250 lb	17
1838, August			18
1843, October	Battersea	280 lb, 9' 6"	19
1846, June	Adelphi Pier		20
1860, April	Greenhithe		21
1861, April	Halfway Reach	125 lb, 6' 6"	22
1863, July	"Mouth of the Thames"	3 feet	23
1867, April	Putney Bridge	15 feet	24
1867, May	Westminster Bridge	60 lb	25
1879, July	River Crane, Isleworth	7 lb	26
1880, June	Charlton	9"	27
1883	Erith		28
1894, June	Erith	280 lb	29

Some of the records in the table warrant a little additional information, especially those from fresh water. The capture of the Windsor fish in 1824 was detailed in a contemporary report thus:-

For some time past the fishermen in the neighbourhood of Maidenhead have been on the alert, in consequence of a fish of immense size, supposed to be a sturgeon, having been seen basking near that place. All their endeavours to take captive this enormous stranger were, however, unavailing, and, it not having been perceived lately, the general belief was that it had returned down the river. This supposition was partly correct, for on Sunday last the fish was discovered at Clewer Point, about a mile from Windsor. On Wednesday, as some bargemen were working a punt down the pound stream of the lock below Windsor, they descried the long-looked-for object of their search, and immediately commenced preparations for its seizure. Having succeeded in driving it into shallow water, they enveloped it in strong nets, and at great personal risk, owing to its strength, succeeded in bringing it to the shore. It proved to be, as expected, a sturgeon, measuring 7ft 4 in in length and weighing upwards of 150 lb.

The capture of the seven pound fish in the River Crane at Isleworth in 1879 at first sight would appear doubtful, except that it was reported by no less an expert than Francis Francis, who lived nearby, however, he did not claim to have seen the fish himself. The nine inch fish reported from Charlton in 1880 may have been a case of mistaken identity, but the fish was reported to have been "preserved" and viewable at the Star and Garter in St Martin's Lane.

The 1843 Battersea fish was trapped in a mill pond (Mr Hutton's at Battersea Fields):-

It had been seen in the mill pond since Saturday morning, but the depth of the water prevented its giant proportions being ascertained. On Monday, however, the water was let off, and the pond being almost dry the monster fish was left at the mercy of its enemies. It was half past five o'clock on Monday evening, however, before ten men succeeded, by dint of great exertion, in drawing this monster from the pond to the lawn in front of Mr Hutton's Mill.

In November 2013 a Siberian sturgeon (*Acipenser baerii*) weighing ten pounds was caught by an angler at Greenhithe[30]. This was almost certainly an escapee or release from aquaculture or an aquarium, rather than a vagrant.

Chinese Mitten Crab

This invader from the Far East is believed to have arrived in Europe in the ballast water of ships, which was discharged in harbours and estuaries before the vessels were loaded with goods for the return journey. The "mitten" refers to the dense covering of hairs on the claws. While they breed in salt and brackish water, they may ascend freshwater rivers for hundreds of miles, before descending once more to spawn.

The first record for the Thames was in 1935, but while the species became well-established in many areas of NW Europe it was many years later before numbers started to appear in our river. Numbers then built rapidly, and it is now an abundant member of the fauna throughout the estuary and lower river. The furthest upstream record so far is at Nuneham Courteney, between Wallingford and Abingdon.

Like the signal crayfish, the introduction of this species to the Thames may be a mixed blessing. While it may have contributed to the rapid growth and large size of several predatory fish species, there is concern about the potential for bank damage to be caused by its burrowing habit, and competition with and predation on native fauna.

Chapter 23 footnotes

[1] The Graphic, November 20 1880.
[2] Fishing Gazette, May 11 1877
[3] Press cutting dated 1751 held at Richmond Library. No other details available.
[4] Witness reported in Anon (1861).
[5] Cornish (1902).
[6] Fishing Gazette December 24 1910
[7] Fishing Gazette January 25 1913.
[8] Illustrated Sporting and Dramatic News, February 18 1882, p553.
[9] Dart (1979).
[10] Wheeler (1969).
[11] Stamford Mercury, July 4 1717
[12] Maidenhead Advertiser, December 24 1889
[13] Field, September 2 1865
[14] Field, February 3 1894
[15] London Courier, May 30 1825
[16] Dublin Observer, July 7 1832
[17] Sun (London) May 18 1835
[18] London Courier and Evening Gazette, August 16 1838
[19] Bell's New Weekly Messenger), October 22 1843
[20] Leicester Journal, June 5 1846
[21] Holborn Journal, April 13 1860
[22] Gravesend Reporter, April 6 1861
[23] Dublin Evening Mail, August 1 1863.
[24] Field, April 27 1867
[25] Field, May 18 1867
[26] Field, August 2 1879
[27] Field, June 9 1881
[28] Murie (1903).
[29] Stonehaven Journal, June 21 1894
[30] Atlantic Salmon Trust Press Release, November 10 2013.

CHAPTER 24

Now and the future

The environment

Water quality in the freshwater river has never been really poor, and in general terms it is probably as good now at any time in the past 200 years. Discharge consent conditions for sewage treatment works have become more stringent and are monitored and enforced. Occasional damaging discharges still happen but generally they are promptly addressed, appropriately punished and often mitigated. For example, for discharging raw sewage from Henley STW in April 2016, which killed more than 1,000 fish, Thames Water was fined £2.3 million[1]. There are some concerns over chronic pollution including levels of nitrate and phosphate causing eutrophication, and regular but intermittent discharge of only partially-treated sewage. A further concern is a list of 45 chemicals that have been gradually incorporated into the Water Framework Directive conditions. Twenty-one of these 45 are identified as "priority hazardous substances". Inclusion of these standards has resulted in a failure of chemical status in every single water body in England in 2019! What the implications of this mysterious development are for fisheries is not clear.

Water temperature is likely to become an issue, as climate change continues. However, with the exception of trout, salmon and smelt none of the Thames fish species is currently exposed to temperatures approaching lethal levels; all the coarse fish species present also occur throughout Europe down to the Mediterranean, and moderate increases in Thames water temperature pose little direct threat in the short to medium term.

Increasing water temperature may enhance the survival and spread of invasive species, especially those occurring as escapes or releases of aquarium and pond fish and other animals, and plants.

The physical configuration of the river, with its weirs and locks, is heavily modified from the natural situation and this has had a significant effect upon the environment for fish and other aquatic biota. There is little prospect of a return to more natural conditions in the foreseeable future. This, coupled with the threat of increasing temperatures, means that creating a significant self-sustaining run of salmon based upon spawning in the main river is unlikely. However, one positive result of the interest in restoring a run of salmon is the fish passes that have been installed on many of the navigation weirs. Although originally conceived to be used by salmon, they do allow passage of many other species; one pass in the Thames catchment, fitted with a trap at the top end, has been recorded passing sixteen species of fish in an upstream direction, including many individuals in the 11-20 cm length range[2]. While generally not essential in the short term for the completion of the life cycle for most species, such movement between river sections reduces any risks associated with genetic isolation of fish populations. Many so-called non-migratory species may make extensive movements of up to many tens of kilometres at spawning time, and may attempt to migrate back upstream when washed out in floods. Effective fish passes allow this.

Reduction in freshwater flow volume due to abstraction has been a major feature of the habitat of the whole river and estuary, steadily having a greater impact over the past 200 years. This may limit populations of lovers of fast water such as barbel, but most fish species are equally happy in moderate flows. Again, little recovery of the natural flow regime appears likely in the foreseeable future.

The extent of boating on the river has fallen significantly from its peak late in the 20th century, but it is likely to remain a popular recreation. One thing we will see is the phasing-out of internal combustion power in favour of electric and non-powered craft (paddled, rowed and sailed) which will reduce the impact both in terms of physical disturbance and water quality.

The fish community

For an assessment of the health and wellbeing of the biota, including the fish community, we would naturally turn to the Water Framework Directive (WFD). This EU initiative was adopted into UK legislation and was implemented in 2009. England was divided into about 5000 separate water bodies (including stretches of river); for the Thames basin there are 498 surface water bodies, although the main stem of the river, from Kemble to Teddington, comprises only ten (Table 24.1). Each of these water bodies is assessed for ecological quality (bad, poor, moderate, good or high), and chemical quality (good or fail) every year. The ecological quality is based upon the weakest of six separate assessments, one of which is fish. These assessments use the same five classes as the overall ecological assessment. Now that we have eleven years of annual assessments, what do the results tell us about the health of the River Thames fish stocks and the trends in their fortunes?

The answer is, not very much! The 2019 results for fish, ecology and chemical quality for 2019 are shown in Table 24.1. It can be seen that for five of the ten reaches between the source and the tidal limit there is no fisheries assessment. This is because the WFD process involves a model that requires a quantitative assessment of fish populations, an aspiration that is unrealistic for such a large river as the Thames. Unfortunately the process does not allow semi-quantitative assessment (such as the electric fishing results using the EA boom boat) or expert judgement (for example based on angling success) to be used as a substitute.

The fish community is generally healthy throughout the river and tideway; in the case of the tideway it is as good as at any time in the past 200 years.

At present very large individuals of several species are present, and are sought and caught by anglers, in the Thames. There are larger barbel, chub, perch and carp in the river now than perhaps any time in history. We can be reasonably confident that this situation will continue at least in the short to medium term, as the conditions that appear to have contributed to this situation (such as climate change, improved water quality and clarity, careful release of almost all fish caught, and abundant food supply) are unlikely to change.

Table 24.1. The Water Framework Directive targets and 2019 status of the twelve waterbodies comprising the Thames main stem.

Waterbody name	Length (m)	Heavily Modified?	2019 status			Target		
			Ecology	Chemical	Fish	Ec	Ch	Fish
Kemble to Waterhaybridge	13,675	No	Moderate	Fail	Good	G	G	G
Waterhaybridge to Cricklade	6,628	No	Moderate	Fail	High	G	G	G
Churn to Coln	22,156	No	Moderate	Fail	?	M	G	-
Coln to Leach	28,025	No	Poor	Fail	Poor	M	G	M
Leach to Evenlode	49,788	Yes	Moderate	Fail	Poor	M	G	M
Evenlode to Thame	63,863	No	Moderate	Fail	Good	M	G	G
Wallingford to Caversham	39,401	Yes	Moderate	Fail	?	M	G	-
Reading to Cookham	38,319	Yes	Moderate	Fail	?	M	G	-
Cookham to Egham	30,056	Yes	Moderate	Fail	?	M	G	-
Egham to Teddington	31,523	Yes	Poor	Fail	?	P	G	-
Upper tidal (Teddington to Chelsea)		Yes	Moderate	Fail	Good	G	G	G
Middle tidal (Chelsea to Tilbury)		Yes	Moderate	Fail	Good	M	G	G

Fishing

The future looks very bright for Thames angling, subject to a couple of concerns which are discussed below. For those that wish to fish the river the situation is as good now as it has ever been. As already discussed, the fish community is generally in a healthy state. Access to good fishing is as easy now as it ever was. There is free fishing from the London Stone at Staines downstream, including the tidal reaches. There is also much effectively free fishing upstream of Staines, wherever the riparian owner does not choose to restrict access. Although much of the fishing is owned or leased by fishing clubs and associations, membership of most clubs is not expensive. For example, £12 annual adult membership (£7 for seniors) of the Littlemore Angling Society in Oxford gives access to the Society's own stretch of the Thames, six miles of the river controlled by the Oxford and District Angling Association (an umbrella organisation for local clubs), and, by reciprocal agreements, access to the Reading and District AA and Thames Valley AA waters on the Thames. This represents astonishing value for money; all this fishing for a season for less than the price of the cheapest ticket to watch a single Oxford United home football match.

The two concerns are the fall in numbers of anglers, which is discussed below, and the connected growth of an anti-fishing sentiment in the population as a whole. While I do not believe that the direct actions of the "antis" will have any great impact upon our sport, the increasing challenge on ethical grounds is a likely present and future factor in the fall in angler numbers. I am fearful that in a matter of a few generations angling may come to be viewed as anachronistic as bear-baiting and cock-fighting are today. But I hope I am quite wrong!

The angler

The demography of angling has changed radically in recent years. As discussed in Chapter 6, there are few reliable figures for anglers fishing the Thames *per se*, but it is likely that the picture for England and Wales as a whole is representative of trends on the Thames. The types and numbers of annual licences purchases nationally for the past ten years are shown in Table 24.2.

Table 24.2. Numbers of annual licences (coarse fish plus trout) sold for England and Wales.

Year	Junior	Adult	Senior	Total
2009/10	119,384	675,088	124,644	919,116
2010/11	110,738	644,578	128,486	883,802
2011/12	103,507	625,900	134,464	863,871
2012/13	82,978	565,813	140,164	788,955
2013/14	71,713	548,808	149,350	769,871
2014/15	61,411	532,747	157,315	751,473
2015/16	56,358	527,283	164,780	748,421
2016/17	48,302	510,901	168,515	727,718
2017/18	69,171	483,001	178,717	730,889
2018/19	48,035	499,673	178,725	693,433
Change 09-18	**-58.8%**	**-30.9%**	**+43.4%**	**-24.5%**

There has been a fall of almost 25% in the overall numbers sold over the ten year period, but this figure masks a real shift in the age composition of the angling population. The numbers of junior licences (for youngsters aged 13-16; up to the age of 12 no licence is required to fish) have fallen by more than 58%; the temporary uptick in the trend in 2017/18 coincided with removing the fee for a junior licence, although one was still required to fish. There has been a considerable upward trend in the number of senior (age 65+) licences; more than 43% over the ten years. These figures are indicative of an ageing population with a much reduced level of recruitment; a situation that would cause alarm if it were apparent in a fish population!

Presumably this decline in youngsters taking up fishing is at least partly a reflection of the burgeoning array of alternative pastimes and interests. Will the trend be halted and reversed? Only time will tell. There has been an increase in outdoor recreation including fishing in the USA in recent years[3], and the Environment Agency reported a major increase in licence sales in England coincident with the relaxation of the Covid 19 lock-down rules in the summer of 2020. Watch this space!

As discussed in Chapter 8, there has been a marked reduction in the popularity of match angling since the peak in the 1960s through 80s. However, interest now appears to have stabilised, albeit at a lower level than formerly. For example, there are several annual matches in the Oxford area that have a steady and reliable participation; one of these is the three-day Thames Festival match, which was inaugurated in 2013. Recent events have been fished between Abingdon and Appleford, and the event is usually a sell-out of the 78 available spaces. Other well-supported matches in the Oxford Area are the summer and winter league series, the Thames Championship (24 teams of six in 2019) and the Turner 400 (25 teams of four in 2019). These matches are well-organised and very popular with the participants, and their future seems assured at least in the short to medium term.

All in all, a cautious optimism about the future of Thames fisheries seems justified.

Chapter 24 footnotes

[1] Reading Chronicle, March 3 2021.
[2] Armstrong *et al* (2010).
[3] www.statista.com/statistics/190202/number-of-participants-in-outdoor-activities-in-the-US/2009

"The Complete Angler"

From The Graphic, Summer number 1882. Artist J C Dollman.

ANNEX 1

Oarsman's and Angler's Map

Ravenstein's "*Oarsman's and Angler's map of the river Thames from its source to London Bridge*" first appeared in 1861. Numerous editions and reprints followed, the one reproduced here being dated 1893. This is copied from a recent reprint and is reproduced by kind permission of Bloomsbury Publishing.

The map was originally produced as a continuous page more than 2.5 m in length. Here it is reproduced in ten sections, with a small overlap at each break.

Map from *The Oarsman's and Angler's Map of the River Thames 1893* by Ernest George Ravenstein ©1991 Old House Books, Bloomsbury Publishing Plc.

Map 1

R. Ray
153

Marston Maisey

152

151

CASTLE EATON
150

The Butts

WILTSHIRE

149   KEMPSFORD

Blackford

148

Hannington

Hannington Br.

GLOUCESTERSHIRE

FAIRFORD STA.

The Thames and Severn Canal. By means of this and the Stroudwater Canal, which joins it at Wallbridge, Stroud, the River Severn may be reached at Framilode. The distance from Inglesham Round House to Wallbridge is 28¾ miles.
Manager's office, Brimscombe Port, near Stroud.

147

Ham Barn

146

Dudgrove?

R. Coln

The Weirs and other obstructions above Lechlade having been removed, it is now possible, in fair seasons, for pleasure boats to reach Cricklade, or even beyond, with comparatively little trouble.

Lechlade Bridge 143 m. 3 f. (31 m. 3 f.)

Inns: New Inn Hotel, Red Lion, &c.

List of Tolls for pleasure boats and steam launches on the Thames and Severn Canal.

From Inglesham.

To Cricklade . . . 10s
„ Daneway basin, Sapperton; or any place on summit level 20s
„ Wallbridge . . . 30s
On *return* passage half only of the above tolls will be charged.
Canoes and Skiffs lifted at all the locks by the crew, half the above rates.

145

Upper Inglesham

R. Cole

Inglesham Round House

INGLESHAM
144

The Stroudwater Navigation is 8 miles long from its junction with the Thames and Severn Canal at Wallbridge to Framilode on the River Severn. It crosses the Glos'ter and Berkley Canal at Saul junction, one mile from Framilode, and affords by way of the Severn, direct communication with the canals of the Midlands, and the Bristol Chanel.

The charge for the passage of pleasure boats, or steam launches, is 10s; or for return within one week 15s.

For further information apply to the manager, Mr. W. J. Snape, Canal Office, near Stroud, Glo'stershire.

Hart's Weir, 140 m. 2 f. (28 m. 2 f.) Falls 1 to 3 ft. Pull out a few paddles and then the piles, or rymers that hold them. Assistance may be had from the adjoining public-house.

214

Map 2

LECHLADE
143
STA.

GLOUCESTER / OXON

St. Johns Bridge & Lock

BUSCOT
142
Buscot Lock

Lechlade Mill

Buscot Park

141

St. John's Lock, 142 m. 6 f. (30 m. 6 f.) Falls 3 ft.
Inn: The Trout.

Buscot Lock, 141 m. 5 f. (28 m. 5 f.) Falls 4 ft.

Hart's Weir
140
KELMSCOT

EATON HASTINGS
139

Grafton Common

C. W. R.

Camden Farm

138

FARINGDON
STA.
G. W. R.

OXFORD SHIRE

Radcot Bridge
Swan
137

CLANFIELD

BERKSHIRE

Thrupp

Weir
136
Site of Old Mans Weir

Barrow

Radcot Bridge, 137 m. 1 f. (25 m. 1 f.). Good accommodation at the Swan Inn, close to the bridge.

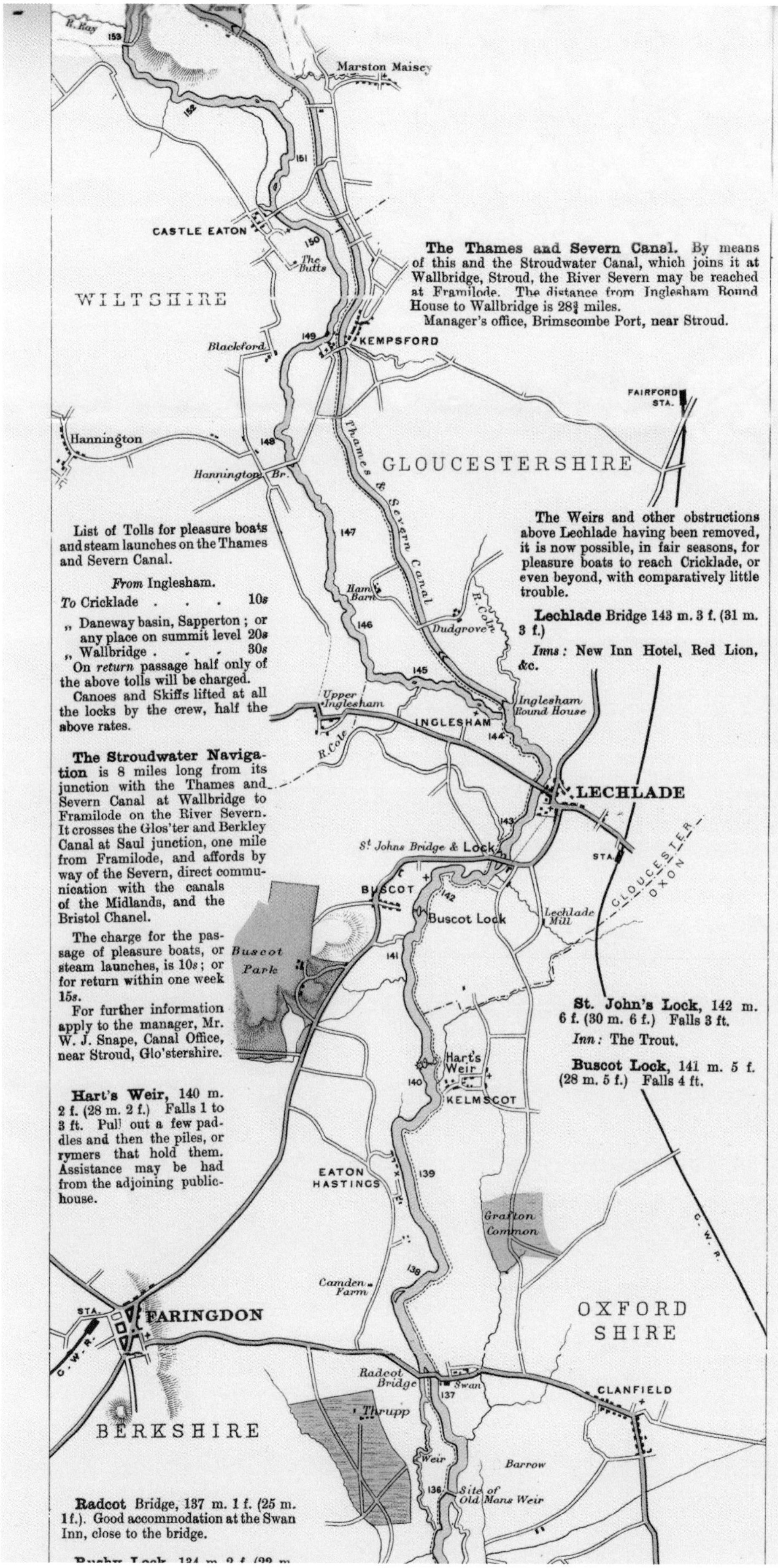

5 km or 3.1 miles

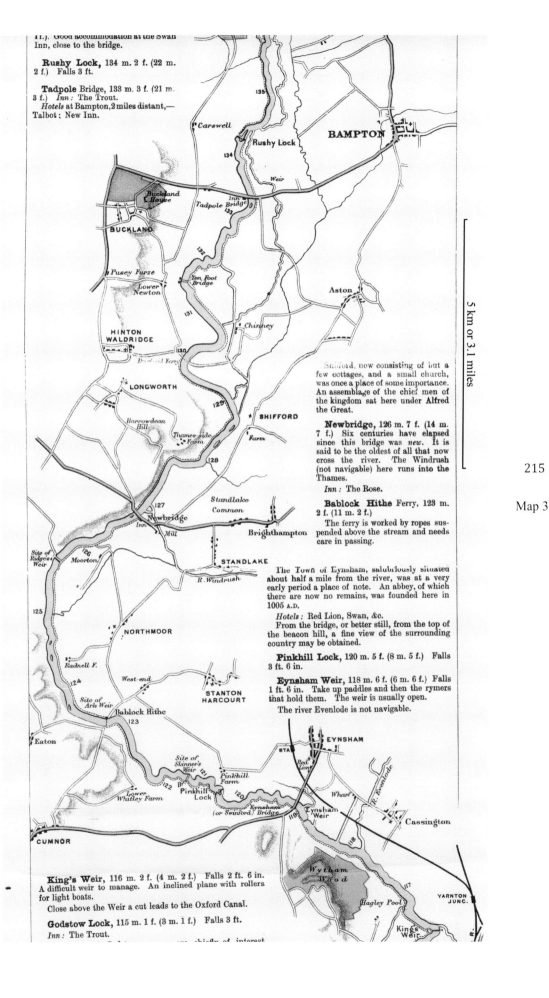

Il.). Good accommodation at the Swan
Inn, close to the bridge.

Rushy Lock, 134 m. 2 f. (22 m.
2 f.) Falls 3 ft.

Tadpole Bridge, 133 m. 3 f. (21 m.
3 f.) *Inn* : The Trout.
Hotels at Bampton, 2 miles distant,—
Talbot ; New Inn.

Shilford, now consisting of but a
few cottages, and a small church,
was once a place of some importance.
An assemblage of the chief men of
the kingdom sat here under Alfred
the Great.

Newbridge, 126 m. 7 f. (14 m.
7 f.) Six centuries have elapsed
since this bridge was *new.* It is
said to be the oldest of all that now
cross the river. The Windrush
(not navigable) here runs into the
Thames.

Inn : The Rose.

Bablock Hithe Ferry, 123 m.
2 f. (11 m. 2 f.)

The ferry is worked by ropes sus-
pended above the stream and needs
care in passing.

The Town of Eynsham, salubriously situated
about half a mile from the river, was at a very
early period a place of note. An abbey, of which
there are now no remains, was founded here in
1005 A.D.

Hotels : Red Lion, Swan, &c.

From the bridge, or better still, from the top of
the beacon hill, a fine view of the surrounding
country may be obtained.

Pinkhill Lock, 120 m. 5 f. (8 m. 5 f.) Falls
3 ft. 6 in.

Eynsham Weir 118 m. 6 f. (6 m. 6 f.) Falls
1 ft. 6 in. Take up paddles and then the rymers
that hold them. The weir is usually open.

The river Evenlode is not navigable.

King's Weir, 116 m. 2 f. (4 m. 2 f.) Falls 2 ft. 6 in.
A difficult weir to manage. An inclined plane with rollers
for light boats.

Close above the Weir a cut leads to the Oxford Canal.

Godstow Lock, 115 m. 1 f. (3 m. 1 f.) Falls 3 ft.

Inn : The Trout.

Godstow Lock, 115 m. 1 f. (3 m. 1 f.) Falls 3 ft.

Inn : The Trout.

The ruins of Godstow nunnery are chiefly of interest from their connection with the story of Fair Rosamond.

The Port Meadow, an extensive pasturage, was given to the citizens of Oxford as a free common by William the Conqueror.

Medley Weir, 113 m. 6. f. (1 m. 6 f.) Falls 1 ft. Take up paddles and then the rymers that hold them.

At a short distance above Osney Bridge a branch stream leads to the Oxford Canal, by which, for a small sum, steam launches and other craft up to 7 ft. beam, may reach the Thames again above King's Weir, avoiding the intervening difficulties of the river.

Osney Lock, 112 m. 7 f. (7 f.) Falls 4 ft. 6 in.

Folly Bridge, 112 miles from London.

Salter's and other boat-houses close to the Bridge.

The **City of Oxford,** renowned for its University, is a place of great antiquity. As a seat of learning it dates from the 9th century. The University consists of 21 colleges and 4 halls. The extensive and beautiful grounds of Christ Church College extend to the river. In front of them, from Folly Bridge to the Cherwell, are moored the College barges and numerous gaily painted boat-houses.

Hotels : Randolph, Clarendon, Roebuck, Mitre, Golden Cross, George, &c.

Inns : The Plough, &c.

The University bathing place is in the backwater, 6 f. above Iffley.

Iffley Lock, 110 m. 4 f. (1 m. 4 f.) Falls 2 ft. 6 in. Inclined plane with rollers for boats. From here to Oxford is the usual course for college matches.

Sandford Lock, 108 m. 6 f. (3 m. 2 f.) Falls 6 ft. 6 in. The pools of Sandford Lasher, in the backwater by the lock, are dangerous for bathing in, and have acquired an ill name from the many fatal accidents which have happened there.

Hotel : The King's Arms.

Abingdon Lock, 104 m. 2 f. (7 m. 6 f.) Falls 6 ft.

Abingdon Bridge, 103 m. 7 f. (8 m. 1 f.)

Hotels : Queen's, Crown and Thistle.

Inns : Anchor, Nag's Head.

Boat-yard : J. Stevens.

The Berks and Wilts Canal communicates by a branch at Swindon with the Thames and Severn Canal ; and at Semington, near Devizes, with the Kennet and Avon.

In coming down, at about 1½ miles below Abingdon, keep the towing path side ; for the cut, leading to Culham Lock, trends abruptly to the left.

216

Map 4

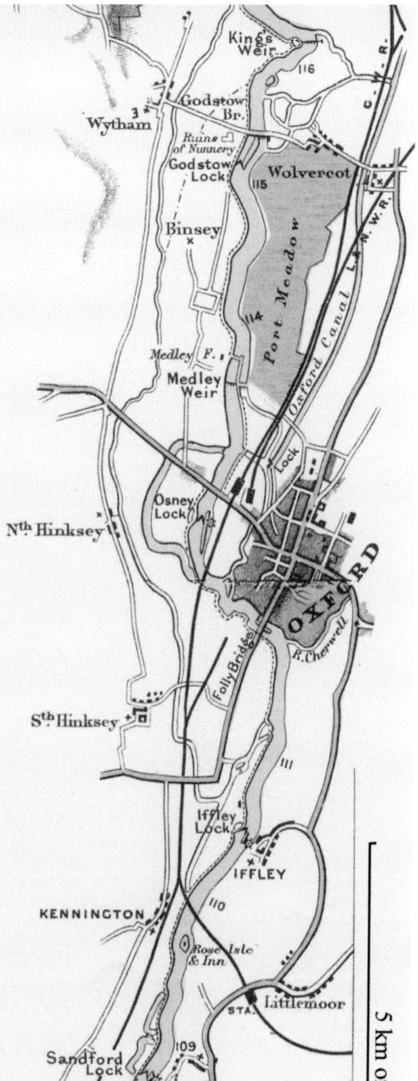

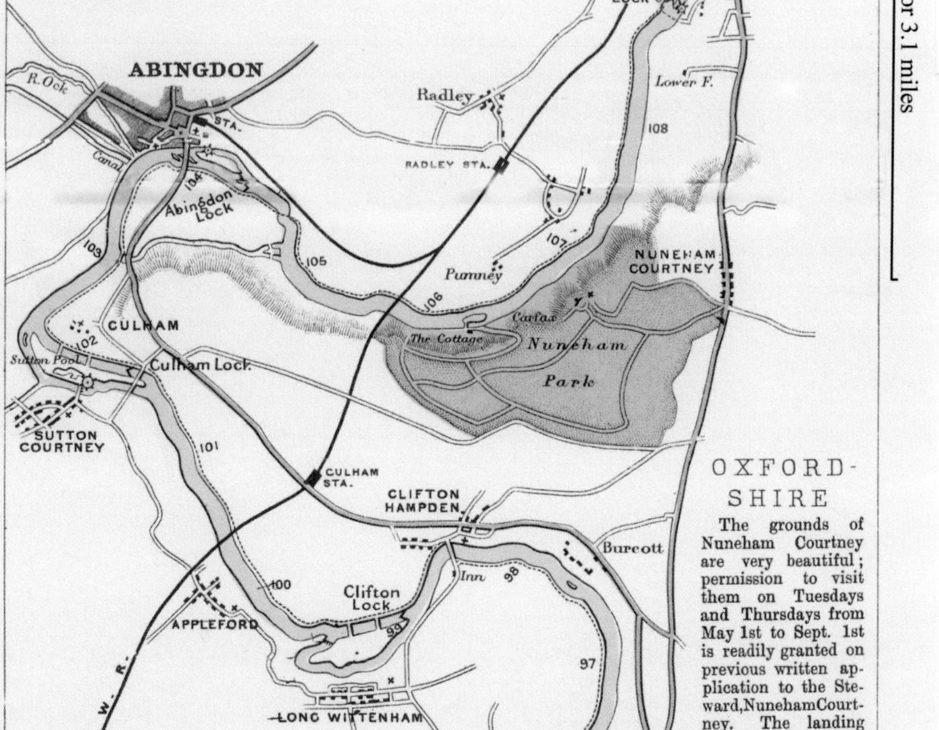

5 km or 3.1 miles

OXFORD-SHIRE

The grounds of Nuneham Courtney are very beautiful; permission to visit them on Tuesdays and Thursdays from May 1st to Sept. 1st is readily granted on previous written application to the Steward, NunehamCourtney. The landing place is by the cottage

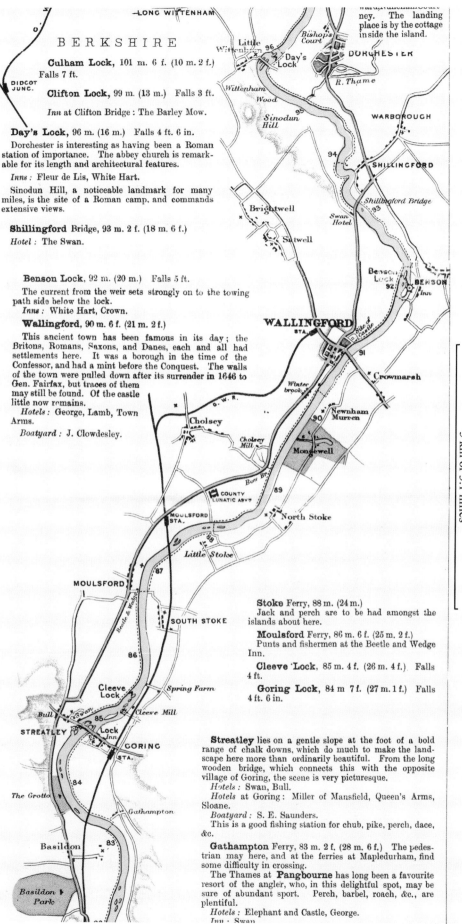

BERKSHIRE

Culham Lock, 101 m. 6 f. (10 m. 2 f.)
Falls 7 ft.

Clifton Lock, 99 m. (13 m.) Falls 3 ft.

Inn at Clifton Bridge : The Barley Mow.

Day's Lock, 96 m. (16 m.) Falls 4 ft. 6 in.

Dorchester is interesting as having been a Roman station of importance. The abbey church is remarkable for its length and architectural features.

Inns : Fleur de Lis, White Hart.

Sinodun Hill, a noticeable landmark for many miles, is the site of a Roman camp, and commands extensive views.

Shillingford Bridge, 93 m. 2 f. (18 m. 6 f.)

Hotel : The Swan.

Benson Lock, 92 m. (20 m.) Falls 5 ft.

The current from the weir sets strongly on to the towing path side below the lock.

Inns : White Hart, Crown.

Wallingford, 90 m. 6 f. (21 m. 2 f.)

This ancient town has been famous in its day ; the Britons, Romans, Saxons, and Danes, each and all had settlements here. It was a borough in the time of the Confessor, and had a mint before the Conquest. The walls of the town were pulled down after its surrender in 1646 to Gen. Fairfax, but traces of them may still be found. Of the castle little now remains.

Hotels : George, Lamb, Town Arms.

Boatyard : J. Clowdesley.

Stoke Ferry, 88 m. (24 m.)
Jack and perch are to be had amongst the islands about here.

Moulsford Ferry, 86 m. 6 f. (25 m. 2 f.)
Punts and fishermen at the Beetle and Wedge Inn.

Cleeve Lock, 85 m. 4 f. (26 m. 4 f.) Falls 4 ft.

Goring Lock, 84 m 7 f. (27 m. 1 f.) Falls 4 ft. 6 in.

Streatley lies on a gentle slope at the foot of a bold range of chalk downs, which do much to make the landscape here more than ordinarily beautiful. From the long wooden bridge, which connects this with the opposite village of Goring, the scene is very picturesque.

Hotels : Swan, Bull.

Hotels at Goring : Miller of Mansfield, Queen's Arms, Sloane.

Boatyard : S. E. Saunders.

This is a good fishing station for chub, pike, perch, dace, &c.

Gathampton Ferry, 83 m. 2 f. (28 m. 6 f.) The pedestrian may here, and at the ferries at Mapledurham, find some difficulty in crossing.

The Thames at **Pangbourne** has long been a favourite resort of the angler, who, in this delightful spot, may be sure of abundant sport. Perch, barbel, roach, &c., are plentiful.

Hotels : Elephant and Castle, George.

Inn : Swan.

5 km or 3.1 miles

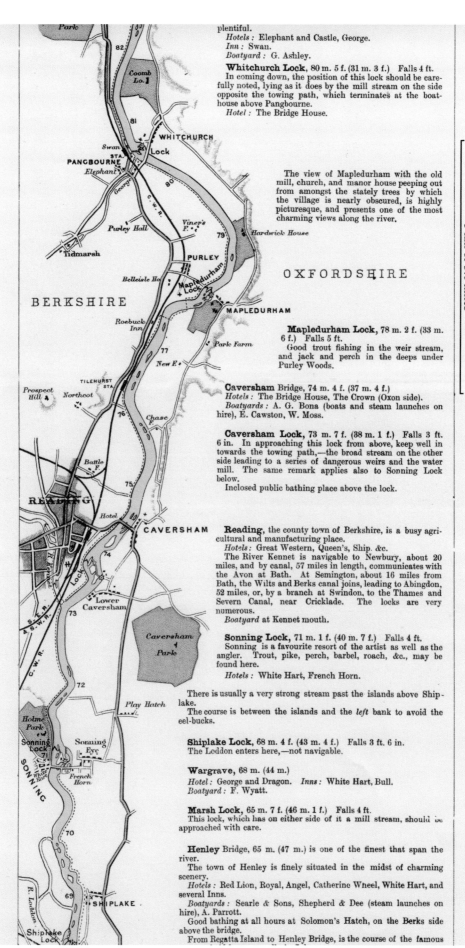

plentiful.
Hotels : Elephant and Castle, George.
Inn : Swan.
Boatyard : G. Ashley.

Whitchurch Lock, 80 m. 5 f. (31 m. 3 f.) Falls 4 ft.
In coming down, the position of this lock should be carefully noted, lying as it does by the mill stream on the side opposite the towing path, which terminates at the boathouse above Pangbourne.
Hotel : The Bridge House.

The view of Mapledurham with the old mill, church, and manor house peeping out from amongst the stately trees by which the village is nearly obscured, is highly picturesque, and presents one of the most charming views along the river.

Mapledurham Lock, 78 m. 2 f. (33 m. 6 f.) Falls 5 ft.
Good trout fishing in the weir stream, and jack and perch in the deeps under Purley Woods.

Caversham Bridge, 74 m. 4 f. (37 m. 4 f.)
Hotels : The Bridge House, The Crown (Oxon side).
Boatyards : A. G. Bona (boats and steam launches on hire), E. Cawston, W. Moss.

Caversham Lock, 73 m. 7 f. (38 m. 1 f.) Falls 3 ft. 6 in. In approaching this lock from above, keep well in towards the towing path,—the broad stream on the other side leading to a series of dangerous weirs and the water mill. The same remark applies also to Sonning Lock below.
Inclosed public bathing place above the lock.

Reading, the county town of Berkshire, is a busy agricultural and manufacturing place.
Hotels : Great Western, Queen's, Ship. &c.
The River Kennet is navigable to Newbury, about 20 miles, and by canal, 57 miles in length, communicates with the Avon at Bath. At Semington, about 16 miles from Bath, the Wilts and Berks canal joins, leading to Abingdon, 52 miles, or, by a branch at Swindon, to the Thames and Severn Canal, near Cricklade. The locks are very numerous.
Boatyard at Kennet mouth.

Sonning Lock, 71 m. 1 f. (40 m. 7 f.) Falls 4 ft.
Sonning is a favourite resort of the artist as well as the angler. Trout, pike, perch, barbel, roach, &c., may be found here.
Hotels : White Hart, French Horn.

There is usually a very strong stream past the islands above Shiplake.
The course is between the islands and the *left* bank to avoid the eel-bucks.

Shiplake Lock, 68 m. 4 f. (43 m. 4 f.) Falls 3 ft. 6 in.
The Loddon enters here,—not navigable.

Wargrave, 68 m. (44 m.)
Hotel : George and Dragon. *Inns :* White Hart, Bull.
Boatyard : F. Wyatt.

Marsh Lock, 65 m. 7 f. (46 m. 1 f.) Falls 4 ft.
This lock, which has on either side of it a mill stream, should be approached with care.

Henley Bridge, 65 m. (47 m.) is one of the finest that span the river.
The town of Henley is finely situated in the midst of charming scenery.
Hotels : Red Lion, Royal, Angel, Catherine Wheel, White Hart, and several Inns.
Boatyards : Searle & Sons, Shepherd & Dee (steam launches on hire), A. Parrott.
Good bathing at all hours at Solomon's Hatch, on the Berks side above the bridge.
From Regatta Island to Henley Bridge, is the course of the famous

218

Map 6

5 km or 3.1 miles

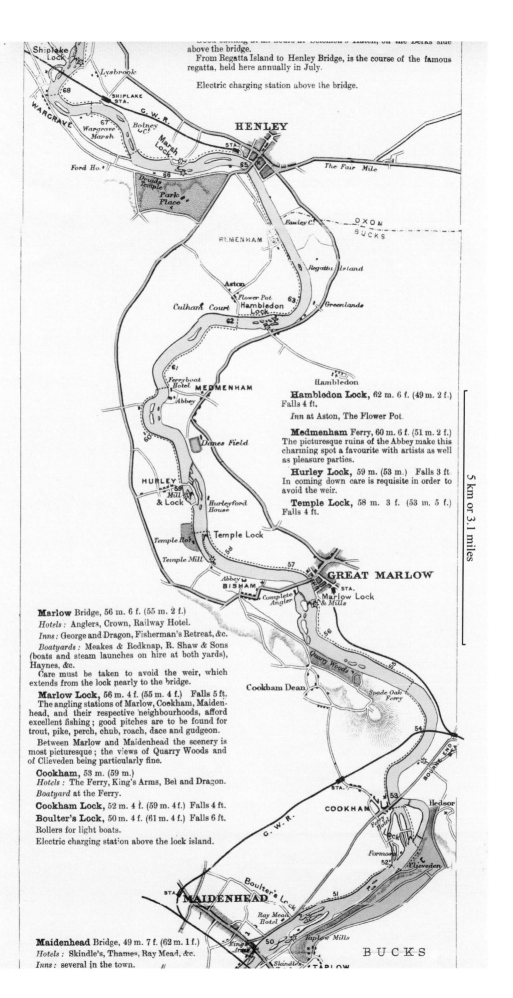

above the bridge.

From Regatta Island to Henley Bridge, is the course of the famous regatta, held here annually in July.

Electric charging station above the bridge.

Hambledon Lock, 62 m. 6 f. (49 m. 2 f.) Falls 4 ft.

Inn at Aston, The Flower Pot.

Medmenham Ferry, 60 m. 6 f. (51 m. 2 f.) The picturesque ruins of the Abbey make this charming spot a favourite with artists as well as pleasure parties.

Hurley Lock, 59 m. (53 m.) Falls 3 ft. In coming down care is requisite in order to avoid the weir.

Temple Lock, 58 m. 3 f. (53 m. 5 f.) Falls 4 ft.

Marlow Bridge, 56 m. 6 f. (55 m. 2 f.)
Hotels : Anglers, Crown, Railway Hotel.
Inns : George and Dragon, Fisherman's Retreat, &c.
Boatyards : Meakes & Redknap, R. Shaw & Sons (boats and steam launches on hire at both yards), Haynes, &c.
Care must be taken to avoid the weir, which extends from the lock nearly to the bridge.

Marlow Lock, 56 m. 4 f. (55 m. 4 f.) Falls 5 ft.
The angling stations of Marlow, Cookham, Maidenhead, and their respective neighbourhoods, afford excellent fishing ; good pitches are to be found for trout, pike, perch, chub, roach, dace and gudgeon.

Between Marlow and Maidenhead the scenery is most picturesque ; the views of Quarry Woods and of Clieveden being particularly fine.

Cookham, 53 m. (59 m.)
Hotels : The Ferry, King's Arms, Bel and Dragon.
Boatyard at the Ferry.

Cookham Lock, 52 m. 4 f. (59 m. 4 f.) Falls 4 ft.

Boulter's Lock, 50 m. 4 f. (61 m. 4 f.) Falls 6 ft.
Rollers for light boats.
Electric charging station above the lock island.

Maidenhead Bridge, 49 m. 7 f. (62 m. 1 f.)
Hotels : Skindle's, Thames, Ray Mead, &c.
Inns : several in the town.

5 km or 3.1 miles

219

Map 7

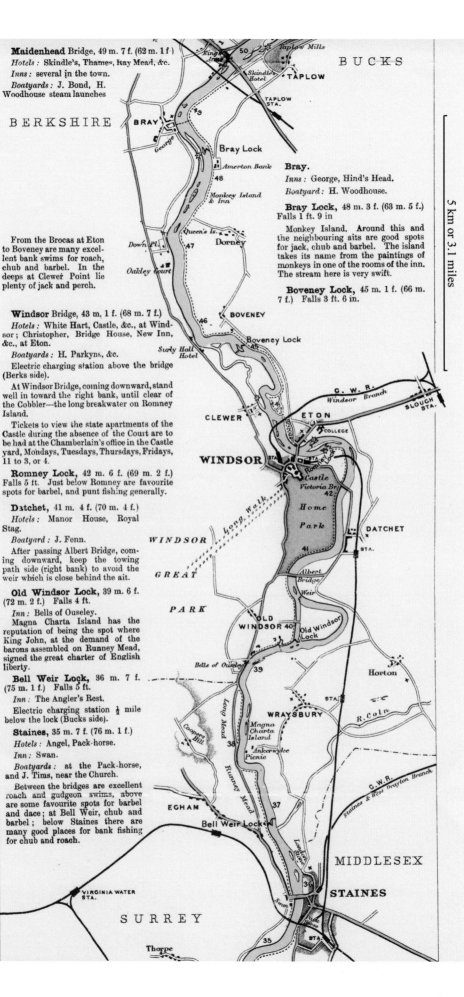

Maidenhead Bridge, 49 m. 7 f. (62 m. 1 f.)
Hotels : Skindle's, Thames, Ray Mead, &c.
Inns : several in the town.
Boatyards : J. Bond, H. Woodhouse steam launches

BERKSHIRE

From the Brocas at Eton to Boveney are many excellent bank swims for roach, chub and barbel. In the deeps at Clewer Point lie plenty of jack and perch.

Windsor Bridge, 43 m. 1 f. (68 m. 7 f.)
Hotels : White Hart, Castle, &c., at Windsor ; Christopher, Bridge House, New Inn, &c., at Eton.
Boatyards : H. Parkyns, &c.
Electric charging station above the bridge (Berks side).
At Windsor Bridge, coming downward, stand well in toward the right bank, until clear of the Cobbler—the long breakwater on Romney Island.
Tickets to view the state apartments of the Castle during the absence of the Court are to be had at the Chamberlain's office in the Castle yard, Mondays, Tuesdays, Thursdays, Fridays, 11 to 3, or 4.

Romney Lock, 42 m. 6 f. (69 m. 2 f.)
Falls 5 ft. Just below Romney are favourite spots for barbel, and punt fishing generally.

Datchet, 41 m. 4 f. (70 m. 4 f.)
Hotels : Manor House, Royal Stag.
Boatyard : J. Fenn.
After passing Albert Bridge, coming downward, keep the towing path side (right bank) to avoid the weir which is close behind the ait.

Old Windsor Lock, 39 m. 6 f. (72 m. 2 f.) Falls 4 ft.
Inn : Bells of Ouseley.
Magna Charta Island has the reputation of being the spot where King John, at the demand of the barons assembled on Runney Mead, signed the great charter of English liberty.

Bell Weir Lock, 36 m. 7 f. (75 m. 1 f.) Falls 5 ft.
Inn : The Angler's Rest.
Electric charging station ½ mile below the lock (Bucks side).

Staines, 35 m. 7 f. (76 m. 1 f.)
Hotels : Angel, Pack-horse.
Inn : Swan.
Boatyards : at the Pack-horse, and J. Tims, near the Church.
Between the bridges are excellent roach and gudgeon swims, above are some favourite spots for barbel and dace ; at Bell Weir, chub and barbel ; below Staines there are many good places for bank fishing for chub and roach.

Bray.
Inns : George, Hind's Head.
Boatyard : H. Woodhouse.

Bray Lock, 48 m. 3 f. (63 m. 5 f.)
Falls 1 ft. 9 in
Monkey Island. Around this and the neighbouring aits are good spots for jack, chub and barbel. The island takes its name from the paintings of monkeys in one of the rooms of the inn. The stream here is very swift.

Boveney Lock, 45 m. 1 f. (66 m. 7 f.) Falls 3 ft. 6 in.

220

Map 8

5 km or 3.1 miles

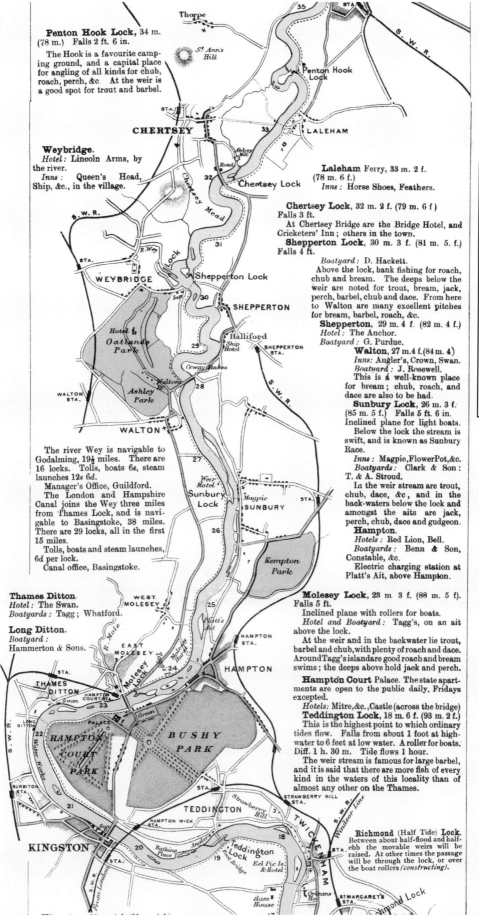

Penton Hook Lock, 34 m. (78 m.) Falls 2 ft. 6 in.

The Hook is a favourite camping ground, and a capital place for angling of all kinds for chub, roach, perch, &c. At the weir is a good spot for trout and barbel.

Weybridge.
Hotel : Lincoln Arms, by the river.
Inns : Queen's Head, Ship, &c., in the village.

The river Wey is navigable to Godalming, 19½ miles. There are 16 locks. Tolls, boats 6s, steam launches 12s 6d.
Manager's Office, Guildford.
The London and Hampshire Canal joins the Wey three miles from Thames Lock, and is navigable to Basingstoke, 38 miles. There are 29 locks, all in the first 15 miles.
Tolls, boats and steam launches, 6d per lock.
Canal office, Basingstoke.

Thames Ditton.
Hotel : The Swan.
Boatyards : Tagg; Whatford.

Long Ditton.
Boatyard :
Hammerton & Sons.

Laleham Ferry, 33 m. 2 f. (78 m. 6 f.)
Inns : Horse Shoes, Feathers.

Chertsey Lock, 32 m. 2 f. (79 m. 6 f) Falls 3 ft.
At Chertsey Bridge are the Bridge Hotel, and Cricketers' Inn ; others in the town.

Shepperton Lock, 30 m. 3 f. (81 m. 5. f.) Falls 4 ft.

Boatyard : D. Hackett.
Above the lock, bank fishing for roach, chub and bream. The deeps below the weir are noted for trout, bream, jack, perch, barbel, chub and dace. From here to Walton are many excellent pitches for bream, barbel, roach, &c.

Shepperton, 29 m. 4 f. (82 m. 4 f.)
Hotel : The Anchor.
Boatyard : G. Purdue.

Walton, 27 m.4 f.(84 m. 4)
Inns : Angler's, Crown, Swan.
Boatyard : J. Rosewell.
This is a well-known place for bream ; chub, roach, and dace are also to be had.

Sunbury Lock, 26 m. 3 f. (85 m. 5 f.) Falls 5 ft. 6 in.
Inclined plane for light boats.
Below the lock the stream is swift, and is known as Sunbury Race.
Inns : Magpie, FlowerPot, &c.
Boatyards : Clark & Son : T. & A. Stroud.
In the weir stream are trout, chub, dace, &c, and in the back-waters below the lock and amongst the aits are jack, perch, chub, dace and gudgeon.

Hampton.
Hotels : Red Lion, Bell.
Boatyards : Benn & Son, Constable, &c.
Electric charging station at Platt's Ait, above Hampton.

Molesey Lock, 23 m. 3 f. (88 m. 5 f). Falls 5 ft.
Inclined plane with rollers for boats.
Hotel and Boatyard : Tagg's, on an ait above the lock.
At the weir and in the backwater lie trout, barbel and chub, with plenty of roach and dace. Around Tagg's island are good roach and bream swims ; the deeps above hold jack and perch.

Hampton Court Palace. The state apartments are open to the public daily, Fridays excepted.
Hotels : Mitre, &c., Castle (across the bridge)

Teddington Lock, 18 m. 6 f. (93 m. 2 f.)
This is the highest point to which ordinary tides flow. Falls from about 1 foot at high-water to 6 feet at low water. A roller for boats. Diff. 1 h. 30 m. Tide flows 1 hour.
The weir stream is famous for large barbel, and it is said that there are more fish of every kind in the waters of this locality than of almost any other on the Thames.

Richmond (Half Tide) **Lock.** Between about half-flood and half-ebb the movable weirs will be raised. At other times the passage will be through the lock, or over the boat rollers *(constructing)*.

5 km or 3.1 miles

221

Map 9

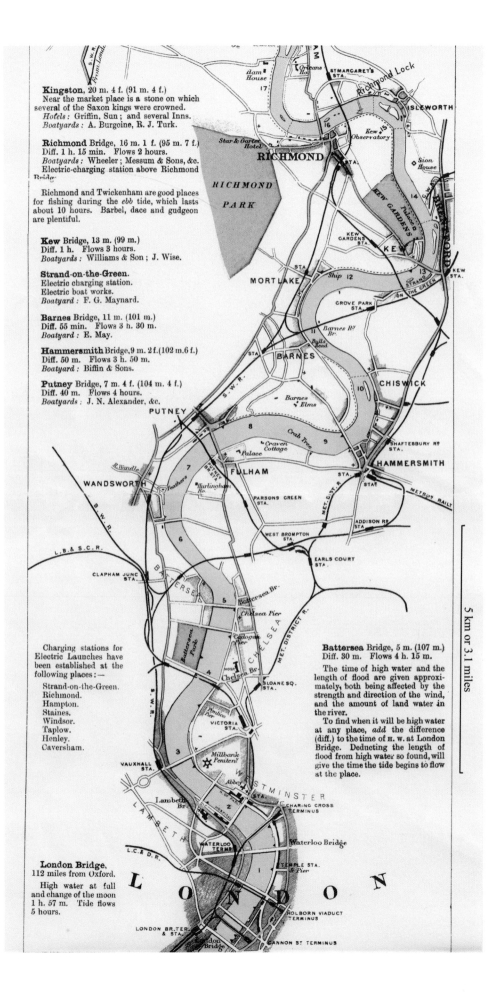

Kingston, 20 m. 4 f. (91 m. 4 f.)
Near the market place is a stone on which
several of the Saxon kings were crowned.
Hotels: Griffin, Sun; and several Inns.
Boatyards: A. Burgoine, R. J. Turk.

Richmond Bridge, 16 m. 1 f. (95 m. 7 f.)
Diff. 1 h. 15 min. Flows 2 hours.
Boatyards: Wheeler; Messum & Sons, &c.
Electric-charging station above Richmond
Bride

Richmond and Twickenham are good places
for fishing during the *ebb* tide, which lasts
about 10 hours. Barbel, dace and gudgeon
are plentiful.

Kew Bridge, 13 m. (99 m.)
Diff. 1 h. Flows 3 hours.
Boatyards: Williams & Son; J. Wise.

Strand-on-the-Green.
Electric charging station.
Electric boat works.
Boatyard: F. G. Maynard.

Barnes Bridge, 11 m. (101 m.)
Diff. 55 min. Flows 3 h. 30 m.
Boatyard: E. May.

Hammersmith Bridge, 9 m. 2 f. (102 m. 6 f.)
Diff. 50 m. Flows 3 h. 50 m.
Boatyard: Biffin & Sons.

Putney Bridge, 7 m. 4 f. (104 m. 4 f.)
Diff. 40 m. Flows 4 hours.
Boatyards: J. N. Alexander, &c.

Charging stations for
Electric Launches have
been established at the
following places:—

Strand-on-the-Green.
Richmond.
Hampton.
Staines.
Windsor.
Taplow.
Henley.
Caversham.

Battersea Bridge, 5 m. (107 m.)
Diff. 30 m. Flows 4 h. 15 m.

The time of high water and the
length of flood are given approxi-
mately, both being affected by the
strength and direction of the wind,
and the amount of land water in
the river.

To find when it will be high water
at any place, *add* the difference
(diff.) to the time of H. W. at London
Bridge. Deducting the length of
flood from high water so found, will
give the time the tide begins to flow
at the place.

London Bridge,
112 miles from Oxford.

High water at full
and change of the moon
1 h. 57 m. Tide flows
5 hours.

5 km or 3.1 miles

Amphlett's guide to fishing from Isleworth to Marlow.

In 1894 there was published a fascinating book entitled "The lower and middle Thames; where and how to fish it". It was written by F H Amphlett (perhaps better known as the author of "Everybody's book on angling") and is important as the author gave great details of individual swims and the fish to be caught in them. This allows comparisons to be drawn with present-day fishing. Because of this, the map showing the location of the swims is reproduced here, with relevant extracts from the text giving details. From here on the words in italics are Amphlett's. The numbers in brackets refer to a swim location shown on the map. Apart from the map there are no illustrations in Amphlett's work; those here interspersed with his text are gathered from elsewhere.

Kew, Richmond and Twickenham.

The fishing from Kew Bridge to Isleworth is principally confined to fly fishing for dace. Immediately above the bridge (1) there is a stretch of water that is much patronised by anglers. The fish, as a rule, are not large, but invariably reach 6 inches, under which size they are not allowed to be taken from the Thames. Another good piece of water for fly-fishing for dace is situated just opposite to Kew Gardens (2), the bottom of which is very level, the water deepening so gradually that the angler who feels inclined to wade has every facility to do so in perfect safety. Fishing should be commenced about two hours before the tide is low, and I could

Figure A2.1. Fishing at Brentford, opposite Kew Gardens, in about 19001. Close to swim 2.

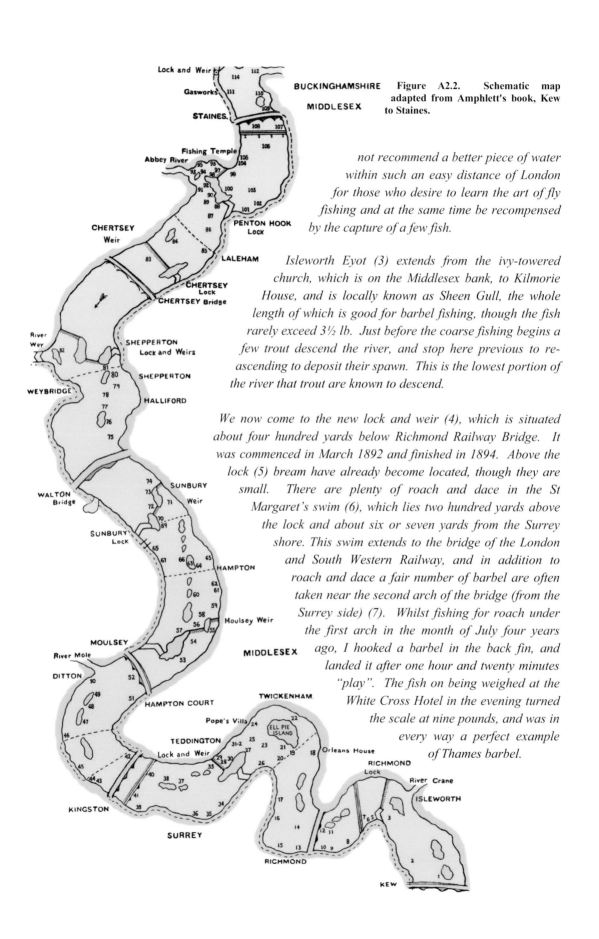

Figure A2.2. Schematic map adapted from Amphlett's book, Kew to Staines.

not recommend a better piece of water within such an easy distance of London for those who desire to learn the art of fly fishing and at the same time be recompensed by the capture of a few fish.

Isleworth Eyot (3) extends from the ivy-towered church, which is on the Middlesex bank, to Kilmorie House, and is locally known as Sheen Gull, the whole length of which is good for barbel fishing, though the fish rarely exceed 3½ lb. Just before the coarse fishing begins a few trout descend the river, and stop here previous to re-ascending to deposit their spawn. This is the lowest portion of the river that trout are known to descend.

We now come to the new lock and weir (4), which is situated about four hundred yards below Richmond Railway Bridge. It was commenced in March 1892 and finished in 1894. Above the lock (5) bream have already become located, though they are small. There are plenty of roach and dace in the St Margaret's swim (6), which lies two hundred yards above the lock and about six or seven yards from the Surrey shore. This swim extends to the bridge of the London and South Western Railway, and in addition to roach and dace a fair number of barbel are often taken near the second arch of the bridge (from the Surrey side) (7). Whilst fishing for roach under the first arch in the month of July four years ago, I hooked a barbel in the back fin, and landed it after one hour and twenty minutes "play". The fish on being weighed at the White Cross Hotel in the evening turned the scale at nine pounds, and was in every way a perfect example of Thames barbel.

Figure A2.3. Isleworth at about the time of Amphlett's work, looking downstream [2]. The "ivy-covered church" can be seen in the centre. The land on the left is Isleworth Eyot.

ISLEWORTH ON THAMES.

Cholmondley Walk (8) is a favourite rendezvous for bank anglers, roach, dace and barbel being the only kind of fish taken, with perhaps an exception in the case of an occasional eel. A little further on is another drain (9), which empties itself into the Thames. This is the best swim along Cholmondley Walk. The professional fishermen are generally to be found along here (10). Their charge is 10s per day for services, and the use of punt, rods, tackle and bait. Two or three anglers may avail themselves of these advantages, but two anglers and the puntsman are usually considered a fair cargo. Towards the opposite shore are two eyots, and near the bridge is an island, the upper end of the latter (11) being good for roach, dace and barbel, whilst on the shallows (12) there used to be capital fly fishing for dace at low tide.

Very fair bank fishing is to be obtained at Richmond Deeps (13), and a famous barbel haunt is close by, and locally known as the Duke of Buccleugh's Hole (14). Many large barbel have been taken here on ledger tackle. A punt or boat is of much service to the angler fishing this swim, but it is possible to throw a ledger line from either bank, though there is much disadvantage in doing this on account of the number of boats which, in the spring, summer and autumn, pass up and down this part of the river. After passing Messum's boathouse there is an excellent roach swim (15), and then we arrive at Glover's Island, off the upper end of which the fishing for barbel, roach and dace fairly good. Petersham Meadows are on the Surrey side, and at certain times of year roach fishing is good near the bank (16 and 17). Orleans House, formerly the residence of the Orleans family during the Second Empire, is a prominent object from the river, opposite to which (18) there are good barbel, roach and dace swims, and sometimes jack are caught there, one of the latter last year being taken with a gentle; it weighed 6 lb.

Figure A2.4. Fishing below Richmond Bridge about 1780[3]. Swims 11 and 12.

Figure A2.5. Punt fishing at Twickenham, about 1900[4]. Looking upstream, Eel Pie Island on right. About swim 19.

We now arrive at Twickenham, the fishing at which is very good, although it has seen better days. It is the largest fishing station on the Thames, there being between thirty and forty fishing punts available for hire, and a large number of professional fishermen to attend the wants of anglers. Twickenham Ferry, famous in the song, is just below Eel Pie Island, and is two and a half miles above Richmond. The first swim met with is just below the island (19); roach and dace are principally taken there; and (20 and 21) are good for dace, the stream being rapid as a rule. On the opposite side of the island, in front of the Swan Hotel (22), there is a well-known barbel swim, and another lies at the head of the island (23), about six or seven yards off the steps on the Surrey bank. From here to Pope's Villa is the chief stretch of water for angling purposes at Twickenham, the portion in front of the villa being the best (24). There is a large bream hole there reputed to be full of large fish. Several members of London angling clubs (there are over 200 clubs in the metropolis) make this a special hunting ground, and it is not unusual to see ten or fifteen punts, each supplied with two anglers, moored between (23) and (24).

Stoney Deeps (25) used to be a favourite place for roach anglers, but it has deteriorated to a large extent. Button's Hole (26) is a gravel pit much frequented by bank anglers, who often obtain a fair amount of sport amongst the roach, and a ledger line for barbel fishing will be found useful. Strawberry Deeps (27) are not so productive of sport as they used to be, though a few small chub may be taken from under the willow trees by whipping with gentles. From Button's Hole to the lock is termed Teddington Reach, and on the shallows on the Middlesex side throughout the whole length of the reach capital dace fishing with the fly may be obtained when the tide is low.

Figure A2.6. Around swims 23 and 24, postcard postmarked 1905.

Teddington to Kingston.

There is good fishing to be had in the weir pool (28), the bottom of which is very foul, with bags of solid cement and concrete blocks. Jack are caught in the dead water (29), and chub are occasionally taken at this spot. At low water the angler can get very close to the weir itself, and can wade the shallows below (30), and obtain good fly fishing for dace. Barbel are sometimes taken as heavy as 9 lb or 10 lb at (31) and (32), but the average weight taken from this water is 4 lb to 6 lb, and the same may be said regarding the weight of jack. There is also at times a plentiful supply of gudgeons, the favourite sportive fish of lady anglers. During the spring, lamprey and lamperns are sometimes caught.

Above the lock there is an excellent stretch of water, extending from the weir-head to Kingston, which is good for jack fishing. A very favourite abode for Esox lucius is just above the weir-head (33). About 100 yards on the other side of the "Danger" board (34) there is a bream and chub swim, but it ought only to be fished at the fall of the leaf, when the fish appear to cross from the other side of the river, in search of food. What is locally known as the "Half mile tree" is a little further on (35), and is a well known spot for barbel and bream. Opposite to the Albany Club (36) there is a barbel swim, from which some fairly large fish have been taken. Tateham's Island is a little higher up stream, and (37 and 38) can be tried for jack. After passing the Island on the Surrey side, is "Kingston Bend" (39), so named on account of the bend in the river. Here is a favourite roach swim, which is suitable for bank anglers, no fewer than 150 of whom were one day recently counted along the bank. Kingston foot bridge is a point at which many people indulge in jack, perch and barbel fishing. There is a good barbel swim just below the bridge, on the Middlesex side (40), and jack and perch are on the Surrey side (41), as a rule. After passing through the bridge, the towing path is on the Middlesex shore, and there is a good roach swim at (42). The Kingston professional fishermen are located on the Surrey side. They are generally to be found close to the steps near the baths at the end of the town, near what is locally known as Town End Hole (43), which holds a good supply of bream. This "pitch" is immediately in front of the fishing tackle shop belonging to Mr Richardson, who has taken a large number of fish from this spot, and has also preserved several fine specimens for other anglers. In addition to bream there are some good barbel holes in this district; and, in addition, there are some roach swims which have yielded good sport, one of the latter being just opposite to the Catholic Church (44). But this is a difficult swim to fish, unless the punt is moored in the exact spot where it should be. A writer in the "Fishing Gazette" (Nov 18 1893), referring to this swim says: "My recollection is that

here were two elm trees with a seat between, and that to be successful one must fish about a length and a half from the promenade, and exactly at right angles to the trees.

Surbiton to Long Ditton

(At Surbiton) there are some good swims, which afford excellent sport, especially amongst roach, dace, and barbel. The most well-known is located near the old sewer (45), which at one time emptied itself into the Thames, the drain pipe passing under the parade. A large number of fish congregate there in search of food. In addition to splendid examples of Thames roach, bream of 3 lb have often been taken there, and a little while ago a rarity in the shape of a carp weighing 9 lb. Opposite the first grating (46) in the wall of the (Surbiton Waterworks), is one of the best bream holes between Surbiton and Ditton. Some specimen fish have been taken here during the past few years, many of which have been preserved, and grace the walls of angling clubs. From here to Ditton there is very fair jack and perch fishing along the side of the wall of the water-works; but a boat or punt is necessary to fish this water. Long Ditton.....there are two eyots here, and on the Ditton side of the first one is a barbel hole, from which as many as thirty-four of these fish have been taken in one day. This is, of course, rather unusual, but it signifies that there is a fair supply of these fish there, and with the judicious use of ground bait no one should find much difficulty in having a fair day's sport. On the channel side of the first eyot (47) there is a barbel swim, and on the channel side of the second eyot (48) there is dace and roach fishing; whilst from under the boughs of two or three willow trees (49), chub are sometimes to be taken.

The river Mole joins the Thames on the Surrey side, and just below the mouth of the former there is another capital roach swim (50).

Hampton Court to Sunbury

A stone pavement has been laid in front of (Hampton Court) Palace, from which anglers are allowed to ply the rod (51). The water is very deep, and holds trout, barbel, roach and jack. Sometimes a few perch are taken here. The swim is well known , and has been much patronised in consequence of its suitability for bank fishing. The fish here average a good

228

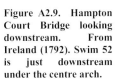

Figure A2.9. Hampton Court Bridge looking downstream. From Ireland (1792). Swim 52 is just downstream under the centre arch.

size, with perhaps the exception of the roach, which have seldom of late been taken here heavier than three-quarters of a pound. We now pass on to Hampton Court Bridge. There is a good roach and dace swim about thirty yards below the bridge (52), and occasionally barbel are taken there. It is quite a favourite spot of the local professional fishermen, who are located on the Surrey shore, and are consequently within two minutes walk of Hampton Court railway station. There are several swims near at hand, so that the fishermen are most conveniently situated. After passing through the bridge the towing path is on the surrey side. There is here a good stretch of water extending to Molesey lock and weir. The weir water (53 and 54) affords the best barbel fishing in the district, the fish often being of large size.

Figure A2.10. Fishing from the structure of Molesey Weir. Swim 54. From Leyland (1897).

Jack, too, are caught there; though they are as a rule under 6 lb. Trout are also taken from the weir pool, and one may not be far wrong in stating that this is the lowest portion of the river where any pretence is usually made to capture trout. The back water at Molesey Weir (55) holds some jack, though it is of little use going as far as the shallow water, which is close to the overfall. Above the weir, too, jack fishing is fairly good. Chub and barbel may be taken at (56), trout and chub occasionally at (57). Roach are taken by bank anglers who fish from Tagg's Island, but the quality if fishing in this district has deteriorated during the past two or three years. There are, however, several swims which can be easily fished from the island, one of the best being at the upper end. Angler's Eyot is on the Middlesex side (58), and a few jack and chub are sometimes taken

Figure A2.11. Upstream end of Hampton Deeps, opposite Garrick's Villa, looking upstream[7]. The chap nearest the camera appears to have just caught an eel. About 1905, swim 61.

there. The "Queen's River", which passes through Bushey Park, empties itself into the Thames at (59), through what is locally known as the Roaring Arch, and in the summer months roach are caught just below this point. The "Swan's Nest" Island is above Tagg's Island, and the water in this vicinity (60) holds jack, one over 20 lb being taken there some years ago. These specimen fish are, however, a rarity in any part of the Thames. A favourite roach swim is opposite Garrick's Villa (61), and bream may sometimes be taken here. The angler will see that from a pipe fixed in the wall some spring water falls into the Thames. He should fix his boat or punt just opposite. Hampton Deeps, which holds jack, roach and bream, extend from Molesey Weir to Garrick Villa, a distance of 1500 yards; and there is an eddy under the willow tree at the end of "Garricks" lawn from which a jack or two may sometimes be taken. Around Plat's Island (63) there are plenty of withies and other shrubbery, from under the boughs of which a few chub have often been enticed. But the best fishing is on the inner side. At (64) there is a quiet eddy, nicely sheltered by shrubs, and this is one of the best places hereabouts for jack fishing; sometimes, too, perch are taken. If "live-baiting" from a boat, anchor just on the outer edge of the eddy, let the float descend with the stream; and after allowing the bait the usual distance to travel, hold the line taut, the float will then work the eddy in the most natural way. Close to the shore the water runs shallow, so it is preferable that the bait shall work up the centre of the eddy. Hampton Waterworks are on the opposite shore, and hot water (waste from the steam engines on the works) falls into the river at (65). Here there is a roach swim, but it is seldom of much use fishing it in the winter months. There are more quiet nooks which will be noticed near Plat's Island as one proceeds up river. These often prove to be the home of small jack, whilst on the other side, in the main stream, there is a barbel hole at (66). The Cherry Orchard swim (67) is situated on the Surrey side, though the roach swim is on a parallel with some bushes at the upper end of the orchard. This, too, is a summer swim, the stream usually being too strong in the winter months. From here to Lambeth waterworks, on the west Molesey side of the river, a few jack can sometimes be caught in the deep water. The Grand Junction Waterworks, which have only recently been built, are opposite, and water from the lake at Kempton Park falls into the river on this bank. There is a roach swim near this inflow. We will now proceed some little distance upstream, past the Grand Junction's intake, and arrive at Clark's Eyot. There are some barbel swims, and jack are occasionally to be met with off the tail end of the lower islands. We are now entering the Sunbury District, and the scenery begins to improve. The main stream is swift, and is known as "The Race". The fishing also improves here, and trout become more abundant. There are two good roach swims off Chelsea Waterworks (68) and barbel are fairly plentiful in most portions of "The Race". There are also some good swims suitable for bank anglers between the waterworks and the lock. Sunbury backwater is somewhat

230

shallow, though there are some deep holes in various places, and roach are sometimes taken there. In the summer time, however, it is very weedy, and the water is much disturbed by boating parties; the tall trees on the islands afford excellent shelter from the sun's rays. After passing the end of Darbey House Island, we again join the main stream, and are close upon a good roach and barbel swim which is opposite to the Magpie Hotel. This is one of the best swims in Sunbury, if we exempt the weir stream. The water from the lock gates to the weir pool is good for fly fishing for dace, and there are several good "pitches" for bank anglers at (69) and (70). The weir pool itself holds trout, barbel, chub, roach, and jack. On the Surrey side the professional fishermen are located. Very often the punt fishing is most successful near the wall on the Surrey side, where the weir stream is rather rapid. There are some good roach and barbel swims there (71). The backwater on the right of the weir is too shallow for fishing, and is somewhat dangerous for boats to negotiate. Above Sunbury Lock there is a small foot-bridge extending from the island to the towing shore, but the next roach swim of importance is locally known as "Black Bough" (72). It is close to a long island on which the Thames camping Club holds sway. In mid-stream too, there is a barbel hole. Bream and barbel are present at (73), and near the tumbling \bay and overfall (74) there are roach and bream. The scenery along this reach is pretty, although the banks continue low. There are no further swims of importance until Walton is reached.

Walton, Shepperton, Chertsey and Laleham.

There is a fair supply of all kinds of Thames fish in the Walton district. A small piece of water on the Surrey side, known as Walton Sale, holds jack, carp, tench and bream. In the summer there are so many weeds to obstruct angling operations that the fish are hard to capture. Winter fishing for jack is often productive of good sport, and there are one or two large fish in this water that have on several occasions baffled all the efforts of the angler to land, though they have been hooked. In the spawning season a large quantity of bream enter the Sale to deposit their ova, and it is a pretty sight to watch hundreds of these fish priming. In the vicinity of the bridge jack and perch are occasionally taken. Cowey Stakes, immediately above the bridge, is noted for roach. Cowey Deeps (75) extend from the two oak trees on the Middlesex bank to the west London Waterworks. They are fairly well stocked with barbel and roach, whilst on the opposite bank there are boughs which shelter chub. A little higher upstream there is a small eyot (76), on the inside of which jack should be tried for. Only a few years ago one of 20 lb was taken here. Halliford \Reach (77) holds barbel, the water in places being 25 ft deep. The village of Halliford is on the Middlesex shore, and there is a roach swim immediately opposite River View House, which can be particularised by the front being covered in ivy. Heart's-ache Deep is above Halliford. The river from here to Shepperton Lock is renowned for the quality of its barbel fishing, though one would be inclined to think that the name Heart's-ache was derived from the inferiority of the sport. The Surrey bank is again studded with withies, which should be fished in the hope of obtaining a few chub. The lawn of the Manor House then is reached, opposite to the end of which is an excellent roach swim (78). The water a little higher up stream is deep and fairly rapid, and barbel may be taken there as well as off Shepperton Point. There is a backwater by the boathouse, called Shepperton Creek, and roach are sometimes taken here in the summer months. Shepperton Reach is just above what is locally termed "the old stop tree", where there used to be an osier bed. It is the only tree *here on the Middlesex side. There is good all-round coarse fishing here, and occasionally good trout are taken.*

We now come to the "Chalk Hole" (79), which is a noted spot for bream and barbel fishing. A large number of fish have been taken here during late years, and it is consequently much patronised by the professional fishermen of the surrounding districts. The summer is the best time to fish here, and so as to localise the identical swim, I may mention it is just above two willow trees, which slightly project over the river from the Middlesex bank. This is not far from the tail of Doyle Carte's Island. The inner side of the latter (80) is the haunt of jack and chub, and extends from "Chalk Hole" past Gitten's Lawn, to Shepperton Ferry. Between the lock and the new weir (81) there is a good roach swim, but it is generally difficult to fix a punt there, unless thoroughly used to the ryepecks, in consequence of the rapid stream. It is sometimes called the "City Yard" swim, and in addition to roach, plenty of barbel are caught there. Below the new weir is capital water for trout fishing, and from here we pass on to the old weir. The most noted part of this backwater is Haliday's Hole (82), which is celebrated for its barbel and bream, and is near the old mill, opposite the bathing hut. The River Wey enters the Thames here. Close to the old weir there are several deep swims, which hold barbel and trout. It is advisable to fish near either shore, rather than the centre of the stream. Above the top of the weir there are some guard piles, near to which jack are now and then caught; and from here we enter the lower part of the Chertsey water.

Docket Eyot is first met, and then Docket Point and reach. Sir Charles Dilke's Eyot is higher up stream and then we enter a more important portion of the water – Chertsey Mead, and Doomsday or Dumsey Deeps. This water is fairly good for all-round fishing, though the swims here are scarcely of sufficient importance to particularise. There is, however, very good bank fishing near Chertsey Bridge and below the weir. The Weir Pool (83), at the upper end of which the Abbey Mill River joins the Thames, holds trout and barbel; whilst chub may be taken here and there under the boughs. The water above the lock to Laleham is chiefly noted for jack fishing, and there are plenty of large barbel in the deeps at (84);

Figure A2.12. Fishing below Chertsey Bridge. From Ireland (1792).

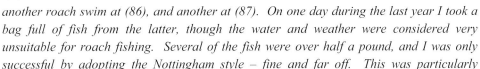

Figure A2.13. Trout fishing at Chertsey Weir[8]. Fishing swim 83 from an unusual vantage point!

roach may also be taken in fair quantities. At Laleham... the principal roach swim is just below the ferry (85), and the punt should be moored on the Middlesex side. This is a quiet swim, and the bed of the river is level. There is another roach swim at (86), and another at (87). On one day during the last year I took a bag full of fish from the latter, though the water and weather were considered very unsuitable for roach fishing. Several of the fish were over half a pound, and I was only successful by adopting the Nottingham style – fine and far off. This was particularly necessary owing to the water being exceptionally clear. Bank anglers are also able to obtain fair sport just here, there being plenty of available places to fish, such as eddies and lay-byes.

Figure A2.14. A family fishing party at Laleham about 1907[9]. Looking upstream towards Penton Hook. Swim 86

Penton Hook and Staines.

(At Penton Hook) bank anglers have every opportunity of fishing all around the Island, which may easily be reached by walking across the footway on the lock gates. There are, however, many portions of this water which can be fished only by using a punt or a boat, and if any craft be used it is better to enter the Hook at the upper end, as the stream is usually very rapid, and difficult to row against. Just off the lower end of the lock (88) there is a very quiet roach swim, though the fish feed here much better after the lock gates have been opened for navigation purposes, because this causes a slight flush of water. One of the best barbel holes in the district is situated between the old Tumbling Bay and the lock (89). Some very fine fish have of late been taken there, and a visit to this swim would undoubtedly repay any angler who used his ledger with ability, although he must be careful to fish "well out". Immediately opposite the Tumbling Bay itself is a bream hole (90), which usually holds a plentiful supply of fish, it being no unusual thing to see a quantity of

them "priming" early on almost any spring or summer morning. A little higher up are what are locally known as the Rocks. On the Surrey side, just below these rocks (91), there is some very deep water, which has yielded good sport to the barbel fisher, and after passing over the rocks there is some more deep water (92) on the Middlesex side, which is most accessible to bank anglers. Chub, roach, dace, and barbel are taken from this swim. There is a stretch of shallow water suitable for fly fishing from here to the Abbey River.

At the mouth of the Abbey River there are some overhanging bushes and tall willow trees. On one of the latter there is a placard, which sets forth that "new and original" notice, "Trespassers beware", presumably as a warning to those who would be so rude as to venture to step on to the land. But the water, just at this very spot (93), contains many trespassers in the shape of portly chub, some of which would obtain a "specimen" if only induced to taste a tempting bait. At (94) there is a noted barbel swim, the water being swift and deep. A roach swim, which is a favourite one with Spicer, a Staines professional fisherman, during the winter months, is on the Surrey side, just above the mouth of the Abbey River (95). At (96) there is a quiet eddy which holds jack. It is sheltered by a large bed of rushes, which divides the stream, and forms, as it were, a quiet backwater just below the tails of these reeds. A very noted barbel swim, is just below the old weir (97). The water is very deep, but the professional fishermen are adepts at mooring a punt in the centre of the swift stream, which is by no means an easy feat. There is a quiet and deep eddy near an old fallen tree at (98), which is much fished by bank anglers, who can throw a ledger line into the barbel swim above referred to, and at the same time enjoy good roach fishing. Trout are also caught in this locality, and on the shallows above the weir on the Surrey side of the river (99) every opportunity is afforded for fly fishing for dace. Barbel, bream, and a few perch are sometimes taken by bank anglers at (100), this being very deep water. We have now passed completely round the hook, and again enter the navigable portion of the Thames, though above the lock.

On the Middlesex side of the river there are roach swims at (101) and (102) well adapted for bank anglers, one being able to obtain a seat on the bank, which is high and rugged. Further towards the centre of the stream (103) barbel make their home, whilst chub lie cosy enough at times under the boughs of the trees which line the Surrey side at this point (104). Near what is known as the "Fishing Temple", a small brick building with a square tower (105), there is a quiet piece of water which holds a few small jack. Near Whitehead's coal-shed there is a reputable roach swim, and off Tress's Island there is another. From here to Staines the bank on the Surrey side is thickly studded with large willow trees and withies, from under which chub can be enticed by whipping with gentles or using a large red and black Palmer. The latter may also be occasionally tipped with a live gentle, and chub will, if feeding, take this bait well. There is some deep water at (106) which holds barbell the swim being opposite the new church. We have now arrived at Staines proper, this portion of the river being about ten minutes walk from either the South-Western or Great Western Railway Stations. After passing under the iron bridge, which here spans the river, there is a very fair stretch of water suitable for Jack fishing at (107). It extends from the bridge to the town Hall, and is on the Middlesex side. Between here and the county Bridge there are several roach swims(108) which have often yielded good sport in days gone by. (Above the County Bridge) there is a barbel swim near the second arch, and Church Eyot is a little

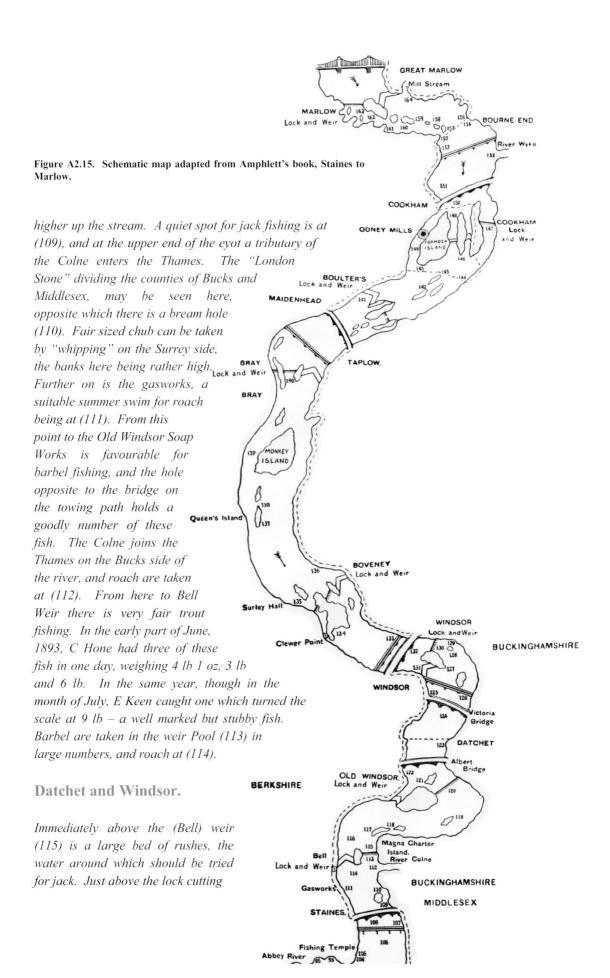

Figure A2.15. Schematic map adapted from Amphlett's book, Staines to Marlow.

higher up the stream. A quiet spot for jack fishing is at (109), and at the upper end of the eyot a tributary of the Colne enters the Thames. The "London Stone" dividing the counties of Bucks and Middlesex, may be seen here, opposite which there is a bream hole (110). Fair sized chub can be taken by "whipping" on the Surrey side, the banks here being rather high. Further on is the gasworks, a suitable summer swim for roach being at (111). From this point to the Old Windsor Soap Works is favourable for barbel fishing, and the hole opposite to the bridge on the towing path holds a goodly number of these fish. The Colne joins the Thames on the Bucks side of the river, and roach are taken at (112). From here to Bell Weir there is very fair trout fishing. In the early part of June, 1893, C Hone had three of these fish in one day, weighing 4 lb 1 oz, 3 lb and 6 lb. In the same year, though in the month of July, E Keen caught one which turned the scale at 9 lb – a well marked but stubby fish. Barbel are taken in the weir Pool (113) in large numbers, and roach at (114).

Datchet and Windsor.

Immediately above the (Bell) weir (115) is a large bed of rushes, the water around which should be tried for jack. Just above the lock cutting

Figure A2.16. Staines Bridge around 1792, looking upstream. The bridge visible through the arches is an old wooden bridge which the nearer one replaced, not the railway bridge shown on Amphlett's map; this was not to be built for many years. The angler in the boat is fishing swim 108. From Ireland 1792.

Figure A2.17. Two boys fishing at Egham, opposite Ankerwyke.[10]

there is a roach swim, and a little further on is Chalk Hole (116), famed for its barbel. This hole is wide and commences at the varnish works on the Surrey side; the local fishermen will tell you that "some rattling good fish" have been caught here, and that the hole contains plenty now. There are plenty of boughs on the Bucks side, which shelter chub; they extend from the weir head to the Ankerwyke estate, at the lower end of which is a slight bend in the river , which causes a quiet eddy. The latter should be tried for jack, and a trifle further on will be noticed some water which enters the Thames from the Ankerwyke estate, this is a very good roach swim in the winter time. One particular tree on the Bucks shore overhangs the river to a greater extent than the others. Some large chub make their home under its boughs, but they are practically safe from the wiles of the angler, because the bottom is foul with submerged brambles. A keeper's lodge will be noted on the Ankerwyke estate, and a little higher up there is a roach swim. Very good bank fishing is to be had from the towing path, and just off the Windsor road there is a jack flat. The withies below the cottage on Magna Carta Island are good for chub (117), the backwater of the island holds a few fish. On the channel side (of the next island up) (118) there are some rush beds from which jack can be taken. The Bucks shore is now again lined with withies, which hold chub, and the upper end of the island, opposite to the "Bells of Ouseley", should also be tried for jack. There is very good bank fishing from here to Old Windsor. Some steps will be noticed, and the ledger should be thrown out here for barbel. Above Mr Ricardo's house there are some more steps, opposite to which will be found an excellent barbel swim. A little above are two drains, which come from Beaumont College. Roach sometimes congregate here in large quantities. (Old Windsor) lock cutting is very good for roach fishing from both banks. The river makes a lengthened detour before the weir is reached, but as this backwater is well stocked with fish a few details concerning it will be useful. When there is a heavy flush of water, the tumbling bay near to the lock is a harbour for roach. On the island are the Royal Tapestry Works, and there is an inlet of water near here which forms an eddy. Bank anglers are able to fish it, and good roach have been taken here. We now come to an island on which there are three clumps of trees. Immediately above is what is locally known as the Old Ruin (119). This swim is noted for barbel, and is always visited by the professional fishermen on August Bank Holiday. They are thus out of the way of the general traffic, and Spicer tells me that many tons of fish have been taken there. It is, in fact, one of the best barbel swims in the district. A boat or punt must be used to fish it, and it may be as well to state that here the stream is very swift indeed. Barbel are also taken at the culvert opposite to the fever hospital. Above it will be noticed that the bank is lines with rush beds and further on is a square inlet; both of these places hold jack. In fact, a good number of these fish are taken along here, and many heavy chub have also fallen victims to either cheese paste or pith and brains. Except where the rush beds are, withies and bushes line both banks, and, as the water is not much disturbed, chub are usually "at home" under the boughs.

Figure A2.18. Fishing at Datchet Bridge about 1790. The bridge was demolished about 1848 when the Victoria and Albert Bridges were commissioned. This view is looking upstream from the location of Datchet waterside. From Ireland (1792).

The weir water (120) holds a large number of trout, chub and barbel. Above the weir there are jack and roach. The latter in winter time can be taken just off the tail of the island above (121). The backwater is not of much account, though occasionally jack and chub are caught there. From here to the Albert Bridge barbel may be taken, but the best spot is just above the bridge. Bank anglers do very well from the towing path at (122). Datchet Reach, which commences just above the bridge, and extends to Datchet, is chiefly noted for roach and barbel. The meadows on the Bucks side are good for winter roach fishing if permission can be obtained from Mrs Fowler. The "Image" swim (123) is just at the lower end of her lawn, and is well known as an excellent place for barbel fishing. The willow tree at the edge of this lawn should be tried for chub, and opposite to Colonel Ellis's pretty riverside residence there is another roach swim. The Berkshire bank is skirted by Windsor Park, and spinning for jack can be

successfully done from here to the Victoria Bridge. There is an old drain near the keeper's house, which has yielded all round sport. The punt or boat should be fixed just above the drain near the keeper's house, and by fishing fine and far off a few roach are sure to be taken if the water is in favourable condition. It is impossible to fish the Buckinghamshire portion of the river in the summer months, because the water is shallow, and thick with weeds. A barbel swim is situated about 100 yards below Victoria Bridge. Just above, there are one or two roach swims, the principal being near the archway over a culvert (125). The river on the towing path side is very shallow in the summer time, though it deepens towards Windsor lock. There are some fine roach swims close to the withies on the Buckinghamshire shore below the railway bridge, and some backwater is a little higher up. It is known as Black Potts and is dear to the memory of fishermen as being the place where Izaac Walton and Sir Henry Wotton used to fish. A jack of 25 lb was caught here (126) a year or two ago. At the end of the cottage garden on the Eton side of the river roach and barbel can be taken. Windsor lock cutting provides very good roach fishing in the summer months, and is much patronised by bank fishermen. Of the tail end of Romney Island (127) jack can generally be taken in the winter. The weir stream (128) affords good fly fishing. The water is about three feet deep in summer, but the stream is rapid. Some fine trout were caught there last year. Captain Leigh, of the Grenadier Guards, captured a 6¾ lb fish when fly fishing. It was foul hooked in the cheek, and had it been in good condition it should have weighed at least 8 lb. There is a small island at the upper end of the stream which is covered with rushes, and on the Eton side is Stuart's Hole (129), a very noted place for barbel. Some backwater enters the Thames here, and forms an eddy, which should be tried for jack. "The Big Elm" tree is about 15 ft above Stuart's Hole. This is a good all round place for fishing, but is specially noted for its large roach. The weir (130) pool is the best water to fish near Windsor. It holds trout, barbel, chub, jack, roach and dace. Each side of the river is well furnished with withies, and "long corking" is very profitable for the chub fisher. The cutting above the lock (131) can be fished from the bank, the principal fish to be taken being roach. Below Eton Bridge (132) is a famous barbel hole, to which I recommend every angler who visits Windsor to give a trial. After passing through Eton Bridge there is another well-known barbel swim, and then we pass to the "Cuckoo" swim (133). This is just above the railway bridge, and between two arches on the towing path. The water has an undercurrent, and an eddy is formed near the bank. In the winter, jack may be taken here, and a few roach. The "Lily" swim is on the Berks side, and generally affords a certain amount of sport among the roach. Clewer Point (134) is another spot where fish can be taken at all seasons of the year.

Figure A2.19. A flood has not discouraged these punt fishermen from having a go. The river is flowing from left to right, and swim 133 (the Cuckoo Swim) is just upstream of the railway bridge, with Clewer Point (Swim 134) just beyond that.[11]

Figure A2.20. Trout fishing at Boveney Weir[12].

The water on the Berkshire side forms a large eddy, and the Windsor fishermen usually place the punt so that when jack fishing a float can work both up and down stream from either side of the punt. In addition to jack and roach, sometimes trout are taken here. After passing round the bend of the river, barbel can be taken at the end of the first island, and then Boveney Lock is reached. Above the lock on the Berks shore, is Surley Hall, a very renowned place for all interested in the art of angling. There is capital jack fishing above the lock, but more particularly in the quiet water opposite to the hall. Bank fishing can be pursued at (136), but the quality of the sport had fallen off somewhat in the last year or two. Down Place, sometimes called Water Oakley Park, is yet another piece of water which holds jack and perch. Queen's Island is famed for its barbel, there being good swims at the tail and upper end on the channel side (137-8). Inside the eyot a few jack are occasionally taken. Round the next small island an occasional jack may fall victim to a lively live bait, and then we arrive at Monkey Island, the boughs round which are sure to give sport among the chub. Jack of 10 lb and 11 lb were taken on the inner side of the island last year (139), and a few smaller fish of the same kind were taken by bank anglers in the Queen's Deeps with paternoster and live bait, close to the bank. The next eyot is a small one, surrounded by rush beds, and it is worth giving the jack a trial here, especially at the upper end. The lower part of Bray weir stream is suitable for fly fishing for dace and trout. The latter are often taken in the weir pool (140). Just below the lock eyot there is a barbel swim, and the bank fishing in this district is better than usual.

Maidenhead, Cookham, and Great Marlow.

After passing through Maidenhead Railway Bridge we come to Ray Mead, opposite to which the water is rather swift, and holds some good barbel, chub and occasional trout; the fishing is generally good, and the Maidenhead Angling Association often places a number of trout in the river. Just below Taplow Mills there are three small islands, the backwater of which is navigable and supplies good sport. We now reach Boulter's lock and weir; the weir pool (141) holding trout, chub and barbel; below the weir lies Taplow court., the water, being rather shallow here, can be fished with a fly. There are three islands before we reach the (Cliveden) ferry, the back of which is good for jack and chub. At 142-3 there are some rushes, and quiet water, which occasionally hold some large fish; at the upper end of the island it is very shallow, and the rushes strong, it is therefore advisable to use the paternoster here. We come next to Cliveden Springs, near which there is a cottage, opposite to the latter (144) is an excellent barbel swim. The withies on the Bucks side should be tried for chub. Just below Odney Weir is another good winter haunt of jack (145-6); the river divides itself into four channels at Cookham Lock, and in the quiet water at the end of each island there are plenty of these fish to be found, and they are generally caught with a very small live bait. The weir pool (147) contains trout, chub, barbel, jack and roach, but permission must be obtained from Lord Boston to fish it. This stretch of water is especially renowned for its trout. The lock cutting is about half a mile in length, and is of little, or indeed no use for fishing. The Odney Weir stream (148) is good for chub, and the stream on the Berks side (149), leading to the mill, holds a large supply of barbel, especially at the tail of the mill; trout are also sometimes taken there, and permission must be obtained from the mill owner to fish it. Immediately below Cookham Bridge (150) there is a very good roach swim, the bed of the river being level, gravelly and free from weeds, the stream exactly suiting roach fishing. Cookham Church, with its square ivy covered tower, is on the Berks side, opposite to which there is a good roach and barbel swim (151). The over-hanging willows and bushes which line the Bucks shore should be tried for chub, whilst at the mouth of the Wyke River (152) there is a fine barbel swim. In the winter the quiet water just above the entrance of the Wyke into the Thames should be tried for jack; in the season an occasional trout is taken from this water. Just below Bourne End Railway Bridge, a wooden structure of several arches, looking scarcely strong enough to bear the weight of a train, is Abney House, opposite which are some excellent roach swims.

Figure A2.21. Opposite Cliveden, about swim 144.[13]

After passing the under the railway bridge there are some newly-erected bungalows, opposite to which are some good summer roach swims (153). On the Bucks side, above the Upper Thames Sailing Club boat house, there are several capital roach swims, which can be fished from the bank. A little further on (154) are one or two quiet corners suitable for jack fishing, and the Spade Oak Ferry is reached. Spade Oak Reach is very good for roach fishing, and the withies at (155) should be tried for chub; the latter may sometimes be caught close to the high clay banks, by using float tackle, the water being rather deep. Stone House Flat is at (156), but will be more localised when stated to be immediately opposite to a black hut on the railway line. Roach and jack can be taken here by bank anglers, it being one of the best stretches of water in the vicinity for bank fishing. Opposite to Stonehouse, which is on the Berks side, is an island, the tail end of which (157) should be tried for jack; some quiet water is formed by the channel stream and the backwater joining. On the inner side of the eyot is "Gibraltar", which is noted for gudgeon fishing. Barbel fishing is fairly good on the channel side (of Quarry Wood) (158), and at (159) jack can be taken after a flood. Opposite to Quarry Wood house there is a roach swim, and "Black Hole" (160) holds jack, both in summer and winter. But the best piece of jack water is at (161), it lies quite out

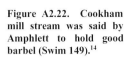

Figure A2.22. Cookham mill stream was said by Amphlett to hold good barbel (Swim 149).[14]

of the way of the main stream, and is most secluded. Mr F C Parker, in an article on "The Thames Trout" says Quarry Head is a spot the jack fisherman, and where many a twenty pounder has made its last meal. At the back of the next eyot gudgeon are numerous, and chub are sometimes taken from under the withies. The weir stream at (162) is shallow, and suitable for fly fishing. The water, however, deepens at (163) where barbel and trout are taken. There are two small islands surrounded by rushes of the Berks side of the weir, the water between the island and the shore being a favourite spot for winter jack fishing. The weir pool holds trout, jack, barbel, and chub, the latter in large quantities. The lock cutting (164) is level, and can be fished from the towing path on the Bucks side. Just before reaching Great Marlow Lock there is a paper mill and a flour mill. The mill stream is especially good for barbel fishing, more particularly near to the concrete wall, but permission must be obtained from Mr Thomas Wright. The fishing from Marlow Lock to the suspension bridge is hardly worth a mention.

Annex 2 footnotes

[1] A Tuck's Oilette art postcard 1907.

[2] A Tuck's Oilette art postcard; postmarked 1913.

[3] From Walpoole 1784.

[4] A Tuck's Oilette art postcard. The artist was Robert Finlay McIntyre, 1846-1906.

[5] Postcard, A.S. Series No.222, produced about 1905.

[6] Frith's postcard, number 38332.

[7] Postcard, AS Series number, number 5156, produced about 1905.

[8] Illustrated Sporting and Dramatic News, May 14 1881.

[9] Frith's postcard, no 58002.

[10] Postcard, Gilberts Photo Series 3; undated, probably 1905-10.

[11] Illustrated London News, January 1866.

[12] Illustrated Sporting and Dramatic News, April 16 1882.

[13] A Strengel postcard (no 25306), postmarked 1903.

[14] Frith's postcard no 43209, postmarked 1909. The picture was dated ten years before this.

Fron The Graphic, Summer number 1882. Artist J C Dollman.

ANNEX 3.

Location of eel bucks on the Thames

Eel bucks are devices for intercepting downstream-migrating adult eels in lowland rivers. Their construction and operation are described in Chapter 5. Here information is presented on all historic locations identified. No bucks have been operated for well over 100 years, and virtually all traces have now disappeared. As this method of fishing was practiced for hundreds of years this inventory represents an significantly incomplete historical picture.

Inglesham Mill Williams (1922) referred to numbers of eels passing the mill, and to a trap net that the miller used to set in the mill sluice. The eels were kept alive in a perforated keep-box moored in the river.

Figure A3.1. Iffley Mill, 1818.[1]

Figure A3.2. Goring, 1897.[2]

Iffley A set of four bucks at Iffley Mill is the subject of an image in Cooke and Cooke (1818). Figure A3.1. National Grid Refereence (NGR) SP 52586 03557.

Benson A map by Richard David in 1788 marks a set of bucks on Benson Weir. NGR SU 61385 91162.

Goring A set of five bucks is the subject of a painting by William Müller, date unknown. A print of the painting appeared in *Art Journal* in 1897. Figure A3.2. NGR about SU 59519 80765.

Tilehurst A set of five bucks with guiding posts and hurdles close to Buck's Eyot, the Fisheries, is shown in good detail on the 1885 OS 25 inch map. The structure appears in the background of at least two Taunt photographs. Dismantled in June 1910[3]. Figure A3.3 and A3.4. NGR SU 69179 74944.

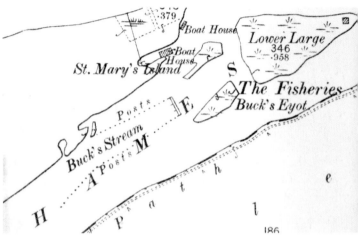

Figure A3.3. Tilehurst bucks in background. **Figure A3.4. OS 25 inch map, Tilehurst bucks,1876.**

Caversham One of the best known and best recorded rank of five bucks was situated immediately upstream of Caversham Bridge, in full view of passing traffic and pedestrians. Good detail is shown on the 1885 25 inch OS map, and literally dozens of photographs exist as postcards and in books, taken between 1870 and 1910. Possibly *Welbeck's Weare* mentioned by Taylor (1632). Dismantled about 1915[3]. Figure A3.5 and A3.6. SU 71115 74640.

Earley In 1783 *the bucks standing below Earley Point in the occupation of Isaac Breach* were considered as a *notorious nuisance*, and it was suggested that moving them to *Hardware Hill would render them less troubledome*[3]. The eventual removal of the bucks was witnessed by John Rennie in 1794. Exact location uncertain.

Sonning In 1721-22 the mill was let jointly with *lock, bucks, wares and fishery*[3].

Sonning Ferry to Partridge Bridge Rennie (1794) refers to the navigation through this reach being *much encumbered by ayts and fishing bucks*.

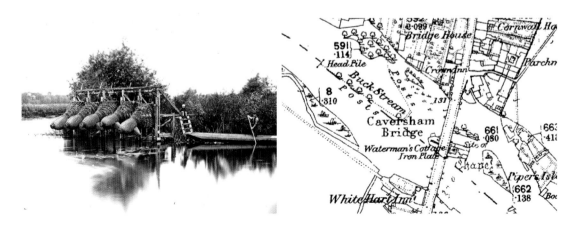

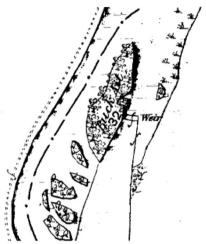

Figure A3.5. Caversham bucks.   **Figure A3.6. OS 25inch map, Caversham bucks, 1885**
Figure A3.7. OS 25 inch map, Shiplake bucks, 1877.   **Figure A3.8. Marsh Weir bucks, 1906.[4]**

Shiplake A fishing weir is shown on the 1885 OS 25inch map between Buck Ait and the Berkshire shore. This may have been the *Haules Weare* referred-to by Taylor (1632). Probably also *Bromley's Bucks*, said by Hobbs (1947) to have been *long gone* by 1914; *they disappeared many years ago after eel-fishing by bucks became unprofitable.* Figure A3.7. SU 76666 77238.

Marsh Weir (at least two sites). Two similar paintings by the Dutch artist Jan Siberechts; *A view of Henley* (1690) and *Henley from the Wargrave Road* (1698) show a set of bucks in the causeway between the main stream and the flash lock. In 1794 John Rennie wrote of Marsh Lock *there are also two sets of fishing bucks, one on the Marshall's and the other Mr Stevens. Joel's bucks* mentioned in a document dated 1703. A photograph in Wack (1906) shows a set of seven bucks apparently built into the weir (Figure A3.8).

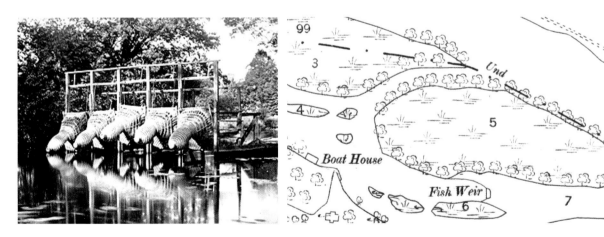

Figure A3.9. Culham Court bucks.   **Figure A3.10. OS 25 inch map Culham Court bucks, 1874.**

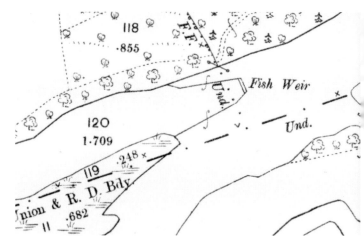

Figure A3.11. Harleyford bucks.[5]   Figure A3.12. OS 25 inch map, Harleyford bucks, 1876.

Medmenham (Culham Court) Set of five bucks in weir between Magpie Island and another small island. Shown as *fish weir* on the 1874 OS 25 inch map. Many contemporary images. Figure A3.9 and A3.10. NGR SU 79468 83798.

Hurley (Harleyford) Set of five bucks between island and the Buckinghamshire shore, downstream of the weir. Shown as *fish weir* on 1885 OS 25 inch map, and in several contemporary photographs. Figure A3.11 and A3.12. NGR SU 82376 84342.

Marlow A set of about 5 bucks was built into the (old) weir and are visible in an estate map of 1753 (Wilson 1977), in an engraving in Ireland (1792) and in a drawing by Havell (see Chapter 5). Apparently destroyed when the weir was rebuilt. *Marlow bucks* mentioned in a document dated 1703.

Marlow Thacker (1920) refers to a fisherman, William Mellet, seeking permission in 1797 to erect a new set of bucks in place of a derelict set in the channel below the weir, between The Great Eyot and the Great Meadow.

Little Marlow An advertisement in the Reading Mercury, Monday April 18 1785, offered to let a fishery *from a place called Mill Pond to Little Marlow Rails, in the Parish of Cookham*. This included several eyots and bucks. This would appear to be the same fishery as that described by Thacker (1920) as being immediately above the millpond fishery, and extending from there upstream to *Cookham over against the rails at the upper end of Little Marlow Mead*.

Cookham Weir Rennie (1794) refers to the navigation in the area being *most dangerous around the fishing bucks and pleasure grounds* of Sir George Yonge, Mr Martindal and others.

Hedsor This was a purpose built weir, with at first six bucks set in the left side (looking upstream). Shown in an 1865 photograph in Wilson (1977) and in a drawing by Leslie (1888, but drawn before 1871). In 1871 the weir was rebuilt with nine bucks at the right-hand end (looking upstream). Shown in Taunt (1887) and Belloc (1907). Said by Chalmers (1932) to be the only bucks still operating on the river at that time; the structure still remains. Figures A3.13 and A3.14. NGR SU 90599 85694.

246

Figure A3.13. Hedsor pre-1871 bucks.[6]   **Figure A3.14. Hedsor post-1871 bucks.**[7]

Maidenhead A set of nine bucks was operated in the weir at Boulters by the Lovegrove family from at least 1794 (Rennie 1794) to 1858 (Venables 1874). These caught salmon as well as eels; see Chapter 20. NGR SU 90378 82753.

Maidenhead A set of four bucks is shown upstream from Maidenhead Bridge in an etching by Havell in about 1813. Figure A3.15. NGR SU 90172 81498

Maidenhead   Set of seven bucks existed in decaying state up to the 1960s, between Guard's Club Island and the Berkshire shore (between the GWR railway Bridge and Maidenhead Bridge).   Shown in many contemporary photographs from about 1880 to 1900. Figure A3.16. NGR SU 90123 81132.

Bray Many contemporary drawings and photographs of set of nine bucks close to Berkshire shore by the church. Figure A3.17 and A3.18. NGR SU 90162 79846.

Figure A3.15. Bucks above Maidenhead Bridge, 1813.[8]   **Figure A3.16. Bucks below Maidenhead Bridge, 1897.**[5]

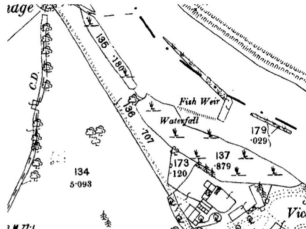

Figure A3.17. Bray bucks, 1885[9].   Figure A3.18. OS 25 inch map, Bray bucks, 1876.

Dorney   Rennie refers to the stretch of water between *Queen's Ait fishing bucks* and *Shooters bucks*. Thacker gives details of Shooters Bucks in 1816. NGR SU 91818 78140.

Water Eaton   *The Fishery* marked on 1880 OS 6" map. NGR SU 93237 77304.

Boveney   *Gills Bucks* are referred-to in a number of old reports. Thacker confirmed the location as being in front of the cottage just downstream of Boveney Lock. NGR SU 94591 77822

Clewer   At one time it is believed that there were bucks in the Clewer Stream, the side branch of the river behind the island where Windsor race course is situated. NGR SU 93891 77289.

Windsor   A painting by J M W Turner, entitled *Near the Thames' Lock, Windsor* dated 1809 (based upon a sketch done in 1805) shows a single buck set into a causeway[10]. The waterway appears to be a side-channel used for swimming by Eton scholars, exact location not known.

Windsor   According to Thacker (1920), at that time the bucks were still in existence at Black Potts (close to the SR railway bridge). NGR about SU 97481 78052.

Old Windsor   Buck weir shown on 1876 25inch OS map at *New Lock* a short distance below Albert Bridge. These were known as Newman's bucks (Thacker 1920). Figure A3.19. NGR SU 98761 75443.

Wraysbury   Rennie refers to Welly Bucks House and Mr Isherwood's bucks. Thacker refers to *Haynes Bucks* and *Welly Bucks* in this area but the exact locations are unknown. Believed to have been on the loop of river now bypassed by Old Windsor lock cut.

Runnymede   Island upstream of Magna Carta Island is called Buck Ait. May be the same installation as the one below.

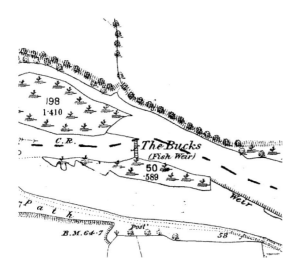

Figure A3.19. OS 25 inch map of Old Windsor bucks, 1876   **Figure A3.20. Runnymede bucks, about 1810.**[11]

Runnymede A colour engraving by George Delamotte, dated around 1810, shows one end of a set of bucks at Magna Carta Island. Figure A3.20.   NGR about SU 99825 73065.

Hampton An aerial photograph of the eyot immediately downstream of Tagg's Island taken in the 1920's shows what appears to be a rank of bucks between the island and the north shore.

Kingston Fishing weir, believed to incorporate bucks, was installed just upstream of Kingston Bridge in about 1555 and remained until at least 1785. Rennie (1794) referred to *Brown's fishing stops* near Kingston.

Teddington What appears to be a set of bucks built into the weir is shown in an engraving dated 1837; see Figure 10.3, Chapter 10. NGR about TQ 17026 71375.

Annex 3 footnotes

[1] Cooke and Cooke (1818).
[2] Art Journal, 1897
[3] Thacker (1920)
[4] Wack (1906),
[5] Leyland (1897)
[6] Leslie (1888)
[7] Belloc (1907)
[8] Drawn by William Havell in 1813. Engraved by Robert Havell, and published by Thomas McClean, 1818.
[9] Postcard, henry Taunt photograph.
[10] Picture reproduced in Hill (1993)
[11] Lithograph, George Delamotte.

Emptying the bucks at Caversham. From Leyland (1897).

REFERENCES

Allnut Z (1810) An essay on the right of angling in the River Thames, and in all other public navigable rivers, in which the public right to angle in all such rivers is stated and proved. Printed by Smart and Cowslade, Reading. Copy in Reading Central Library.

Amphlett F H (1894) The lower and middle Thames; where and how to fish it. London, Sampson Low, Marston and Co.

Amphlett F H (1897) Thames season 1897-98. Fishing Gazette, June 12 1897, 413-4.

Amphlett F H (1901) Everybody's book on angling. London, F V White and Co.

Anon (1757) An act for the more effectual preservation and improvement of the spawn and fry of fish in the River of Thames, and the waters of the Medway; and for the better regulating the fishery thereof. London, Act of Parliament.

Anon (1861)   Report of the Commissioners appointed to inquire into Salmon Fisheries (England and Wales); together with the minutes of evidence. London, HMSO.

Anon (1880) Report of the committee of the Thames Rights Defence Association.

Anon (1884)   Report of the select committee on the Thames river preservation; together with the proceedings of the committee, minutes of evidence, and appendix. London, HMSO.

Anon (1891) Rivers of Great Britain – the Thames from source to sea. London, Cassell & Co Ltd.

Anon (1925) Haunts and hints for Anglers. London, Great Western Railway Company.

Anon (undated – about 1925) A pictorial and descriptive guide to the Thames from Putney to Cricklade. London, Ward Lock and Co.

Anon (1961) Pollution of the Tidal Thames. Report of the Departmental Committee on the effects of heated and other effluents and discharges on the condition of the tidal reaches of the River Thames (The Pippard Committee).   Ministry of Housing and Local Government. London, HMSO.

Anon (1964) Effects of polluting discharges on the Thames Estuary. The Reports of the Thames Survey Committee and of the Water Pollution Research Laboratory. Department of Scientific and Industrial Research, Water Pollution Technical Paper no 11. London, HMSO.

Armstrong G S, Aprahamian M W, Fewings G A, Gough P J, Reader N A and Varallo P V (2010) Environment Agency Fish Pass Manual. EA Document GEHO 0910 BTBP-E-E.

Armstrong W (1887) The Thames from its rise to the Nore. 2 volumes. London, J S Virtue and Co.

Baddeley J (1834) The London angler's book or Waltonian chronicle. London, published by the author.

Banks J (1979) River Thames fish surveys. Proceedings of the First British Freshwater Fish Conference. Liverpool, University of Liverpool.

Barclay W G (1963) Pollution in the Thames Valley during the last century. Effluent and Water Treatment Convention at Seymour Hall. 8pp.

Beighton H (1731) A description of the water-works at London Bridge. Philosophical Transactions of the Royal Society of London, 37, 5-12.

Belloc H (1907) The historic Thames. London, J M Dent and Co.

Bickerdyke J (1894) Thames rights and Thames wrongs. London, Archibald Constable and Co. ("John Bickerdyke" was the *nom de plume* of C H Cook.)

Bickerdyke J (1901) Days of my life on water fresh and salt. London, Longmans, Green and Co.

Binnell R (1758) A description of the River Thames. London, T Longman.

Bond C J (1988) Monastic fisheries. pp 69-112 in:-Aston M (Ed) Medieval fish, fisheries and fishponds in England. Oxford, BAR.

Brigham T (2001) The Thames and Southwark waterfront in the Roman period. In:- Watson B, Brigham T and Dyson T. (Eds) London Bridge, 2000 years of a river crossing. MoLAS Monograph 8, 12-27, Museum of London.

Brookes R (1781) Art of angling.

Brooks C E P and Glasspool J (1928) British floods and droughts. London, Ernest Benn.

Buckland F (1871) Curiosities of natural history. London, Richard Bentley.

Buckland F (1883) The natural history of British fishes. London, SPCK.

Burrett J (1960) Freshwater fishing – the lower Thames. Peterborough, Angling Times Book, Ernest Benn.

Burrett J (1968) Fishing Famous Rivers – The lower Thames. Angling Times publication.

Burrett J and Pearson A (1961) Anglers Angles. London, George Allan and Unwin.

Callcut W G (1924) The history of the London Angler's Association. London, W G Callcut.

Cargill C (1969) The River Thames – historical survey of the rights over the river and their conservancy. Thames Angling Preservation Society.

Cargill C (1972) The Thames Angling Preservation Society – past, present and future. Pamphlet produced by TAPS.

Chalmers P R (1932) At the tail of the weir. London, Phillip Allan.

Chaplin P H (1982) The Thames from source to tideway. London, Whittet Books.

Cholmondeley-Pennel H (1886) Fishing – pike and other coarse fish. 2nd edition. London, Longman's Green and Co.

Cohen B (1985) The Thames 1580-1980 – a general bibliography. London, Ben Cohen.

Coles B J (1998)   Doggerland – a speculative survey. Proceedings of the Prehistoric Society. Published online; https://doi.org/10.1017/S0079497X00002176

Cornish C J (1902) The naturalist on the Thames. London, Seeley and Co.

Courtney Williams (1945) Angling diversions. London, Herbert Jenkins.

Cowie R and Blackmore L (2008)   Early and middle Saxon rural development in the London region. Museum of London Archaeology Monograph 43.

Cox J (1686) The gentleman's recreation. Part 4 Art of angling. London, J Cox.

Darby H C (1977) Domesday England. Cambridge University Press.

Dart M C (1979) The recovery of the river Thames. Proceedings of the IFM Study Course, 18-20 September 1979.

Day F (1887) British and Irish Salmonidae. London; Williams and Norgate.

De Mare, E (1958) London's riverside; past, present and future. London, Max Reinhardt

Dickens C (Jr) (1887) Dickens's dictionary of the Thames. London, Charles Dickens and Evans.

Doxat J (1977) The living Thames. Hutchinson Benham, London.

Duffield J E (1933)   Fluctuations in numbers among freshwater crayfish, *Potamobius pallipes*. Journal of Animal Ecology, 2(2), 184-196.

Dyer C (1988) The consumption of fresh-water fish in medieval England. pp 27-35 in:- Aston M (Ed) Medieval fish, fisheries and fishponds in England. Oxford, BAR.

Eaton R (1956) Where to fish. London, Harmsworth.

Englefield J ("Red Quill") (1912) A delightful life of pleasure on the Thames. Windsor, Field Press.

Environment Agency (1997)   The water quality of the tidal Thames.   London: The Stationery Office.

"Faddist" (1951) Coarse fish "briefs". Hertford, Gilbertson and Page.

Faulkner T (1813) An historical and topographical account of Fulham including the hamlet of Hammersmith. London, T Egerton.

Fearnside W G (1850) Eighty picturesque views on the Thames and Medway. London, Black and Armstrong. ("Tombleson's Thames").

Fennell G (1867a) The rail and the rod, Vol II, Great Western Railway.

Fennell G (1867b) The rail and the rod, Vol III, South Western Railway.

Fennell G (1870) The book of the roach. London; Longmans, Green, Reader and Dyer.

Fisher P (1835) The anglers souvenir. London, Charles Tilt.

Francis F (1867) A book on angling, 1st Edition. London; Longmans Green and Co.

Francis F (1876) A book on angling, 4th Edition. London; Longmans Green and Co.

Francis F (1880) Hot pot, or miscellaneous papers. London, The Field.

Francis J M and Urwin A C B (1991). Francis Francis 1822-1886; angling and fish culture in Twickenham, Teddington and Hampton. Borough of Twickenham Local History Society Paper no. 65.

Gerhold D (2019) London Bridge and its houses, c 1209-1761. London, London Topographical Society Publication 182.

Gollock M, Curnick D and Debney A (2011) Recent recruitment trends in juvenile eels in tributaries of the River Thames. Hydrobiologia 672; 33-37.

Good G L, Jones R H and Ponsford (1988) (Eds) Waterfront archaeology- Proceedings of the third International Conference, Bristol. Council for British Archaeology Research Report 74.

Goodburn D and Davis S (2010) Two new Thames tide mills and a brief up-date on archaeological evidence for changing medieval tidal levels. Pages 1-14 in Galloway J A (Ed) Tides and floods – new research on London and the tidal Thames from the middle ages to the twentieth century. Centre for Metropolitan History, Working papers series no 4.

Graham C (1972) Woodbine Angling Yearbook 1972. London, Queen Anne Press.

Graham C (1973) Woodbine Angling Yearbook 1973. London, Queen Anne Press.

Griffiths R (1748) An essay to prove that the jurisdiction and conservancy of the river Thames is committed to the Lord Mayor and the City of London. London, Robert Brown.

Hall S C and Hall Mrs (1853) The book of the Thames. London, J S Virtue.

Halliday S (1999) The great stink of London. Sutton Publishing, Stroud.

Hastings W (1955) The monarch of the Thames. Published privately.

Havell W and Havell R (1818) Picturesque views of the River Thames.

Herbert A P (1966) The Thames. London, Weidenfield and Nicolson.

Hickley P and Dexter K F (1979) A comparative index for quantifying the growth in length of fish. Fisheries Management, 10(4), 147-152.

Hill D (1993) Turner on the Thames. London, BCA.

Hobbs A E (1947) Trout of the Thames. London, Herbert Jenkins.

Hodgson H (1787) A letter to a proprietor of a fishery in the River Thames, in which an attempt is made to shew in whom the right of fishing in public streams now resides. Second edition. Printed and sold by Smart and Cowslade, Reading. Copy in Reading Central Library.

Hofland T C (1839) The British angler's manual. London, Whitehead.

Hofland, T C (1848) The British angler's manual. Revised and enlarged by Edward Jesse. London, H G Bohn.

Holinshed R (1587) Holinshed's Chronicles. London, Lucas Harrison.

Houghton Rev W (1879) British freshwater fishes. London, William Mackenzie.

Howes W (1969) Niclolson's guide to Thames fishing. London, Robert Nicholson.

Huddart R and Arthur R D (1971) Lampreys and teleost fish, other than whitebait, in the polluted Thames estuary. International Journal of Environmental Studies 2, 143-152.

Hulme M and Barrow E (1997) Climates of the British Isles. London, Routledge.

Ingram J (1837) Memorials of Oxford. London and Oxford, J H Parker.

Ireland S (1792) Picturesque views on the River Thames. London, T and J Egerton.

Jardine A (1904a) Perch. Chapter in in Hutcinson H G (Ed) Fishing; Country Life Library of sport, Volume 2. London, George Newnes.

Jardine A (1904b) Pike. Chapter in Hutcinson H G (Ed) Fishing; Country Life Library of sport, Volume 2. London, George Newnes.

Jeremiah J (1997) The upper and middle Thames from source to Reading – a pictorial history. Phillimore, Chichester.

Jeremiah J (2009) The middle and lower Thames from Sonning to Teddington – a pictorial history. Phillimore, Chichester.

Jesse E (1834) Gleanings in Natural History. London, John Murray.

Jesse E (1836) An angler's rambles. London, Van Voorst.

Leslie, G D (1888) Our river; personal reminiscences of an artist's life on the river (2nd Edition). London, Bradbury Agnew and Co.

Leyland J (c1897) The Thames illustrated. London, George Newnes Ltd.

London Angler's Association (1951) Rule Book; general rules and standing orders, benevolent fund rules, appendix to rules and maps of waters. LAA, London.

London Angler's Association (1962) The anglers guide and member's handbook. LAA, London.

MacMahon A F M (1946) Fishlore. Pelican A161. London, Penguin Books.

Maidenhead, Cookham and Bray Angling Association (1877) Third Annual Report.

Maiklem L (2019) Mudlarking; lost and found on the river Thames. London, Bloomsbury Circus.

Manning S and Green S G (1890) English pictures. London, Religious Tract Society.

Marston A N (1963) Newnes angling encyclopedia. London, Newnes.

Martin J (1854) The anglers guide, the most complete ever written. London, G Cox.

Maxwell H (1902) Stocking the Thames with salmon. The Tatler, January 8 1902.

Maylin R (2019) (Editor) Thames carping. Bountyhunter Publications.

Maxtone Graham J (1990) To catch a fisherman. Privately published.

Moore S A and Moore H S (1903) The history and law of fisheries. London, Stevens and Haynes.

Murgett F (1960) How to fish the lower Thames. London, Putnam.

Murie J (1903) Report on the sea fisheries and fishing of the Thames estuary. London, Waterlow Bros and Layton.

Naismith I A and Knights B (1993) The distribution, density and growth of the European eel, *Anguilla anguilla*, in the freshwater catchment of the River Thames. Journal of Fish Biology, 42, 217-226.

Nash J P ("Piscator") (1826) Observations on the public right of fishing by angle or nets in public navigable rivers in general and the River Thames in particular. Printed for the author by G Cannon, Marlow. Copy in Reading central Library.

Osborn S (1896) The history of Datchet, 2nd Edition. Windsor, Oxley and Sons.

"Otter" (1864) The modern angler. London, Alfred and Sons.

Overton L, Bayley M, Paulsen H and Wang T (2008) Salinity tolerance of cultures Eurasian perch, *Perca fluviatilis*; effects on growth and survival as a function of temperature. Aquaculture 277, 282-286.

Pearson A (1961) Angles on Huchen. Chapter in Burrett and Pearson (1961).

Pennant T (1790) Of London. London, Robert Faulder.

Phillips H (1951) The Thames about 1750. London, Collins.

Pilcher M (1989) Tidal Thames Fishery Survey, Thames East, 1989. National Rivers Authority, Thames Region.

Prior M (1982) Fisher Row – fishermen, bargemen and canal boatmen in Oxford, 1500-1900. Oxford, Clarendon Press.

Ransome A (1929) Rod and line. London, Jonathan Cape.

Ravenstein E G (1893) The oarsman's and angler's map of the River Thames from its source to London Bridge. London, James Reynolds and Sons.

Read S (1989) The Thames of Henry Taunt. London, Alan Sutton.

Reading and District Angling Association (1878) First Annual Report.

Reading and District Angling Association (1880) Report for 1879 and 1880.

Reading and District Angling Association (1882) Fifth Annual Report.

Reading and District Angling Association (1883) Sixth Annual Report.

Regan C T (1911) The freshwater fishes of the British Isles. London, Methuen.

Rennie J (1794) A survey of the river Thames from Reading to Isleworth. Undertaken for the Commissioners of Thames Navigation.

Robertson H R (1875) Life on the upper Thames. London; Virtue, Spalding and Co.

Rogers P (2008) Below the weir –methods and memories of Thames trout angling. Little Egret Press.

Salter T F (1814) The anglers guide, or compleate London angler. London, published for the author by T Tegg.

Senior W (1885) Waterside sketches. London, Sampson Low, Marston, Searle and Rivington.

Sheringham H T (1910) An open creel. London, Methuen and Co.

Sheringham H T (Editor) (1928) Where to fish – the angler's diary. 56th edition, London, Field Press.

Smeaton J (1763) Report on improving, widening and enlarging London Bridge.

Smith A (1860) The Thames angler (2nd Edition). London, Chapman and Hall.

Solomon D J (1975) The decline and reappearance of migratory fish in the tidal Thames, with particular reference to the salmon. London Naturalist 54, 35-37.

Solomon D J (2006) Migration as a life-history strategy for the sea trout. In:- Harris G and Milner N (Eds). Sea trout – biology, conservation and management. Oxford, Blackwell Publishing.

Spillett P G (1979) Fisheries research in the Thames Water Authority. Proceedings of the First British Freshwater Fisheries Conference, pp325-335. University of Liverpool and the National Federation of Anglers.

Steane J M and Foreman M (1988) The archaeology of medieval fishing tackle. pp 88-101 in:- Good et al (1988).

Stone P (1997) Old Father Thames. Medlar Press.

Strype J (1720) A survey of the cities of London and Westminster.

Taunt H (1887) A new map of the upper Thames. Reproduced in facsimile with annotations as Read (1989).

Taylor J (1632) Thame Isis, a poem.

Taylor W (1960) Fishing Famous Rivers – The Upper Thames. Peterborough, Angling Times Books.

Taylor W (1968) Freshwater fishing the Upper Thames. London, Ernest Benn.

Thacker F S (1914). Thames highway; Volume 1, a history of the inland navigation. London, Fred S Thacker. Reprinted 1968 by David and Charles, Newton Abbot.

Thacker F S (1920). Thames highway; Volume 2, a history of the locks and weirs. London, Fred S Thacker. Reprinted 1968 by David and Charles, Newton Abbot.

Thames Angling Preservation Society (1934) Blue Book, 1934. TAPS, London.

Tombleson W and Fearnside W G (1834) Tombleson's Thames. London, Tombleson and Co.

Varley M E (1967) British Freshwater Fishes. London, Fishing News (Books) Ltd.

Venables G (1874) Salmon in the Thames and other rivers. London, Macintosh.

Wack H W (1906) In Thamesland. London, G P Putnam and Sons.

Walpoole G A (1784) The New British traveller. London, Alex Hogg.

Walton I (1676) The compleat angler. 5th Edition, revised by the author.

Wheeldon J P (1878) Angling resorts near London. London, Trübner &Co.

Wheeldon J P (1883) The angling clubs and preservation societies of London and the provinces. London, William Clowes and Co. International Fisheries Exhibition.

Wheeler A C (1958) The fishes of the London area. London Naturalist 37, 80-101.

Wheeler A C (1969) Fish-life and pollution in the lower Thames: a review and preliminary report. Biological Conservation, 2(1), 25-30.

Wheeler A C (1979) The tidal Thames. London, Routledge and Kegan Paul.

Wheeley C H (1897) Coarse fish. London, The Anglers Library, Lawrence and Bullen.

Whymper F (1883) The fisheries of the world; an illustrated and descriptive record of the International Fisheries Exhibition, 1883. London, Cassell and Co.

Williams A (1922) Round about the Upper Thames; glimpses of rural Victorian life. London, Duckworth and Co.

Williams WP (1967) the growth and mortality of four species of fish in the River Thames at Reading. Journal of animal Ecology, 36, 695-720.

Williams W P (1963) A study of fish populations in the River Thames. Proceedings of the first British Coarse Fish Conference, held at the University of Liverpool.

Wilson D G (1987) The Thames – record of a working waterway. London, Batsford.

Wisdom A S (1957) The government of the Thames. The River Board's Association Yearbook for 1957, 70-77.

Wright W (1858) Fishes and fishing. London, Thomas, Cautley and Newby.

Yarrell W (1859) A history of British Fishes, Third Edition. London, John Van Voorst.

Young A M (1926) The story of the stream. London, William Heinemann Ltd.

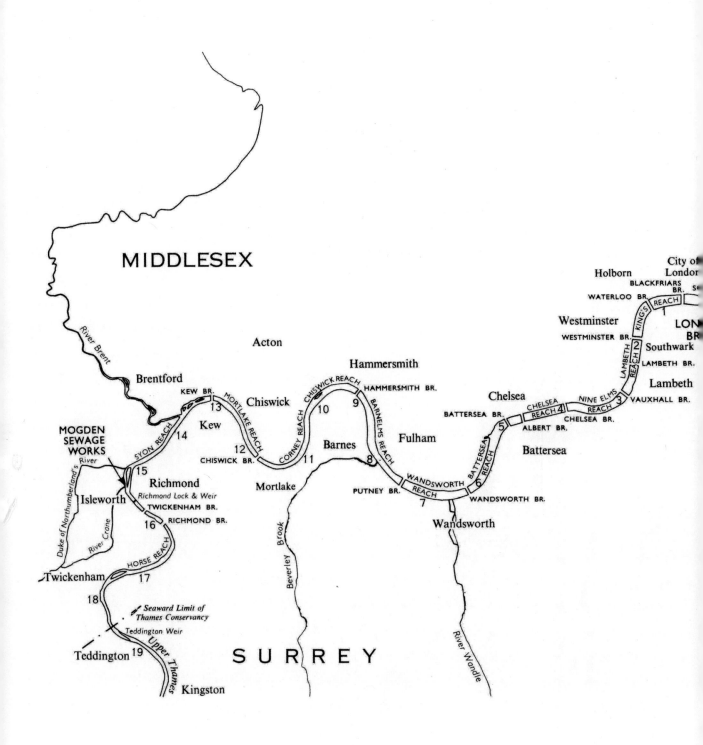

MIDDLESEX

City of
Holborn   London

Acton

Hammersmith

Brentford

KEW BR.
Chiswick
13

MORTLAKE REACH

SYON REACH
14

Kew
12

CHISWICK BR.

CORNEY REACH

CHISWICK REACH

10
9

HAMMERSMITH BR.

BARNELMS REACH

Barnes

Fulham

BLACKFRIARS
BR.   S

WATERLOO BR.
REACH
KING'S
1

Westminster
WESTMINSTER BR.
LON
BR

LAMBETH REACH
2
Southwark

LAMBETH BR.
Lambeth

Chelsea
NINE ELMS REACH
3
VAUXHALL BR.

BATTERSEA BR.
CHELSEA REACH 4
CHELSEA BR.

ALBERT BR.
5

Battersea

MOGDEN
SEWAGE
WORKS

River

15
Richmond
Richmond Lock & Weir
TWICKENHAM BR.
RICHMOND BR.

Isleworth

Duke of Northumberland's River

River Crane

Mortlake

HORSE REACH

16

17

18

Twickenham

Seaward Limit of
Thames Conservancy

Teddington Weir

Teddington   19

Kingston

Upper Thames

Beverley Brook

PUTNEY BR.

8

WANDSWORTH
REACH
7

Wandsworth

BATTERSEA REACH
6
WANDSWORTH BR.

River Wandle

S U R R E Y

The Tidal Thames Teddington to

Numbers are miles above and below London B